LANGUAGE ARTS: LEVEL D

Full Course PDF

Educator Information and Directions

- This packet contains a collection of every student PDF that is available for Language Arts: Level D. Educators who choose to print this PDF set at the beginning of the course will not need to print additional PDFs for this course.
- Please note that individual lesson PDFs are subject to minor edits.
- Answer keys can be found in the Curriculum tab of your parent account.
- This packet was compiled on 08/28/2025.

Unit 1: What Authors Write: Informational Texts

Day 1

- ❏ Video and Guided Notes
- ❏ Read and Respond
- ❏ Online Practice Level 1

Day 2

- ❏ Language Lab
- ❏ Connect and Reflect
- ❏ Online Practice Level 2
- ❏ Optional: Dig Deeper or Climb Higher

Lesson Goal: I can describe what I will learn in Language Arts: Level D and explain how to use the lesson materials.

Record your thoughts:
If you could travel anywhere, where would you go? Why do you want to go there?

Record your thoughts on the right! →

A Word To Explore:

To move or travel around

Day 1: Guided Notes

Follow along with Bea to complete the guided notes below.

Guided notes

are the lesson materials I can use to ______________ along with Bea.

Draw or write something you're looking forward to learning about with Bea.

I'm looking forward to...

____

____

____

____

____

____

Today we learned...

Bea has a lot of great lessons in store! You're going to learn new reading and writing skills, and why they matter in your everyday life!

Day 1: Read and Respond

Read or listen to the text below, then answer the questions that follow the passage. Scan or click the QR code below to listen along with Bea.

A letter from Bea:

Hey there!

I'm so glad you're here! When I started Read and Roam, I wanted to show how reading and writing aren't just for school — they're part of how we explore the world.

But here's something you might not know yet: This adventure isn't just about where I go; it's about what you learn and discover along the way.

Throughout my videos, you'll look at all kinds of everyday reading, from signs and stories to things you write yourself. You'll ask questions, spot patterns, and try out new ideas. Most importantly, you'll grow as a learner.

You don't need perfect handwriting or great spelling skills to be a great reader and writer! You just need curiosity and the goal to learn more every day!

I can't wait to start exploring with you! But first, I want to hear more about you!

See you soon!
-Bea

Day 1: Read and Respond

Use Bea's letter and your own opinions to answer the questions below.

1. What's one thing Bea said you'll be doing with her in her videos?

____

____

2. What did Bea say you need to become a great reader and writer?

____

____

3. What kind of stories or books do you like most? Why?

____

____

4. What is one thing you are curious to learn more about?

____

____

Draw or write how you feel about starting a new language arts course!

Day 2: Language Lab

Read the mini-lesson. Then, practice the skill in parts 1 through 2.

In this course, you'll hear the word **text** a lot! What exactly is text, though?

Text is any words or letters that we read or write. Text can help teach us, guide us to understand something, or share ideas.

When we read a book, look at signs, or even follow a recipe, we're looking at text. Below are some examples and nonexamples of text.

Examples: storybooks, street signs, menus, comics, written instructions, journal entries

Nonexamples: a pencil, paintings, a blank piece of paper

Part 1: Text or not? Look at each item below, and circle if it has or does not have text.

Sign with the word "stop"	Picture of a dog	Speech bubble in a comic
Text / No text	Text / No text	Text / No text

Cup of water	Glasses	Chapter book
Text / No text	Text / No text	Text / No text

Day 2: Language Lab

Part 2: Text is everywhere, not just in books! Look around your learning space, home, or neighborhood (with an adult's permission). Try to find different examples of text — that means anything with words or letters.

Your task:
Record examples of text you find, but don't repeat the same type over and over. For example, you can write down a book, a toy with writing on it, and a note, but don't list only books.

An example has been recorded for you.

Item (What did you find?)	Where was it?	What did the text say or do?
A label on a pack of fruit snacks	Kitchen cabinet	It said the ingredients of the snack.

Day 2: Connect and Reflect

Follow the prompts to deepen your understanding of the lesson.

Focus on your favorite moment. Write down or draw your favorite part of today's lesson.

Pack your bags! What's something you learned that you want to take with you and remember later?

Make a real-world connection. How do you think learning about reading and writing will help you outside of school?

Rate how you feel about this week's "Language Lab" skill: I can identify examples and nonexamples of text.

Rate how you feel about this week's skill: I can describe what I will learn in Language Arts: Level D and explain how to use the lesson materials.

Optional Support

Dig Deeper

What better way to get to know your materials than with a scavenger hunt? You can answer each question below using this lesson PDF! Look through the pages to find the answers you need, and record your answers in each box below the question.

What is Mia holding on p. 6?	How many steps are listed in the Climb Higher activity?	What is the Word To Explore for this lesson?
In what activity is there an icon of a camera?	How many days does the suggested schedule show for this lesson?	What animal is there a picture of in the Language Lab?
How many Mias are there in this PDF?	How many levels of online practice go with this lesson?	**Bonus:** Which activity was or looks like the most fun in this lesson?

Optional Support

Climb Higher

Before we jump into the rest of the course, take a moment to think about *yourself* as a reader and writer. This will help you set goals and get ready for the adventure ahead!

Step 1: Think about how you currently feel about reading and writing.

Color in the face that shows how you feel about **reading**.

I enjoy reading!

I feel OK about reading.

I don't really like reading.

Color in the face that shows how you feel about **writing**.

I enjoy writing!

I feel OK about writing.

I don't really like writing.

Step 2: Now that you know where you're starting, think about where you want to go! What's something you want to get better at during this course?

I want to get better at ____________________

____

Why do you want to get better at that? ____________________

____

Step 3: Everybody learns differently. To reach your goal, think about what will help you learn best. Draw or write the things that help you learn best (ideas: your favorite place to learn, someone who supports you, a tool or supply that helps you).

Day 1

- ❑ Video and Guided Notes
- ❑ Read and Respond
- ❑ Online Practice Levels 1 and 2

Day 2

- ❑ Language Lab
- ❑ Connect and Reflect
- ❑ Online Practice Levels 3 and 4

Day 3

- ❑ Extend Your Skills
- ❑ Online Practice Level 5
- ❑ Optional: Dig Deeper or Climb Higher

Lesson Goal:
I can explain how informational texts are different from stories.

Record your thoughts:
Would you rather read to learn or read to be entertained?

Record your thoughts on the right! →

A Word To Explore:

Not often found or seen

Day 1: Guided Notes

Follow along with Bea to complete the guided notes below.

Informational texts

are texts that are written to give readers ________________

or ______________________ about a certain _____________.

Read the informational text along with Bea below.

Axolotls

Axolotls are a type of salamander that live in water their whole lives. Originally, wild axolotls were found in one lake in Mexico. Axolotls live in fresh water, which means they could not survive in salt water, like the ocean.

Today, axolotls are critically endangered and are rare in the wild, but many people keep them as pets all over the world.

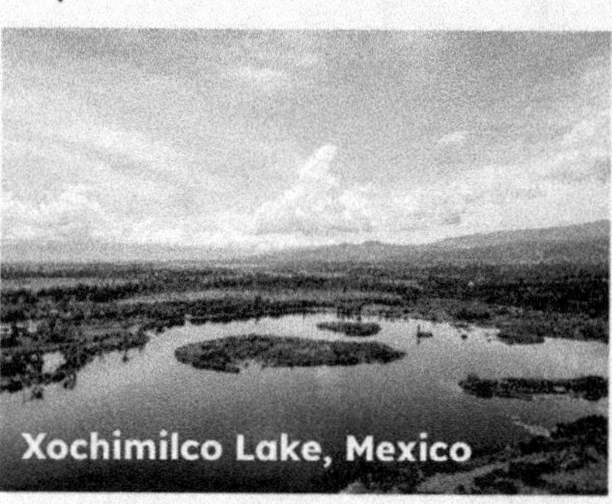

Xochimilco Lake, Mexico

Day 1: Guided Notes

Follow along with Bea to complete the guided notes below.

Record what you know in the chart, then fill out the rest with the lesson.

Informational Texts	Fictional Stories

The Secret Zoo

The National Parks

Twister on Tuesday

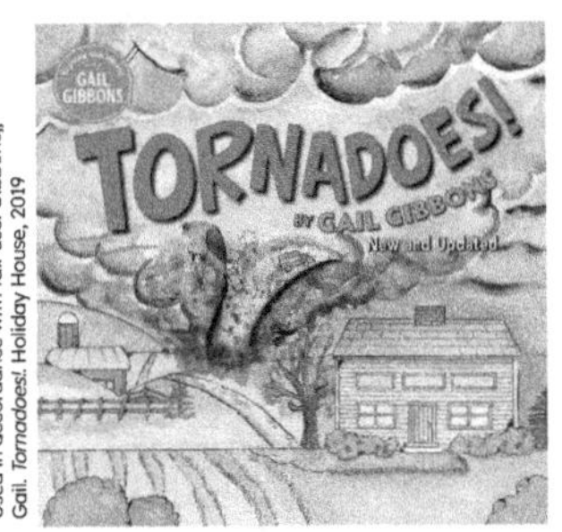

Tornadoes!

Draw lines from the books to where they belong in the chart above.

Today we learned...

Stories are made up to entertain readers

Informational texts use true facts to teach the reader about a topic

Day 1: Read and Respond

Step 1: Read or listen to each book passage below, then decide if each text is informational or a fictional story by circling the correct type.

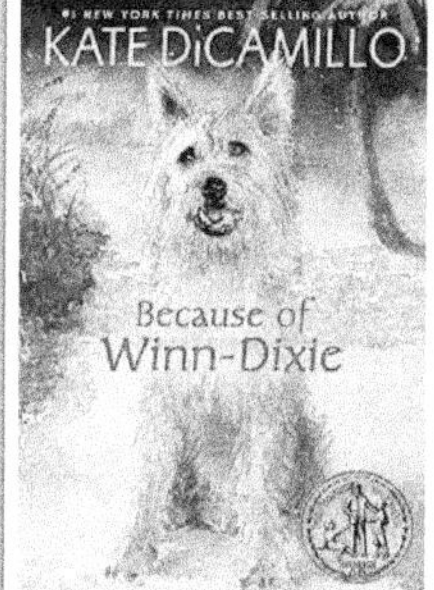

1

"Winn-Dixie looked up at me and wagged his tail. He was kind of limping like something was wrong with one of his legs. And I have to admit, he stunk. Bad. He was an ugly dog, but already, I loved him with all my heart."

Informational text
OR
Fictional story

Excerpt is used in accordance with fair use.
DiCamillo, Kate. *Because of Winn-Dixie*. Candlewick Press, 2000.

2

"Stink and his friends crawled on hands and knees through the grass. Stink peered into an empty box of mood flakes at one end. A furry hair ball with dark brown eyes, a wet pink nose, and twitchy whiskers peered back at him."

Informational text
OR
Fictional story

Excerpt is used in accordance with fair use.
McDonald, Megan. *Stink and the Great Guinea Pig Express*. Candlewick Press, 2013

3

"Sea turtles are reptiles ... Most reptiles lay eggs and breathe air through their lungs, as opposed to having gills like a fish. This means that while turtles are excellent swimmers and can stay underwater for hours, they eventually must come up for air."

Informational text
OR
Fictional story

Excerpt is used in accordance with fair use.
Young, Karen Romano. *National Geographic Kids Mission: Sea Turtle Rescue: All About Sea Turtles and How to Save Them*. National Geographic Kids, 2015

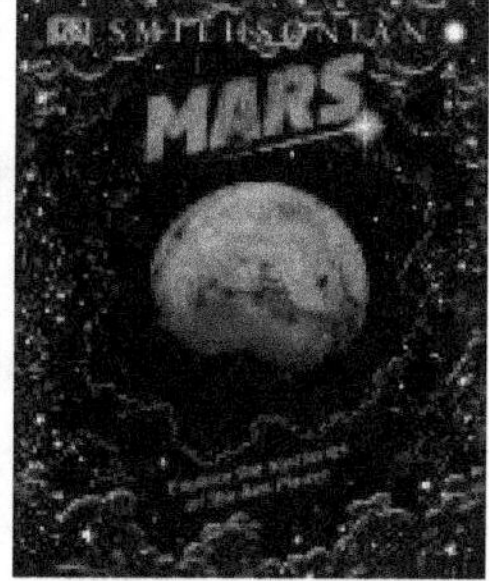

4

"The biggest volcano in the solar system, Olympus Mons lies a little north of Mars's equator. It is a type of volcano known as a shield volcano. Formed by lava erupting for about two billion years, the volcano rises high above the flat ground that surrounds it."

Informational text
OR
Fictional story

Excerpt is used in accordance with fair use.
Edson, Shauna; Sparrow, Giles. *Mars: Explore the Mysteries of the Red Planet*. DK Children

Day 1: Read and Respond

Step 2: Support your answers from Part 1 by recording **why** you chose the type of text you did.

- Circle the type of text you chose in Step 1 in the table below.
- Then, explain why you selected that type. Try to identify two reasons from each passage that explain your answers.

Text	Type	Reasoning
1. *Because of Winn-Dixie* by Kate DiCamillo	Informational text OR Fictional story	
2. *Stink and the Great Guinea Pig Express* by Megan McDonald	Informational text OR Fictional story	
3. *Mission Sea Turtle Rescue* by Karen Romano Young	Informational text OR Fictional story	
4. *Mars* by Shauna Edson and Giles Sparrow	Informational text OR Fictional story	

Step 3: Share your opinion. If you could choose one of these books to read, which would it be? Why?

____

____

____

____

Day 2: Language Lab

Read the mini-lesson. Then, practice the skill in parts 1 through 4.

Nouns are words that name a person, place, or thing.

Common nouns are nouns that are used to describe general or common people, places, or things. They are not capitalized and do not include specific names for people, places, or things.

Examples of common nouns:

- **People:** teacher, friend, girl, uncle
- **Places:** library, school, park, city
- **Things:** book, car, ball, toy

Part 1: For each sentence, underline or circle **all** of the nouns you find.

1. The boy got a hamburger at the restaurant.
2. A large pig was rolling in the mud.
3. The woman went to the store to buy some candy.
4. The computer almost died when I couldn't find the charger.
5. The girl checked out one book from the library.
6. The door slammed shut as the wind blew.

Part 2: Revisit Step 1 from the "Read and Respond" activity on Day 1. Find and circle at least two nouns in each passage.

Day 2: Language Lab

Part 3: Find all of the common nouns in the chart below and color them based on whether they are telling about person, place, or thing.
Be careful, not every word in the chart is a noun!

Create your color key by coloring in each crayon based on the colors you have:

Person | Place | Thing

table	sing	doctor	museum
kick	pencil	mall	artist
hospital	chef	pretty	phone

Part 4: Use nouns from the table above to fill in the blanks in the sentences.
NOTE: Not all nouns will be used.

1. I couldn't wait to visit the ____________ and see the new exhibit about ancient Egypt.

2. Jerry got upset when he stubbed his toe on the leg of the ___________.

3. The ______________ loved working at the restaurant making desserts.

4. We saw the ambulance pull into the parking lot of the ______________.

5. I kept breaking off the tip of my ____________ when I pushed down too hard.

Day 2: Connect and Reflect

Follow the prompts to deepen your understanding of the lesson.

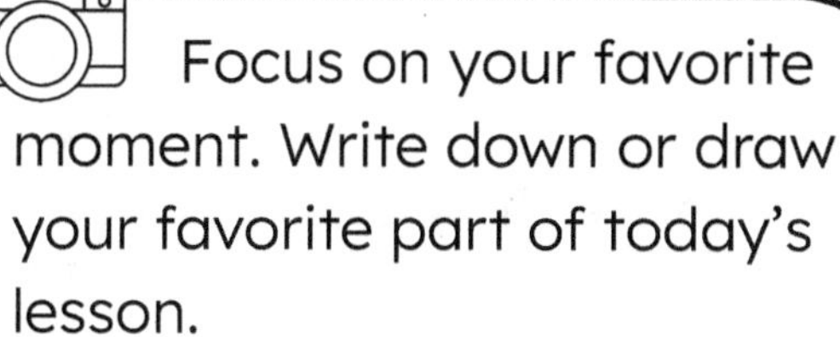

Focus on your favorite moment. Write down or draw your favorite part of today's lesson.

Pack your bags! What's something you learned that you want to take with you and remember later?

Make a real-world connection. How might knowing the difference between informational text and stories help you in real life?

Rate how you feel about this week's "Language Lab" skill: I can define and identify common nouns.

Rate how you feel about this week's skill: I can explain how informational texts are different from stories.

Day 3: Extend Your Skills

Follow the steps below to build your skills in differentiating between informational text and fictional stories.

Step 1: Read both passages. For each one, circle whether it is an informational text or a fictional story.

Dolphins are intelligent marine animals that live in oceans all over the world. They have smooth, gray skin and use their fins to swim quickly through the water. Dolphins must come up to the surface to breathe through a blowhole on top of their heads. They often live in groups called pods, where they work together to find food and stay safe. Dolphins communicate by making clicking and whistling sounds, and they eat a variety of fish and squid to survive.

Informational text OR fictional story

Sarah held onto the side of the boat, staring at the clear blue water below. She and her family had traveled to Florida for vacation, and today they were going to swim with dolphins. As she slipped into the water, a dolphin swam up beside her. It clicked and whistled, and Sarah laughed as it circled around her. The instructor told her the dolphin's name was Sunny and that she liked to play. They swam together for a few minutes before the dolphins headed off toward deeper water. Sarah climbed back onto the boat, excited to tell her family all about it.

Informational text OR fictional story

Day 3: Extend Your Skills

Step 2: This chart is called a Venn diagram. It is used to find the similarities and differences between two things. You'll be using it to compare the passages you read in Step 1.

1. Write things you notice about the fictional story in the left circle.
2. Write things you notice about the informational text in the right circle.
3. Write things you notice that are true for both texts in the middle where the circles overlap.

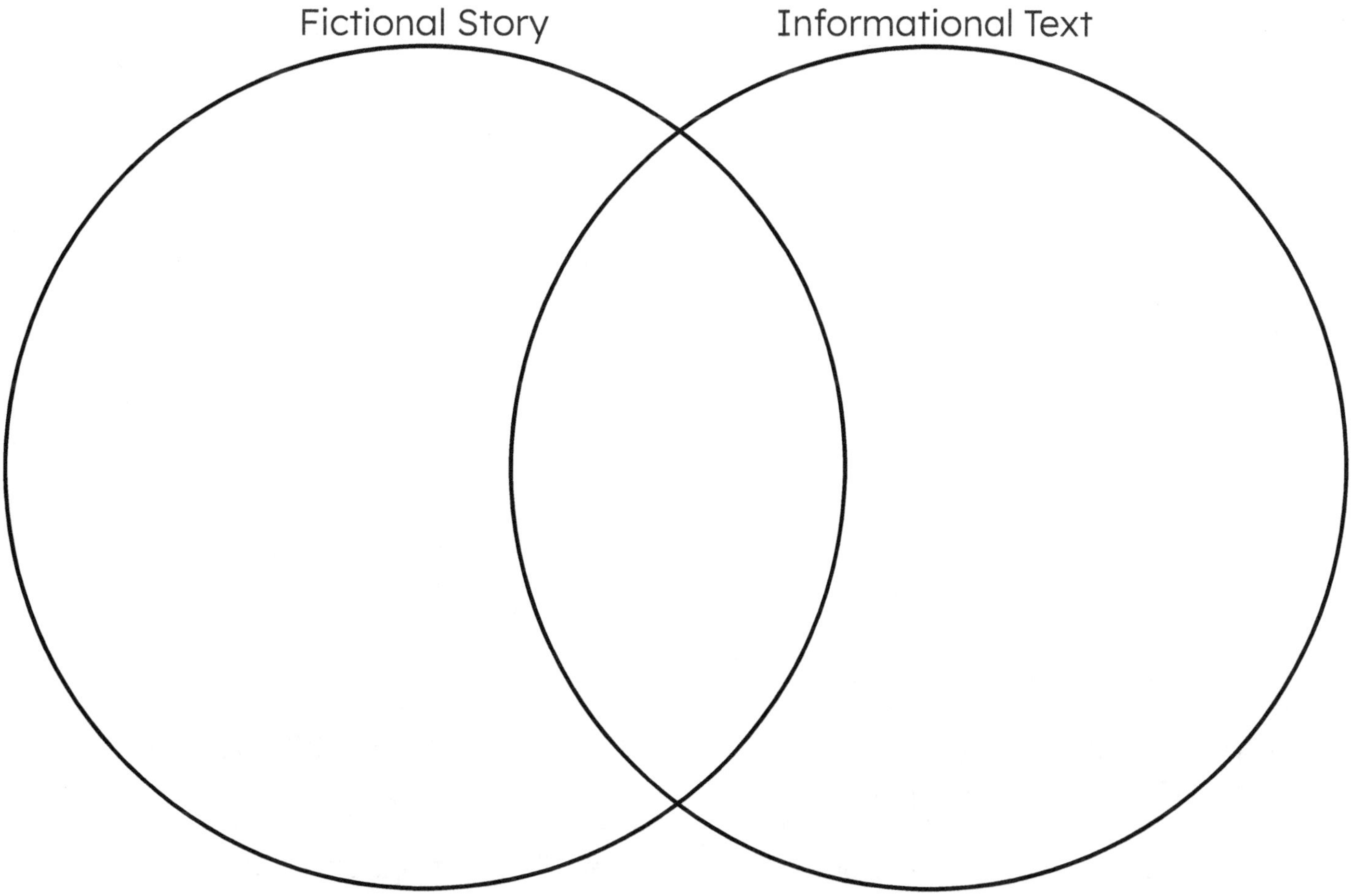

Fictional Story | Informational Text

Venn diagrams help us organize information and see how things are alike and different!

Optional Support

Dig Deeper

Want more practice with telling the difference between fact and fiction?

Step 1: Cut out each sentence below along the dotted lines
Step 2: Read each sentence. Decide if the sentence is presenting a fact (something true that teaches us something) or a fiction (something made up that is entertaining).
Step 3: Sort each sentence into the fact or fiction sections. Then, glue them down when you have checked your answers.

Fact	Fiction

The dragon loved to toast marshmallows with his fiery breath.	The human body has 206 bones.
The first airplane flight took place in 1903.	A friendly giraffe invited me to a tea party.
All of the planets in our solar system orbit the sun.	My robot cat just traveled to the moon.
Her magical sneakers helped her jump over buildings.	There are 12 months in one year.

Optional Support

Climb Higher

Ready for a challenge when it comes to telling the difference between fact and fiction?

Step 1: Choose one informational text and one fictional story to read. Try to find books about the same topic if you can!

Step 2: Reflect on your reading by completing the book reviews below and on the next page. Think about what you liked and disliked about each and how you know if each text is fiction or nonfiction.

Book Review

Title: ______________________________

Author: ______________________________

My rating: ☆ ☆ ☆ ☆ ☆

What I liked and didn't like:	I know this is nonfiction/fiction because...

Optional Support

Book Review

Title: ______________________________

Author: ______________________________

My rating: ☆ ☆ ☆ ☆ ☆

What I liked and didn't like:	I know this is nonfiction/fiction because...

Want another challenge? Read a page of your book and see how many nouns you can find! You can record them below!

Nouns

Day 1

- ❏ Video and Guided Notes
- ❏ Read and Respond
- ❏ Online Practice Levels 1 and 2

Day 2

- ❏ Language Lab
- ❏ Connect and Reflect
- ❏ Online Practice Levels 3 and 4
- ❏ Optional: Dig Deeper or Climb Higher

Lesson Goal: I can define the main idea, the most important idea in a text.

Record your thoughts: What is one topic you would like to learn more about? Why?

Record your thoughts on the right! →

A Word To Explore:

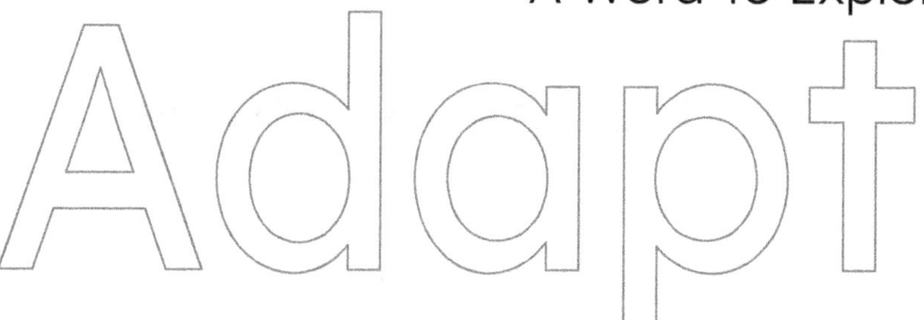

To change for a certain use or become used to something

Day 1: Guided Notes

Follow along with Bea to complete the guided notes below.

Topic is what a text is __________ about, usually one word or term.

Picnic Areas

There are many picnic areas along the main trail. At each picnic area, you will find picnic tables, trash cans, and restrooms. Grassy areas perfect for picnic blankets can also be found within the boundaries of the picnic areas. For the safety of our wildlife, please do not feed any animals.

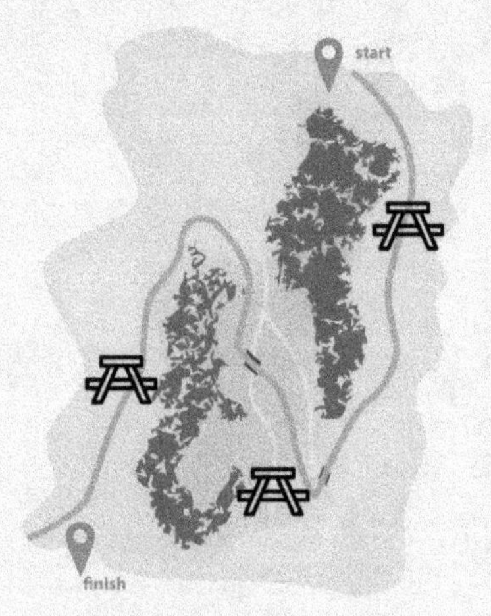

Picnic areas are marked on the map with this symbol:

Topic → Picnics

Main idea

is the most ______________ idea the author wants the reader to know.

Day 1: Guided Notes

Follow along with Bea to complete the guided notes below.

Butterfly Migration

Have you seen these species of butterflies?

If not, you're in luck! This month, our nature park will be in the path of a butterfly migration. As the butterflies start migrating south for the season, these beautiful creatures will pass right through the park. Keep an eye out so you don't miss them!

Topic: ______________________________

Main Idea: Butterflies are currently migrating through the nature park.

Hiking Trail Notice

There are many trail systems throughout the park. As you hike, remember to stay on the trail at all times. Due to recent changes in our wildlife populations, many animals have made their homes near trails. In order to protect the local ecosystem, note that any movement off of the trails is **prohibited**.

Topic: ______________________________

Main Idea:

There are hiking trails throughout the nature park.

OR

Hikers should stay on the trails in order to keep wildlife safe.

Today we learned...

The **topic** is what a text is mostly about

The **main idea** is the most important idea the author wants the reader to know

Day 1: Read and Respond

Step 1: Read the passages below and record the topic of each passage, then answer the questions on the following page.

1 **How Do Cacti Survive?**

The desert is hot and dry, but cacti survive with special features. Their thick, waxy skin keeps water inside, and their sharp spines protect them from predators. Cacti store water in their thick stems and have shallow roots that quickly soak up rain. These smart adaptations help cacti thrive in dry places!

Topic: ______________________

2 **How Do Icebergs Float?**

Icebergs are giant chunks of ice that break off from glaciers and float in the ocean. Even though they are big and heavy, they don't sink. This happens because ice is lighter than water. When water freezes, it takes up more space, which helps ice float. Most of an iceberg is actually hidden underwater, with only a small part sticking out! That's why people say "It's just the tip of the iceberg!"

Topic: ______________________

Day 1: Read and Respond

Step 2: Answer the following questions about each passage.

1. Which of the following best describes the main idea of the passage "How Do Cacti Survive?"
   a. Cacti are really cool plants that have sharp spines.
   b. Cacti have special adaptations that help them survive in the desert.
   c. The desert is a hot and dry place where nothing can live.
   d. Cacti survive in the desert because people take care of them.

2. Which of the following best describes the main idea of the passage "How Do Icebergs Float?"
   a. Icebergs float because the ice is warmer than the water.
   b. Icebergs are big chunks of glaciers that float in the ocean.
   c. The saying "That's just the tip of the iceberg" doesn't make sense.
   d. Icebergs float because ice is lighter than water.

Step 3: Record your answers to the following questions.

1. Look at the title of each passage. How does it help you understand what the text is about?

____

____

____

____

2. Do the titles of each passage help you find the main idea? Why or why not?

____

____

____

____

Day 2: Language Lab

Read the mini-lesson. Then, practice the skill in parts 1 through 3.

Verbs are words that usually show actions. There are three main types of verbs: action verbs, linking verbs, and helping verbs. Today's focus is on...

Action verbs - show what someone or something does

- Examples: kick, show, eat, sing, drive
  - In a sentence: The boy **jumped** over the puddle.

Part 1: Circle the action verb in each sentence.

1. Sarah hit the baseball high into the air.
2. Randall pushed the swing.
3. John wraps birthday presents with green paper.
4. My dog chomped on the bone.

Part 2: Look at the images below. In each box, record an action verb that matches the action in the picture.

Part 3: Write one full sentence describing one of the pictures above. Circle the action verb in your sentence!

___

___

Day 2: Connect and Reflect

Follow the prompts to deepen your understanding of the lesson.

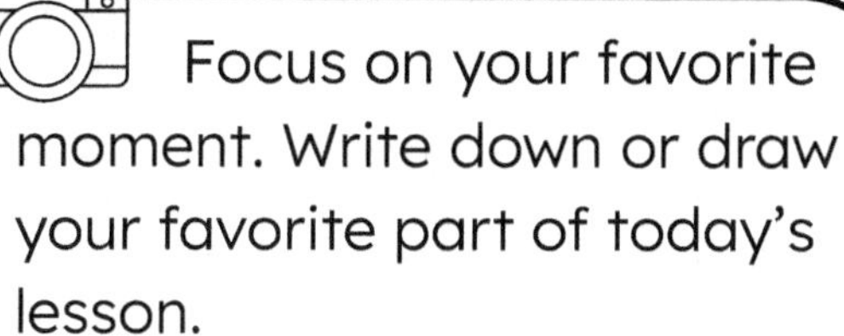

Focus on your favorite moment. Write down or draw your favorite part of today's lesson.

Pack your bags! What's something you learned that you want to take with you and remember later?

Make a real-world connection. How do main ideas help us understand a text?

Rate how you feel about this week's "Language Lab" skill: I can identify and use action verbs.

Rate how you feel about this week's skill: I can define the main idea, the most important idea in a text.

Optional Support

Dig Deeper

Want more practice with knowing the difference between topic and main idea?

In an informational text, the **topic** is what the text is about in general. The **main idea** is the big idea the author wants you to know. Main ideas are complete thoughts, but topics are usually just a word or term.

Step 1: Cut out each rectangle along the dotted lines at the bottom of the page.
Step 2: Sort and glue each piece so a topic is on the left and the main idea that matches the topic is on the right.

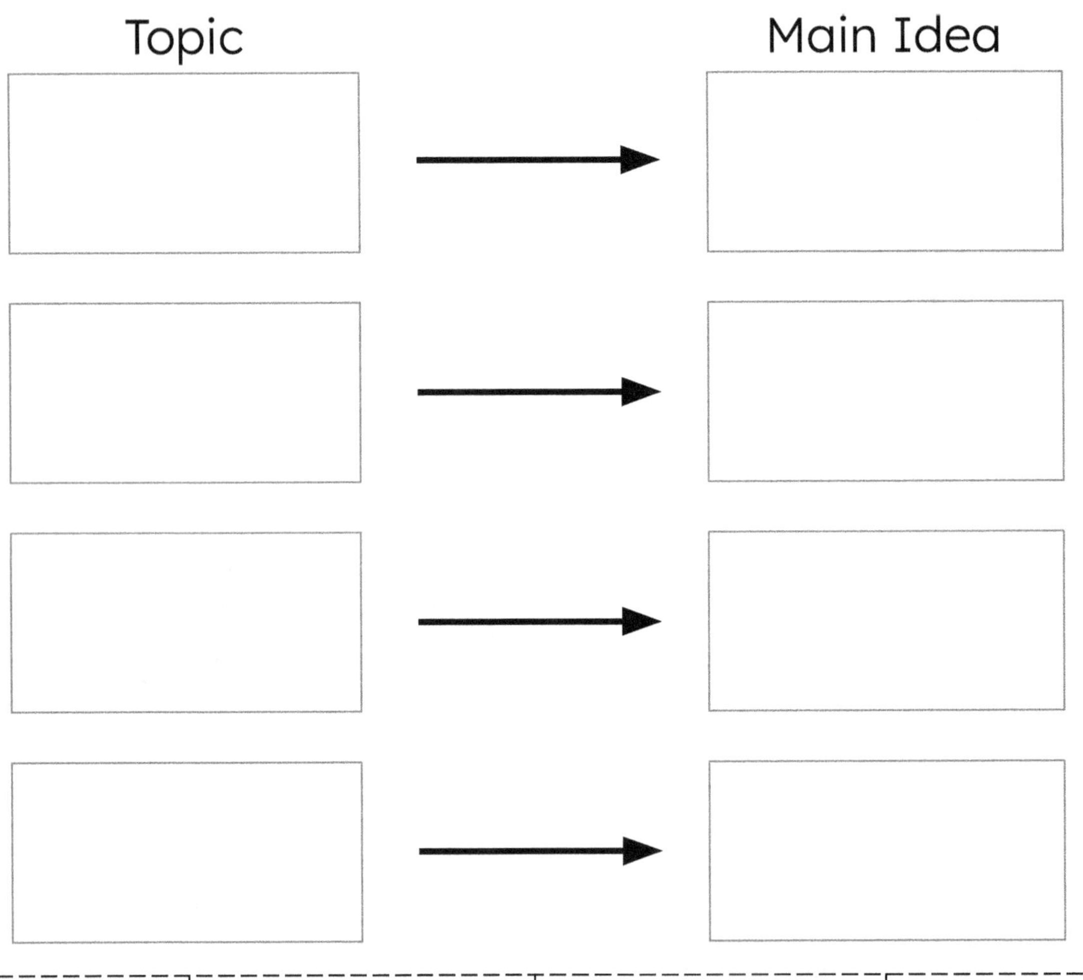

Frogs	Soap helps remove dirt and germs.	Germs	The sun
Fireflies glow to communicate.	The sun gives Earth light and heat.	Many types of frogs live in the rainforest.	Fireflies

Optional Support

Climb Higher

Ready for a challenge
when it comes topic and main idea?

Mystery Main Ideas

Step 1: Read the four words in each group and think about what they have in common.
Step 2: Write a topic that matches the connection between the four words.
Step 3: Create your own main idea that matches the topic of the words.

Set 1 is completed for you as an example.

Set 1

Tent, firewood, marshmallows, sleeping bags

Topic: Camping

Main Idea: People bring special supplies when they go camping.

Set 2

Apple, banana, grapes, orange

Topic: ______________________

Main Idea: ______________________

Set 3

Dog, cat, fish, bird

Topic: ______________________

Main Idea: ______________________

Set 4

Airplane, train, car, bus

Topic: ______________________

Main Idea: ______________________

Day 1

- ❑ Video and Guided Notes
- ❑ Read and Respond
- ❑ Online Practice Levels 1 and 2

Day 2

- ❑ Language Lab
- ❑ Connect and Reflect
- ❑ Online Practice Levels 3 and 4

Day 3

- ❑ Extend Your Skills
- ❑ Online Assessment
- ❑ Optional: Dig Deeper or Climb Higher

Lesson Goal: I can identify main ideas that are directly stated in the text.

Record your thoughts: What are some ways that you share what you think about something?

Record your thoughts on the right! →

A Word To Explore:

Loyal

Faithful to someone or something, especially in hard times

Day 1: Guided Notes

Follow along with Bea to complete the guided notes below.

Stated main idea

a sentence in the text that contains both the ______________ AND the author's most ________________________ ______________ about the topic.

Wetlands: Nature's Cleanup Crew

Did you know that wetlands are more than just a home to animals and plants? They also help keep the environment clean! Wetlands can act like a sponge, soaking up rainwater to prevent flooding. They also filter dirty water, making it cleaner before it flows into rivers and streams. Wetlands keep nature clean and healthy for all living things.

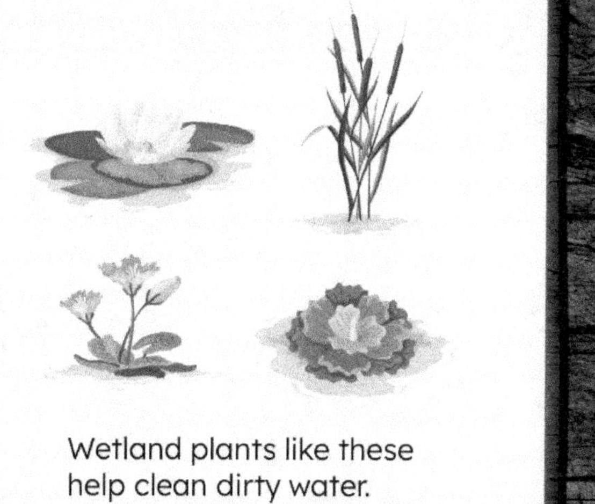

Wetland plants like these help clean dirty water.

Topic: ______________________

Underline the stated main idea you found with Bea.

Day 1: Guided Notes

Follow along with Bea to complete the guided notes below.

Owl Adaptations

Owls have many adaptations that help them survive in the wild. Their long talons and sharp beaks help them catch and eat prey like mice and insects. They also have soft feathers that help them fly silently! Some owls can even turn their heads almost all the way around to look for danger.

Great Horned Owl

⏸ Highlight or underline the stated main idea of the text.

Today we learned...

A **stated main idea** is a sentence in the text that contains both the topic AND the author's most important point about the topic

How to find the stated main idea:

1. Read the text.
2. Find the topic.
3. Find the sentence that mentions the topic AND the author's main point.

Day 1: Read and Respond

Step 1: Read or listen to each text below. Use the checklist under each text to find the stated main idea.

Dogs are known as loyal and friendly pets. They enjoy playing games like fetch and can be trained to follow commands. Many families choose dogs because they are protective and can be great friends. With proper care, dogs can live long, happy lives alongside their owners.

1

- ❏ Read the text.
- ❏ Find the topic: ___________________
- ❏ Highlight the stated main idea.
  - ❏ Circle the topic.
  - ❏ Underline the main point.

Many things we use every day, like paper, glass, and plastic, can be used again instead of being thrown away. This is called recycling. It can help reduce waste in landfills and conserve natural resources. Recycling also saves energy and keeps the planet clean. Recycling helps protect our environment and planet.

2

- ❏ Read the text.
- ❏ Find the topic: ___________________
- ❏ Highlight the stated main idea.
  - ❏ Circle the topic.
  - ❏ Underline the main point.

Day 2: Language Lab

Read the mini-lesson. Then, practice the skill in parts 1-2.

Verbs are words that usually show actions. Action verbs show the action of the subject, but there are two other types of verbs.

Helping verbs - come before the main action verb and <u>help</u> by showing time or adding meaning

- Examples: am, should, has, are, will, is
    - In a sentence: The cat **is** chasing the squirrel.

Linking verbs - link or connect the subject to more information in the sentence; usually show an action

- Examples: am, is, are, was, were, be (common forms of the verb "to be")
    - In a sentence: She **is** a doctor.
- They can also be sensory words like look, feel, smell, sound
    - In a sentence: That food **smells** delicious.

NOTE: Some words can be used as helping verbs and linking verbs, but the difference is that a helping verb is ALWAYS paired with an action verb.

Part 1: Circle the helping OR linking verbs in Mia's text conversation.

Those movies were so funny!

I know! I was laughing the whole time!

We should have more movie nights.

For sure! That new robot movie looks so good!

I am SO down to see it!

Day 2: Language Lab

Part 2: Sort each statement based on whether it has a helping verb or a linking verb.

Step 1: Cut out each sentence below along the dotted lines.

Step 2: Read each sentence. Decide if the sentence is using a helping verb (helps the main action verb) or a linking verb (connects the subject to more information in the sentence).

Step 3: Sort each sentence into the helping verb or linking verb sections.

Step 4: Glue them down after checking your answers.

Helping Verbs	Linking Verbs

Jack is happy.	I will finish my homework.
The ducks are eating the bread.	She was too cold in the snow.
Emery will invite her friends to the party.	Those rocks are heavy.
Those boys are twins.	They are going to the movies tonight.
I am very hungry.	We should eat pizza for dinner.

Day 2: Connect and Reflect

Follow the prompts to deepen your understanding of the lesson.

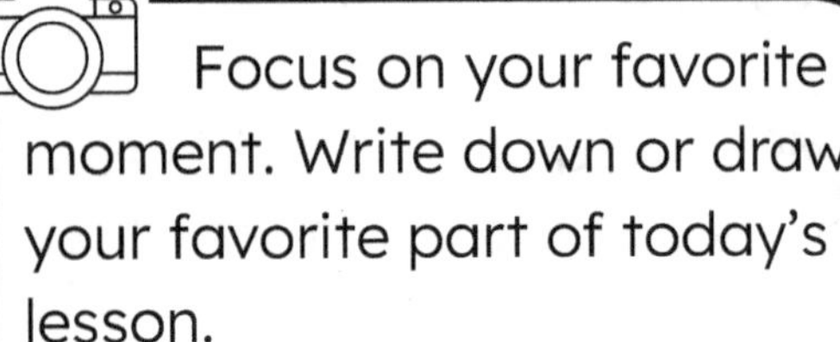

Focus on your favorite moment. Write down or draw your favorite part of today's lesson.

Pack your bags! What's something you learned that you want to take with you and remember later?

Make a real-world connection. How do you best communicate your ideas to others?

Rate how you feel about this week's "Language Lab" skill: I can identify and use helping and linking verbs.

Rate how you feel about this week's skill: I can identify main ideas that are directly stated in the text.

Day 3: Extend Your Skills

Write the Room!

Step 1: Cut out the write-the-room cards on this and the following page.
Step 2: Ask an adult to hang up the cards around your learning space.
Step 3: For each card, read the text, then find the stated main idea of the passage. Circle the answer that matches the stated main idea you find.
Step 4: Use the recording sheet to record your answers to each card. Each card has a number in the corner that matches the space for its answer on the recording sheet.

Example: The answer to Card 1 is choice B. So, you write B in Box 1 on the recording sheet.

Step 5: Use the key at the bottom of the recording sheet to arrange your answer choices. If you're correct, they'll spell out the answer to Mia's joke!

Write-the-Room Cards

(1) Firefighters help keep people safe. They put out fires in homes and buildings. Firefighters also rescue people in danger and teach fire safety. Their job is very important.

J. Their job is very important.
B. Firefighters help keep people safe.
T. They put out fires in homes and buildings.

(2) Bees fly from flower to flower collecting nectar. As they do this, they carry pollen from one plant to another. This helps new flowers and plants grow. Bees help flowers grow by spreading pollen.

O. This helps flowers and plants grow.
R. Bees fly from flower to flower collecting nectar.
B. Bees help flowers grow by spreading pollen.

Day 3: Extend Your Skills

Write-the-Room Cards

3. Trees help the Earth in many ways. They clean the air by taking in carbon dioxide and giving off oxygen. Trees also provide homes for animals and shade for people. Their roots help keep the soil in place.

E. Trees help the Earth in many ways.
F. Their roots help keep the soil in place.
M. Trees also provide homes for animals and shade for people.

4. Sharks have very sharp teeth that help them catch prey. They can smell even the tiniest drop of blood in the water. Some sharks swim fast to chase fish. Sharks are powerful hunters in the ocean.

M. Sharks have very sharp teeth that help them catch prey.
O. Sharks are powerful hunters in the ocean.
D. Some sharks swim fast to chase fish.

5. Cheetahs have long legs and strong muscles. They can run up to 70 miles per hour to chase their prey. No other land animal can run as fast as a cheetah. Cheetahs are the fastest animals on land.

S. Cheetahs have long legs and strong muscles.
G. They can run up to 70 miles per hour.
I. Cheetahs are the fastest animals on land.

6. Robots help people in many ways. Some build cars in factories. Others assist doctors during surgeries. In the future, robots may be able to do even more tasks.

E. Robots help people in many ways.
L. Others assist doctors during surgeries.
K. Some build cars in factories.

Write-the-Room Cards

7

Space travel is hard because astronauts face extreme conditions. There is no air, so they wear special suits. They float because there is no gravity. Astronauts train for years before they go to space.

O. Space travel is hard because astronauts face extreme conditions.
L. They float because there is no gravity.
D. There is no air, so they wear special suits.

8

The first airplane was built in 1903. It was small and couldn't fly very far. Over time, airplanes became bigger and faster. Now, they can carry people around the world. The invention of the airplane changed how people travel.

T. The first airplane was built in 1903.
R. The invention of the airplane changed how people travel.
P. Now, they can carry people around the world.

9

Camels have special adaptations that help them survive in the desert. Their humps store fat, which gives them energy when food is scarce. They also have long eyelashes to keep sand out of their eyes.

V. They also have long eyelashes.
S. Camels have special adaptations that help them survive in the desert.
N. Their humps store fat.

10

Jane Goodall spent years studying chimpanzees in the wild. She watched how they used tools and cared for each other. Her research showed that chimpanzees are smart and social. Jane Goodall changed how people understand and protect chimpanzees.

W. Chimpanzees are smart and social.
M. She watched how they used tools.
R. Jane Goodall changed how people understand and protect chimpanzees.

Day 3: Extend Your Skills

Use this recording sheet to write down the letter that matches your answer for each card.

(1) B	(2)
(3)	(4)
(5)	(6)
(7)	(8)
(9)	(10)

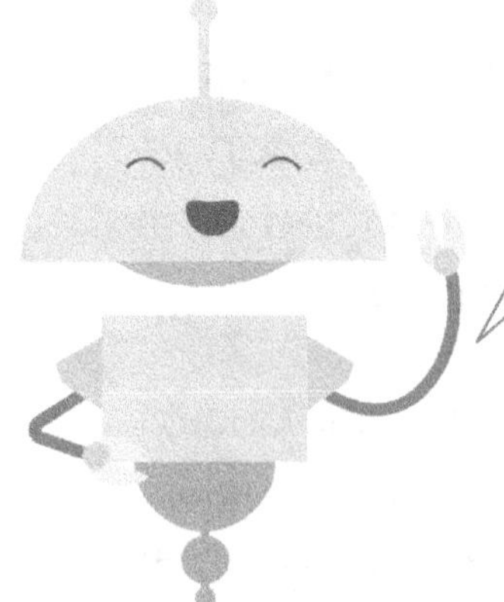

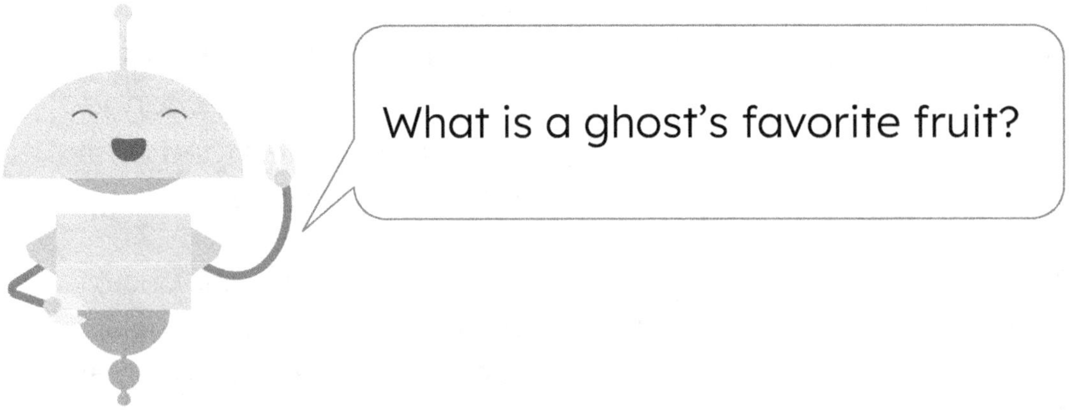

___ ___ ___ – B ___ ___ ___ ___ ___ ___

(2) (4) (7) (1) (6) (8) (10) (5) (3) (9)

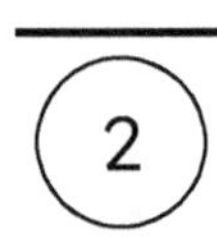

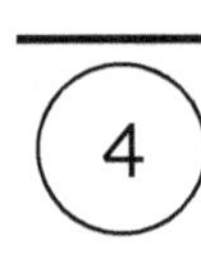

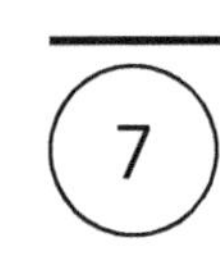

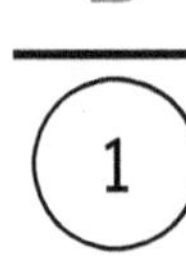

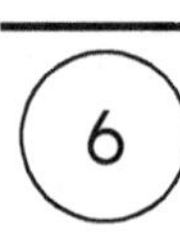

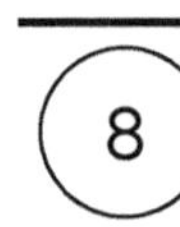

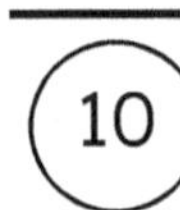

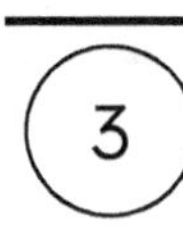

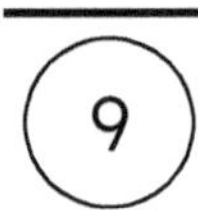

Optional Support

Dig Deeper

Want more practice with finding the stated main idea?

When deciding if a sentence could be the stated main idea, it's important to check that it can stand alone. That means it can make sense if it's read outside of the text. To stand alone, a sentence needs to have a **topic** and the **author's most important point**. If a sentence is missing either the topic or main point, it cannot be the stated main idea.

Directions:

1. Read each sentence in the table below.
2. Figure out if the sentence is missing the topic, the main point, or if it's a complete, stated main idea.
3. Color in the box matching the type of missing part you found or color the box "complete" if nothing is missing.
4. At the bottom of the page, write the **letter** from the colored box in the blank that matches the shape at the start of the row.

The first example has been completed for you.

		Missing topic	Missing main point	Complete
♡	Firefighters help make the town a safer place.	M	V	S
☺	They have many ways to survive in the wild.	T	Y	K
◺	Bumblebees do just that!	E	M	F
☁	It made a big impact on how people travel.	F	N	L
ϟ	Beavers are important to the river ecosystem.	S	L	E
◇	Robots help with that.	O	I	V
✚	Sharks are great hunters in the ocean.	R	T	Y
☾	It is a great way to help your city.	L	J	S

Why did the student throw her watch out the window?

She wanted to

S ___ ___ ___ ___ ___ ___ ___ ___ ___ !

     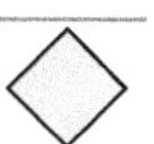 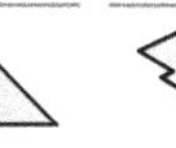   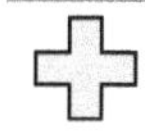

Optional Support

Climb Higher

Ready for a challenge
when it comes to stated main ideas?

Main Idea Build

In this activity, you will identify the main idea of a text and then use your creativity to come up with a way to build or make something that shows the main idea.

Step 1: Read one of the passages on the following page.
Step 2: Find the stated main idea of the passage.
Step 3: Think about what materials you have (Lego, blocks, clay, paper, or other household items) and how you can represent the main idea.
Step 4: Build your model!
Step 5: Explain your model to someone else or have them try to guess the main idea based on your model!
Step 6: Repeat with any of the other passages!

Example: Mia read a passage and found this main idea: "Bridges help people travel to new places." So, she built a bridge out of plastic blocks and used a toy person to show someone traveling.

Optional Support

Climb Higher

Ready for a challenge
when it comes to stated main ideas?

Beaver dams can change entire ecosystems. Beavers use sticks, mud, and leaves to build dams across rivers. These dams create ponds where beavers can live safely. By building dams, beavers also help other animals by making new habitats.

Wind turbines are tall machines with blades that spin when the wind blows. The spinning blades create electricity that people use to power homes and buildings. Wind energy is a clean way to make power without pollution.

Have you ever wondered why cities have skyscrapers? Skyscrapers are tall buildings that are designed to save space. Instead of taking up a lot of space on the ground, they allow many people to live and work in a small area of land.

When a volcano erupts, it sends out hot lava, ash, and gas. Over time, the lava cools and hardens, creating new land. Some islands, like Hawaii, were formed by volcanic eruptions. Volcanoes have the power to change Earth's surface by erupting.

Day 1

- ❏ Video and Guided Notes
- ❏ Read and Respond
- ❏ Online Practice Levels 1 and 2

Day 2

- ❏ Language Lab
- ❏ Connect and Reflect
- ❏ Online Practice Levels 3 and 4
- ❏ Optional: Dig Deeper or Climb Higher

Lesson Goal: I can tell the difference between details that help explain or support the main idea and details that do not.

Record your thoughts: How could you convince someone that your favorite food is the best?

Record your thoughts on the right! →

A Word To Explore:

To take in, or soak something up

Day 1: Guided Notes

Follow along with Bea to complete the guided notes below.

Supporting details

are details that explain, describe, or ____________ the main idea of a text.

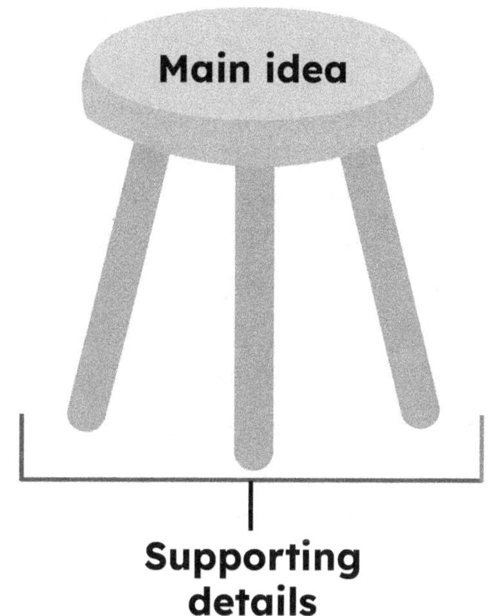

Oak Trees: The Forest's Protectors

Oak trees are important to the forest biome. Their large branches provide shelter for birds and small animals. Their acorns are a valuable food source for many creatures. Oak trees also help clean the air by absorbing carbon dioxide.

Circle the topic and underline the stated main idea of the text.

Follow along with Bea to complete the guided notes below.

Dragonflies: The Unlikely Hunters

Dragonflies are expert hunters. They have large eyes that help them spot tiny insects from far away. Their fast wings allow them to chase and catch their prey in mid air. Dragonflies can also hover like a helicopter before quickly changing direction to catch up to prey. Some dragonflies are bright blue or green.

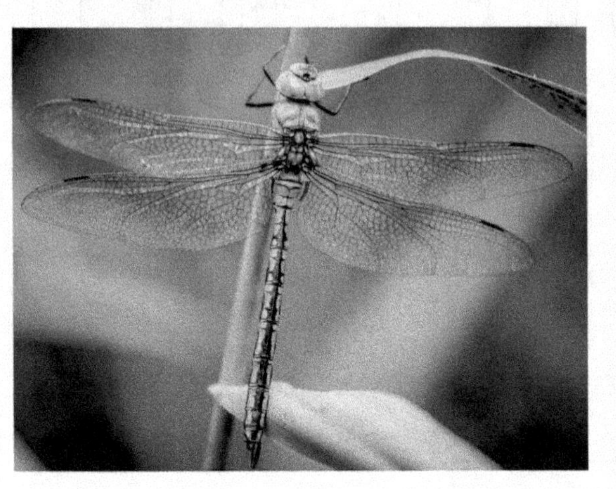

Find three supporting details in the text. Look for details that explain, describe, or prove that the main idea is true.

Today we learned...

Supporting details explain, describe, or prove the main idea of a text

Remember! Not every detail is a supporting detail!

Day 1: Read and Respond

Spiral review questions help you circle back to things you've already been taught to keep them fresh in your brain. If you're ever not sure how to solve a spiral review problem, feel free to look back in your notes or revisit earlier lessons!

For each passage, follow the steps and check them off as you go!

Blinking is important because it keeps our eyes moist and clean. Every time we blink, our eyelids spread tears across the surface of our eyes. This helps wash away dust and dirt. Blinking also gives our eyes a quick break from bright lights or screens. Some animals, like snakes, do not have eyelids and cannot blink.

- ❏ Read or listen to the passage.
- ❏ Find the topic: ____________________
- ❏ Highlight the stated main idea.
- ❏ Underline the supporting details.
- ❏ Draw a box around the detail that does NOT support the main idea.

Day 1: Read and Respond

Spiral review questions help you circle back to things you've already been taught to keep them fresh in your brain. If you're ever not sure how to solve a spiral review problem, feel free to look back in your notes or revisit earlier lessons!

For each passage, follow the steps and check them off as you go!

Penguins have special adaptations to survive in freezing temperatures. Their thick feathers trap heat and keep their bodies warm. Some penguins have black feathers. Penguins also huddle together in large groups to share body heat. Some species of penguins have a layer of fat, called blubber, that helps protect them from the cold.

- ❑ Read or listen to the passage.
- ❑ Find the topic: ____________________
- ❑ Highlight the stated main idea.
- ❑ Underline the supporting details.
- ❑ Draw a box around the detail that does NOT support the main idea.

Day 2: Language Lab

Read the mini-lesson. Then, practice the skill in parts 1 through 2.

Adjectives are words that describe nouns. They give us more information about the nouns and can tell us more about qualities like...

Size (huge, tiny, large, little)	**Color** (blue, colorful, dull, red)	**Taste** (sweet, sour, delicious)
Shape (round, square, curvy)	**Smell** (stinky, fresh, flowery)	**Behavior** (mean, nice, funny)
Sound (loud, quiet, faint)	**Speed** (fast, speedy, slow)	**Texture** (bumpy, smooth, fuzzy)

NOTE: Adjectives can describe more than what is in this chart.
As long as the word is describing the noun, it's an adjective!

Part 1: Read the story below. Find and highlight all of the adjectives in the text and record them in the table below. One has been found for you.

The fluffy cat jumped onto the soft couch and curled up in a warm ball. Outside, the bright sun shone in the blue sky, and a gentle breeze made the tall trees sway. The cat purred happily, enjoying the quiet afternoon. Suddenly, a small bird chirped outside. The cat opened one sleepy eye but decided to stay cozy.

fluffy				

Day 2: Language Lab

Part 2: Complete the silly story below by filling in the blanks with your own adjectives.

1. Read the story until you reach a blank.
2. Using a paper clip and pencil, create a spinner with the circle below.
3. When you reach a blank, spin the paper clip.
4. Use the word you land on to help guide the kind of adjective you fill in the blank.

Example: Mia reads the first sentence and comes to the blank at "_____ dog." She spins the spinner and lands on **color**, so to make her story silly, she writes in pink!

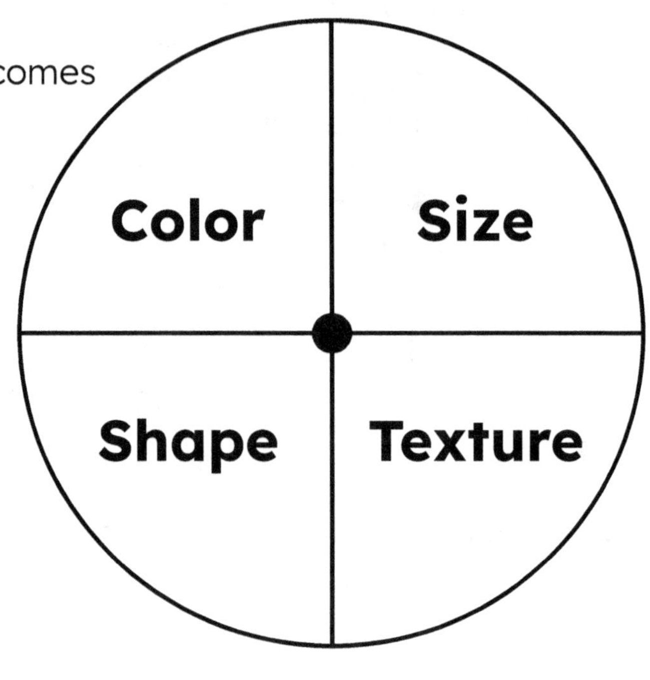

One day, I went to the park and saw a(n) __________ dog chasing a __________ ball. The ball bounced off a(n) __________ bench and rolled into a(n) __________ hole!

I ran to pick it up, but suddenly, a(n) __________ squirrel with a(n) __________ tail grabbed it first! The squirrel scurried up a(n) __________ tree and dropped the ball into a(n) __________ pond.

"Oh, no!" I shouted. But then, a(n) __________ duck with __________ feathers swam over and pushed the ball back to me! What a crazy day at the park!

Day 2: Connect and Reflect

Follow the prompts to deepen your understanding of the lesson.

Focus on your favorite moment. Write down or draw your favorite part of today's lesson.

Pack your bags! What's something you learned that you want to take with you and remember later?

Make a real-world connection. How can using supporting details help you express yourself in a discussion?

Rate how you feel about this week's "Language Lab" skill: I can identify and use adjectives.

Rate how you feel about this week's skill: I can tell the difference between supporting details and other details in text.

Optional Support

Dig Deeper

Want more practice with supporting details?

Step 1: Read the passage below.
Step 2: Cut out the sentences at the bottom of the page. One sentence is the main idea, and the other three are supporting details.
Step 3: Decide where the sentences belong on the organizer, and glue them in the right spots.

Elephants have long trunks that help them grab food and drink water. Their big ears help them stay cool in hot weather. They also have strong tusks that they use to dig and protect themselves. Elephants have many special features that help them survive in the wild.

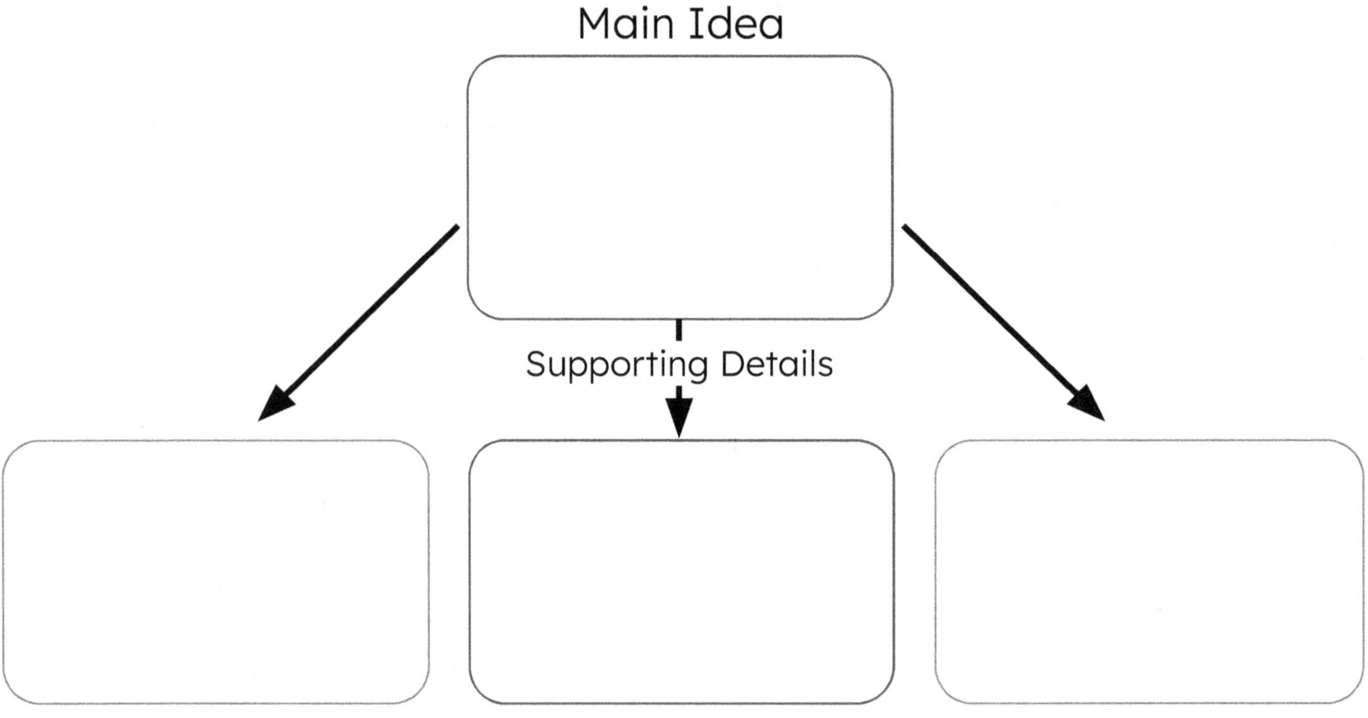

Their big ears help them stay cool in hot weather.	Elephants have many special features that help them survive in the wild.	They also have strong tusks that they use to dig and protect themselves.	Elephants have long trunks that help them grab food and drink water.

Optional Support

Climb Higher

Ready for a challenge when it comes supporting details?

Help Mia get through the maze and find her new book! Read the main idea. Find the path that leads from Mia to the lost book by shading in only the details that support the main idea.

Main Idea: Snowstorms can be dangerous and make it hard for people to stay safe.

Heavy snowfall can make roads slippery and cause cars to slide.	Some animals grow thicker fur in the winter to stay warm.	Not all places in the world get snow in the winter.
Strong winds can blow snow around, making it hard to see and knocking down power lines.	Many people like to play outside after it snows.	Snowflakes have unique patterns, and no two are exactly alike.
Ice on sidewalks and roads can make people slip and fall.	Freezing temperatures and strong winds can make people very cold and even cause frostbite.	To be prepared for snow, you should wear warm layers and a coat.
Many people drink hot chocolate when it snows.	Snowstorms can cause power outages, leaving people without heat or electricity.	Emergency workers may have trouble reaching people who need help during a snowstorm.

Day 1

- ❏ Video and Guided Notes
- ❏ Read and Respond
- ❏ Online Practice Levels 1 and 2

Day 2

- ❏ Language Lab
- ❏ Connect and Reflect
- ❏ Online Practice Levels 3 and 4

Day 3

- ❏ Extend Your Skills
- ❏ Online Practice Level 5
- ❏ Optional: Dig Deeper or Climb Higher

Lesson Goal: I can ask and answer questions to show understanding of a nonfiction text.

Record your thoughts: How do questions help you learn new information?

Record your thoughts on the right! →

A Word To Explore:

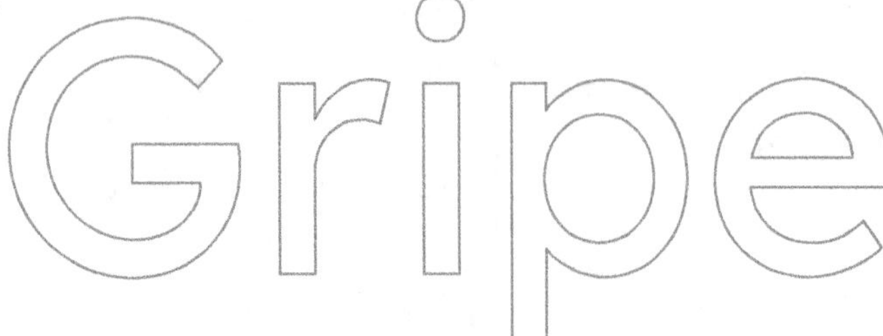

To complain about something

Day 1: Guided Notes

Follow along with Bea to complete the guided notes below.

Good readers _________ and _____________ questions before, during, and after reading.

Before	During	After
• Look at the title and pictures. • Think about what you already know. • Make a prediction.	• Ask questions to help understand the text. • Think about what confuses you or makes you curious.	• Look for text evidence that answers your questions. • Think about what you still want to know. • **Ask "Did I understand what I just read?"**

Follow along on screen as Bea asks and answers questions about the museum exhibit!

Use the five W's and H to ask questions!

Who What When Where Why How

My questions before reading:

My prediction:

Day 1: Guided Notes

Follow along with Bea to complete the guided notes below.

Sharks have lived in the oceans for millions of years. There are more than 500 types of sharks, and each one has special ways to stay alive. Great white sharks swim in open water to hunt for food, while hammerhead sharks use their wide heads to find fish that are hiding. Sharks are very important for the ocean. They help keep the number of fish balanced, which is good for the environment. Scientists study sharks to learn more about how they live and why some types are disappearing. Learning about sharks can help us protect them and keep the ocean healthy.

Pause as often as needed to record questions while reading.

My questions during reading:

Find any answers to your questions, and underline the text evidence.

Today, we learned...

Good readers ask questions before, during, and after reading to...

- Help with understanding
- Make reading more engaging and exciting

Day 1: Read and Respond

Part 1: Before reading, look at the picture and title of this new museum exhibit. In the box, record any questions you have and make one prediction about what you will learn.

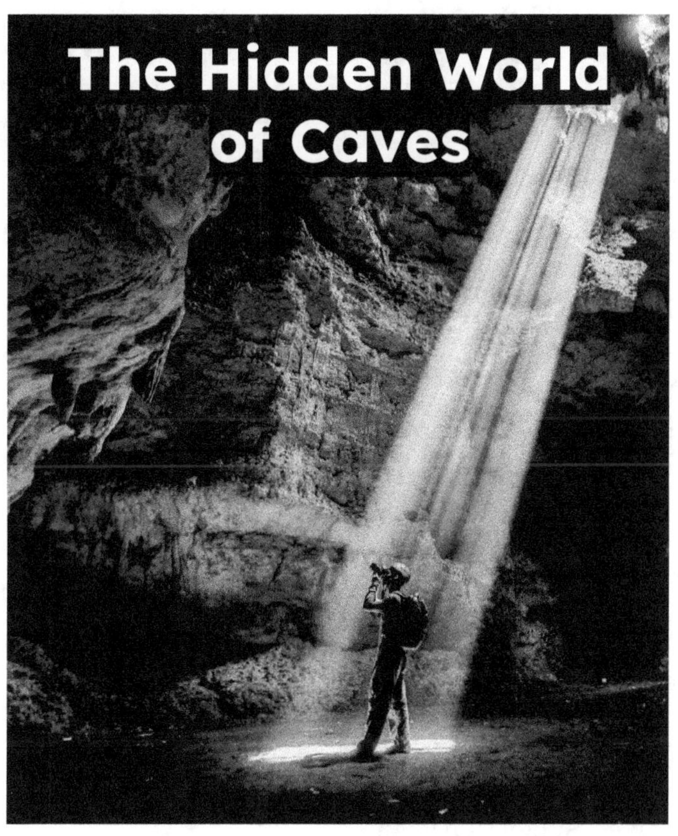

My Questions:

I predict...

____

____

____.

Day 1: Read and Respond

Part 2: During reading, stop to record any questions you have in the box next to the text. Don't be afraid to reread the text multiple times! You can also click or scan the QR code to listen.

Use the five W's and H to ask questions!

Who What When Where Why How

Caves are dark places deep underground. Some caves are made when water wears away rock. Others form from lava or rocks that fall in. Many caves have big rock shapes that take a very long time to grow!

Even though caves are dark, many animals live inside. Bats sleep there during the day and fly out at night to find food. Blind fish and salamanders use their other senses to see where they are. Some caves even have glowworms, tiny creatures that shine like stars!

Scientists go into caves to study animals, old bones, and hidden rivers. These things help us learn about Earth's past. Caves may seem spooky, but they are full of amazing things to discover!

Day 1: Read and Respond

Part 3: After reading, reread the text and underline any text evidence that answers your questions. Then, answer the reflection questions below.

1. Was it easier to ask questions before, during, or after reading? Why?

____

____

____.

2. Were all of your questions answered in the text? If not, what could you do to find the answers?

____

____

____.

3. What questions do you have after reading?

____

____

____.

Day 2: Language Lab

Read the mini-lesson. Then, practice the skill in parts 1 through 3.

An **adverb** is a word in a sentence that describes more about the verb, adjective, or another adverb. An adverb gives us information about how something is done. Adverbs almost always answer questions that start with the following question words.

Note how the underlined adverbs describe the word they're pointing to.

How? I worked quietly.

- Examples: quickly, happily, softly, sadly, carefully, patiently

Where? I played outside.

- Examples: there, away, upstairs, here, somewhere, nearby

When? I will study today.

- Examples: later, never, soon, early, tomorrow, now

How often? You never buy me treats!

- Examples: always, often, sometimes, hardly, usually

NOTE: Many adverbs end with -ly, but not all of them!

Part 1: Read through the sentences and underline the adverb in each sentence.

1. The squirrel ran happily on the branch.
2. Mia played downstairs with her friends.
3. Can we get dinner now?
4. I looked around for a place to sit.
5. I always eat my french fries with ketchup.

Day 2: Language Lab

Part 2: Find the adverbs in the box in the word search below! Words can appear horizontally, vertically, or diagonally. Words can also be forward or backward!

Y	O	C	R	W	E	I	R	Y	T
M	L	S	K	D	A	E	Q	L	H
P	H	L	I	V	T	H	B	T	G
O	H	S	U	A	Z	E	Q	E	I
Y	N	A	L	F	N	N	N	I	N
I	Q	R	V	J	E	E	W	U	O
A	B	O	V	E	N	R	V	Q	T
O	Y	L	I	S	A	E	A	E	D
S	L	O	W	L	Y	N	Q	C	R
S	O	M	E	T	I	M	E	S	F

- ❑ Tonight
- ❑ Sometimes
- ❑ Inside
- ❑ Later
- ❑ Never
- ❑ Slowly
- ❑ Carefully
- ❑ Above
- ❑ Quietly
- ❑ Easily

Part 3: Pick two adverbs from the word search and use them to write your own sentences.

1. ____

____.

2. ____

____.

Day 2: Connect and Reflect

Follow the prompts to deepen your understanding of the lesson.

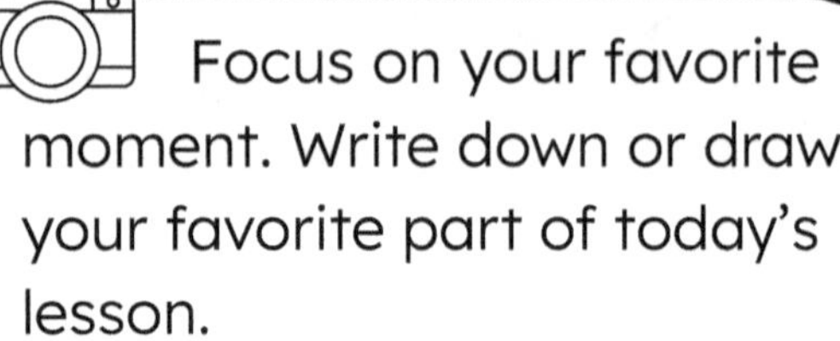

Focus on your favorite moment. Write down or draw your favorite part of today's lesson.

Pack your bags! What's something you learned that you want to take with you and remember later?

Make a real-world connection. How could you learn new information without asking questions?

Rate how you feel about this week's "Language Lab" skill: I can identify and use adverbs.

Rate how you feel about this week's skill: I can ask and answer questions to show understanding of a text.

Day 3: Extend Your Skills

Read the passage below, or click or scan the QR code to listen to it. Then, answer the questions on the next page.

The World of Lions

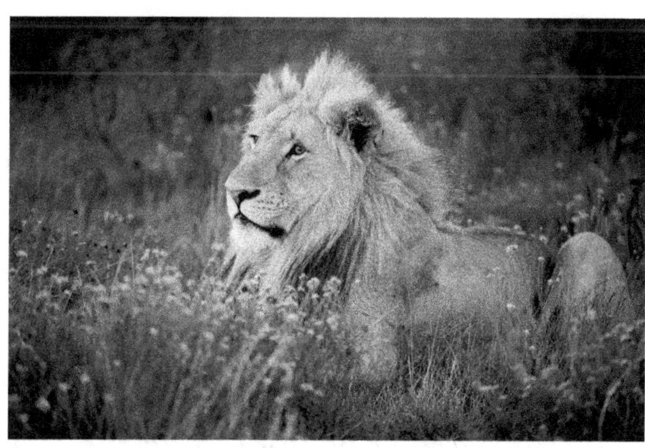

Lions are large cats that live in grasslands and open plains. They have golden fur and a loud roar that can be heard from miles away. Male lions have thick manes around their necks, while female lions do not.

Lions live in groups called prides, which are made up of several lion families. The females do most of the hunting, working together to catch animals like zebras and antelope. Male lions help protect the pride from danger.

Lions are known as the “King of the Beasts” because they are powerful and strong. However, fewer lions live in the wild today because their homes are being destroyed. Scientists work to protect lions and make sure they do not disappear.

Day 3: Extend Your Skills

Below are six questions about the text. Look at the text again and use the shown color to highlight/underline the text evidence that helps you answer the questions. Then, record your answers on the lines.

1. What is a group of lions called? Red

____

____

2. Where do lions live? Orange

____

____

3. Who does most of the hunting in a lion pride? Yellow

____

____

4. Why are lions known as the "King of the Beasts"? Green

____

____

5. Why are there fewer lions today in the wild? Blue

____

____

6. List two kinds of animals that lions hunt. Purple

____

____

Optional Support

Dig Deeper

Want more practice with asking and answering questions?

It is easy for our minds to wander when we read, and that can lead to questions that are not very helpful. In this activity, you'll practice deciding if a question is meaningful or not.

Meaningful questions help teach us more about the main idea and guide our thinking about the text.

Step 1: Read the text "The Moon."
Step 2: Cut out the questions below along the dotted lines.
Step 3: Sort the questions based on whether they are meaningful or not. Then, glue them onto the correct category.

The Moon

The moon is Earth's closest neighbor in space. It controls ocean tides, making water rise and fall. The moon also reflects sunlight, lighting up the night sky. Long ago, astronauts traveled to the moon to learn more about it. Scientists still study the moon to understand how it affects Earth.

Meaningful Questions	**Not Meaningful Questions**

What shape is the moon in the sky tonight?	How does the ocean control tides?	What did astronauts learn about the moon?	Who was the tallest astronaut to walk on the moon?
What would happen if Earth had no moon?	What does the surface of the moon feel like?	What color is the moon?	How does the moon give us light at night?

Optional Support

Climb Higher

Ready for a challenge when it comes to asking and answering questions?

Create a Quiz

Note: You can use the text below or any other nonfiction text to complete this task.

Step 1: Read any short nonfiction passage.

Step 2: On a new sheet of paper, create a set of questions about what you read. The answers must be found in the text.

Step 3: Make an answer key for each question.

Step 4: Use your quiz to test a friend or family member to see if they can find all of the answers!

Soaring Hunters

Eagles are large birds of prey known for their sharp eyesight and strong talons. They have powerful wings that help them fly high in the sky. Some eagles can spot small animals from far away before swooping down to catch them.

Eagles build large nests high in trees or on cliffs. They use sticks, grass, and leaves to make their nests strong. Most eagles live near lakes, rivers, or mountains, where they can find plenty of food.

Bald eagles, which have white heads and dark brown bodies, are the national bird of the United States. Long ago, there were fewer bald eagles, but today, scientists help protect them so they can keep soaring in the sky.

Day 1

- ❑ Video and Guided Notes
- ❑ Read and Respond
- ❑ Online Practice Levels 1 and 2

Day 2

- ❑ Language Lab
- ❑ Connect and Reflect
- ❑ Online Practice Levels 3 and 4
- ❑ Optional: Dig Deeper or Climb Higher

Lesson Goal: I can show understanding by paraphrasing facts from informational text.

Record your thoughts:
Have you ever read or heard something confusing? What helped you understand it?

Record your thoughts on the right! →

A Word To Explore:

To find or notice something

Day 1: Guided Notes

Follow along with Bea to complete the guided notes below.

Paraphrasing

is putting an idea or text into your ___________ words.

Paraphrasing makes text easier to **understand** and **remember**!

Steps to paraphrase:

1. Read the text carefully.
2. Identify the important details (the big ideas!).
3. Cover up the text.
4. Say it in your own words.
5. Check your paraphrase — did you keep the important details?

Original Text	Bea's Paraphrase
Great white sharks have around 300 teeth that they are losing constantly! Unlike humans, sharks continually regrow teeth and can grow a new tooth within 24 hours of losing it!	Sharks have a lot of teeth that they lose all the time. But they are always growing new teeth back quickly!

Day 1: Guided Notes

Follow along with Bea to complete the guided notes below.

Sharks use many different senses to find food. Their excellent sense of smell helps them detect prey from a quarter mile away and their sharp vision allows them to see even in dark waters.

Underline the most important details you want to remember.

Cover up the text and record your own paraphrase.

____

____

____

____

Check to make sure you remembered the important details and used your own words!

Today we learned...

Paraphrasing is NOT copying; it's putting information in your own words in a way that helps you understand and remember it

Everyone's paraphrase will look a little different, and that's OK

Day 1: Read and Respond

Step 1: Read the text from the shark exhibit below, or click or scan the QR code to listen.

Unlike most fish, which have smooth scales, a shark's skin is covered in tiny, tooth-like scales called denticles. These help sharks swim faster and more silently through the water.

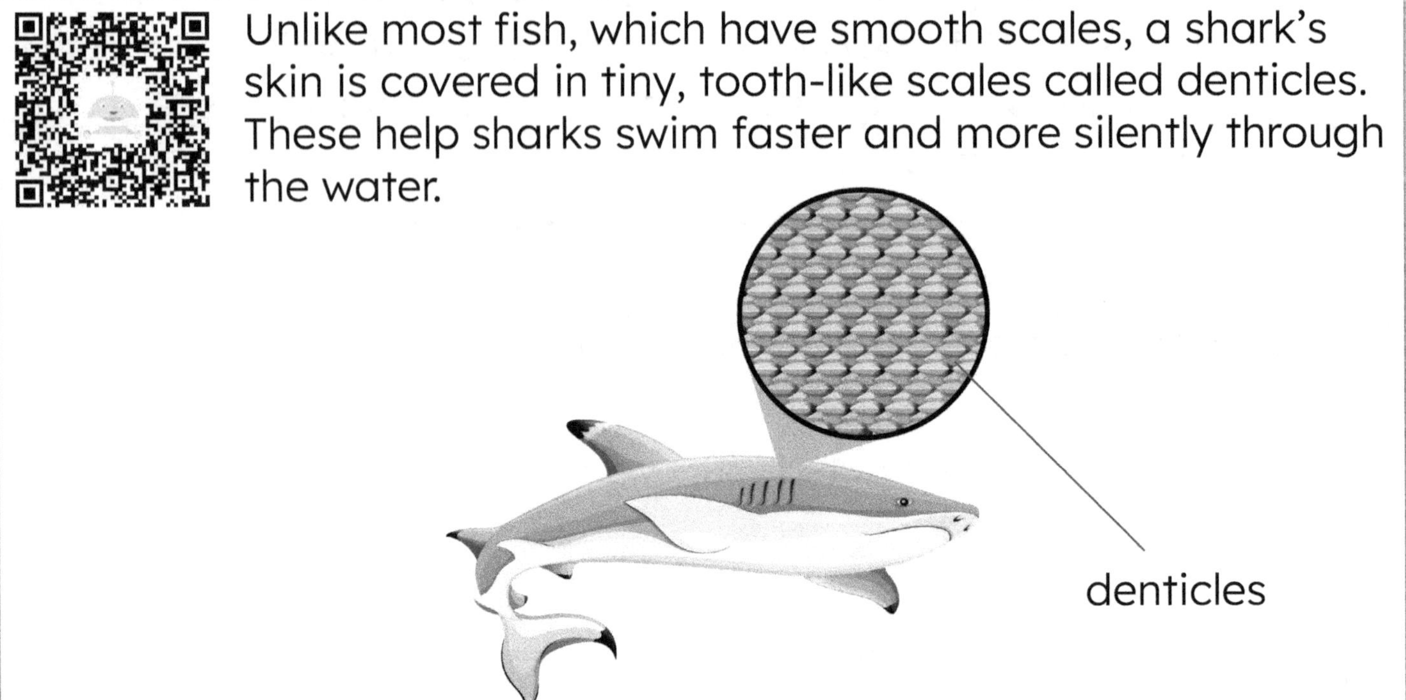

Step 2: Underline the most important information from the text you want to remember. Remember to focus on the big ideas and not just the tiny details!

Step 3: Cover up the text and record your paraphrase below.

____

____

____

____

____

Step 4: Uncover the text and check your paraphrase. Did you keep all of the important details while changing the wording? If not, give it another try!

Day 1: Read and Respond

Step 5: Read or listen to the next text from the shark exhibit below.

Many sharks have lighter undersides and darker backs, which is a type of camouflage called countershading. This helps them blend in with the ocean when hunting prey.

Step 6: Underline the most important information from the text you want to remember. Remember to focus on the big ideas and not just the tiny details!

Step 7: Cover up the text and record your paraphrase below.

____

____

____

____

____

Step 8: Uncover the text and check your paraphrase. Did you keep all of the important details while changing the wording? If not, give it another try!

Day 2: Language Lab

Read the mini-lesson. Then, practice the skill in parts 1 and 2.

Verbs are words that describe actions.
When the action is in the past (it already happened), the verb needs to be in the **past tense**.

Most of the time, to make a verb past tense, we add the ending -ed to the verb. For example: walk → walked. "I walked to the store yesterday."

There are rules we can use to figure out how to change a verb to the past tense.

Spelling Rules	Examples
General Rule: add -ed to the base verb	look → looked play → played
Verb ends in a consonant + y: change the y to i and add -ed	try → tried cry → cried
Verb ends in -e: add -d	love → loved bake → baked
Verb is one syllable, has one vowel, and ends in a consonant: double the final consonant and add -ed	nod → nodded rip → ripped

NOTE: Some verbs don't follow the regular rules, and we just have to learn them through practice! Here are some examples:

eat → ate
run → ran
see → saw
know → knew

Use these notes to help you with the questions on the next page!

Day 2: Language Lab

Part 1: Fill in the sentence with the **past tense** of the verb in parentheses.

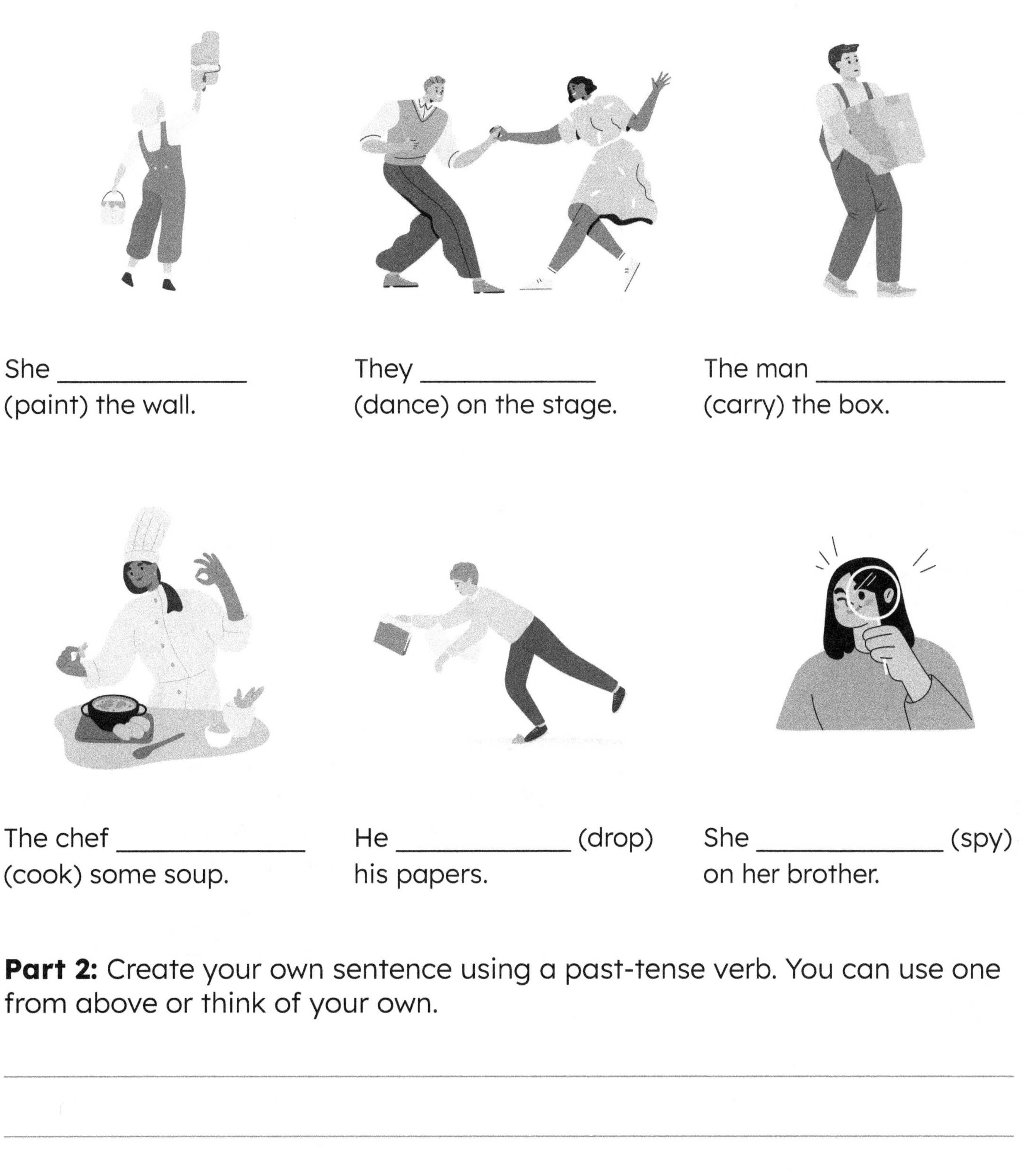

She ______________ (paint) the wall.

They _____________ (dance) on the stage.

The man ______________ (carry) the box.

The chef ______________ (cook) some soup.

He _____________ (drop) his papers.

She ______________ (spy) on her brother.

Part 2: Create your own sentence using a past-tense verb. You can use one from above or think of your own.

____

____

____

Day 2: Connect and Reflect

Follow the prompts to deepen your understanding of the lesson.

Focus on your favorite moment. Write down or draw your favorite part of today's lesson.

Pack your bags! What's something you learned that you want to take with you and remember later?

Make a real-world connection. How could paraphrasing help you explain something new to a friend?

Rate how you feel about this week's "Language Lab" skill: I can identify and use regular past-tense verbs.

Rate how you feel about this week's skill: I can show understanding by paraphrasing facts from an informational text.

Optional Support

Dig Deeper

Want more practice with paraphrasing?

Match each sentence on the left with a paraphrase on the right that keeps the same meaning. These are examples of how thoughts can be paraphrased.

Today was a really good day for me. ●	● It's a wet day!
Soccer is my favorite sport. ●	● I liked the movie a lot.
It's pouring down rain today! ●	● The beach is far from where I live.
I really enjoyed the movie. ●	● I don't want to hike.
I live 1,245 miles from the beach. ●	● I had a great day today.
I would rather not go hiking. ●	● The sport I like the most is soccer.

Optional Support

Climb Higher

Ready for a challenge when it comes to paraphrasing?

Can you fix the mistakes? Find the mistake in each paraphrase, then fix it so the paraphrase is correct!

1. **Original Sentence:** Blue whales are the largest animals on Earth and can grow up to 100 feet long.
   Paraphrase: Blue whales are the biggest animals in the world and can weigh a lot.
   What's Wrong? ______________________________
   ____
   Fix it! ______________________________
   ____

2. **Original Sentence:** Cacti store water in their thick stems, which helps them survive in dry deserts.
   Paraphrase: Cacti don't need any water, which helps them live in the desert without much water.
   What's Wrong? ______________________________
   ____
   Fix it! ______________________________
   ____

Challenge: Create your own paraphrase of the sentence below and include a mistake! See if a friend or family member can find what's wrong.

Original sentence: Astronauts wear unique suits that protect them from the freezing temperatures of space.

Day 1

- ❏ Video and Guided Notes
- ❏ Read and Respond
- ❏ Online Practice Levels 1 and 2

Day 2

- ❏ Language Lab
- ❏ Connect and Reflect
- ❏ Online Practice Levels 3 and 4

Day 3

- ❏ Words To Explore
- ❏ Online Practice Level 5
- ❏ Optional: Dig Deeper or Climb Higher

Lesson Goal: I can define summaries and evaluate if a summary is complete and accurate.

Record your thoughts:
Think about a skill you have. What are some ways you can improve that skill?

Record your thoughts on the right! →

A Word To Explore:

Resource

Something that helps or supports someone

Day 1: Guided Notes

Follow along with Bea to complete the guided notes below.

Summary

is a short ________ of the main idea and supporting details of a text.

Original Text	Justin's Summary
There are many ways that current space exploration is helping us learn about the universe. Astronauts in the International Space Station are studying how space affects the human body. Some are even testing new technology in zero gravity! Scientists are also sending robotic rovers to Mars to learn if life could survive there. Scientists are still researching how to send humans to Mars one day. In deep space, telescopes and probes are helping scientists study faraway galaxies and understand how the universe was formed. Some probes have traveled billions of miles to collect data.	Right now, there are a lot of ways space exploration is teaching us about the universe. Astronauts in the International Space Station are learning how space changes the human body. Scientists are sending rovers to Mars to see if life could survive there. And in deep space, there are telescopes and robots that are helping scientists learn how the universe was made.

What do you notice about Justin's summary compared to the original?

____

____

____

____

____

Day 1: Guided Notes

Follow along with Bea to complete the guided notes below.

Original Text

There are many ways that current space exploration is helping us learn about the universe. Astronauts in the International Space Station are studying how space affects the human body. Some are even testing new technology in zero gravity! Scientists are also sending robotic rovers to Mars to learn if life could survive there. Scientists are still researching how to send humans to Mars one day. In deep space, telescopes and probes are helping scientists study faraway galaxies and understand how the universe was formed. Some probes have traveled billions of miles to collect data.

Justin's First Summary

There are many ways space exploration helps us learn about the universe. Astronauts in the International Space Station study how space affects the human body. Scientists are working on ways to send people to Mars, which would be the most exciting thing ever! Telescopes help scientists study faraway galaxies.

Find the supporting detail from the original text that Justin missed.

A complete summary...

- ❏ Includes the main idea
- ❏ Includes the supporting details
- ❏ Is paraphrased in the summarizer's own words
- ❏ Includes only the ideas in the original text

Today we learned...

Summaries are short recaps that tell us the most important information

Knowing how to identify a strong summary makes it easier to understand and remember key ideas

Day 1: Read and Respond

Step 1: Read the informational text below, or click or scan the QR code to listen.

Original Text

Octopuses have unique features that help them survive in the ocean. They have eight arms and no bones, which lets them squeeze into small spaces to hide from predators. Octopuses also use their arms to taste things! They can change the color and texture of their skin to camouflage themselves and avoid predators. Some octopuses even squirt dark ink to distract predators while they swim away. Scientists have even seen octopuses open jars to get food!

Step 2: Read or listen to the summary of the text below.

Summary

Octopuses have many special abilities that help them survive. They have no bones, so they can hide from predators in tight places. It would be pretty awesome if humans could do that. Octopuses can also change the color and look of their skin to blend in with the ocean so predators don't see them.

Day 1: Read and Respond

Step 3: Use the checklist to evaluate the summary. Circle the check mark ✓ if the summary follows the rule or the ✗ if it does not. Explain your choices.

✓ ✗	Includes the main idea
Explanation:	
✓ ✗	Includes all of the key supporting details
Explanation:	
✓ ✗	Paraphrased into the summarizer's own words
Explanation:	
✓ ✗	Only includes information from the original text (no opinions or extras added)
Explanation:	

Step 4: Choose one of the rules from the checklist above that you found the summary did NOT follow. Suggest a way that the author could change their summary so that it follows the rule.

____

____

____

____

____

Day 2: Language Lab

Read the mini-lesson. Then, practice the skill in parts 1 through 3.

Verbs are words that describe actions.
When the action is happening now, the verb needs to be in the **present tense**.

Most of the time, to make a verb present tense, we add -s to the end of the verb. For example: Live → lives. "She lives in the red house."

★ If the subject of the sentence is "I," "we," "you," or "they," the verb stays in its base form.
Examples: "I **play** baseball." "We **love** pizza." "You **like** cookies." "They **run** fast."

If the subject of the sentence is "he," "she," "it," or a specific person, follow these rules:

Spelling Rules	Examples
Verb ends in ch, sh, ss, x, z, or o: add -es	watch → watches fix → fixes
Verb ends in consonant + y: drop the y and add ies	try → tries cry → cries
Most other verbs: add s	love→ loves swim → swims

Part 1: Circle the correct present-tense verb for each sentence.

1. He (walk/walks) to the park every day.
2. I (feed/feeds) my cat.
3. Lily (try/tries) her best on every test.
4. The boy (catch/catches) the ball.
5. We (eat/eats) pasta every Friday after practice.

Day 2: Language Lab

Part 2: Complete the sentences by making the verb in parentheses present tense.

Lucas ____________ (eat) chocolate ice cream.

I ____________ (study) math facts every day.

My sister ____________ (carry) the heavy bag.

The bee ____________ (buzz) around the yellow flower.

We ____________ (sit) at the round table for lunch.

He ____________ (get) up early to go to the gym.

It ____________ (rain) in the springtime.

Erin ____________ (go) to every soccer game.

Part 3: Find the present-tense verbs you created in the blanks in the words search below! Words can appear horizontally, vertically, or diagonally.

S	Y	M	S	Y	Y	U	D	L	Q
I	O	T	D	E	W	U	P	R	L
T	E	U	C	A	R	R	I	E	S
G	T	T	B	E	D	W	M	B	G
S	K	Q	S	U	L	H	Z	A	G
S	M	A	T	S	Z	A	G	K	N
E	A	T	S	H	I	Z	M	R	C
F	M	L	G	E	F	R	E	Q	K
R	A	I	N	S	X	Q	T	S	S
M	P	X	Y	G	O	E	S	B	V

Day 2: Connect and Reflect

Follow the prompts to deepen your understanding of the lesson.

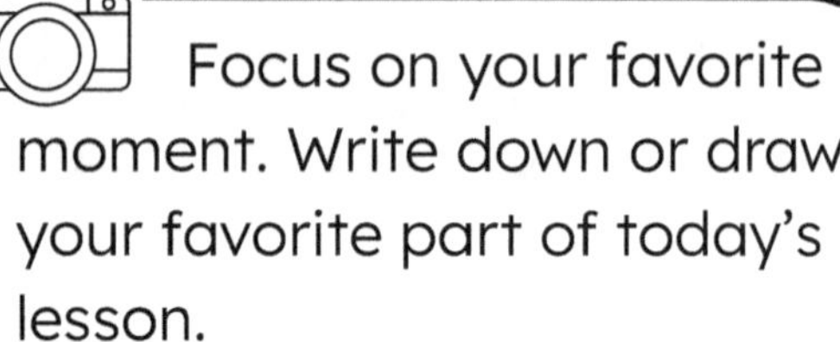

Focus on your favorite moment. Write down or draw your favorite part of today's lesson.

Pack your bags! What's something you learned that you want to take with you and remember later?

Make a real-world connection. Why is it important to think of ways to get better at something?

Rate how you feel about this week's "Language Lab" skill: I can define and use present-tense verbs.

Rate how you feel about this week's skill: I can define summaries and decide if a summary is complete and accurate.

Day 3: Words To Explore (Unit 1)

Explore and review the words to explore from this unit. Add in your own picture to help you remember what the word means.

Word	Definition/Example	Picture
Rare	- not often found or seen *They found a rare gem in the old mine.*	
Adapt	- to change for a certain use or become used to something *When the lights went out, we had to adapt by using flashlights.*	
Loyal	- Faithful to someone or something, especially in hard times. *Emily was a loyal friend that helped when I was sick.*	
Absorb	- to take in or soak something up *The sponge could absorb the water I spilled.*	
Gripe	- To complain about something *John couldn't help but gripe when his dinner was served cold.*	

Day 3: Words To Explore (Unit 1)

Explore and review the words to explore from this unit. Add in your own picture to help you remember what the word means.

Word	Definition/Example	Picture
Detect	- to find or notice something *The dog detected the treat in my hand.*	
Resource	- something that helps or supports someone *This book is a great resource for teaching me how to sew!*	

Day 3: Words To Explore (Unit 1)

Use your knowledge of the vocabulary words from this unit to complete the crossword puzzle. Fill in each blank with the word from the word bank that makes the most sense in the sentence. Feel free to look back at your notes if you get stuck!

rare	adapt	loyal	absorb	gripe	detect	resource

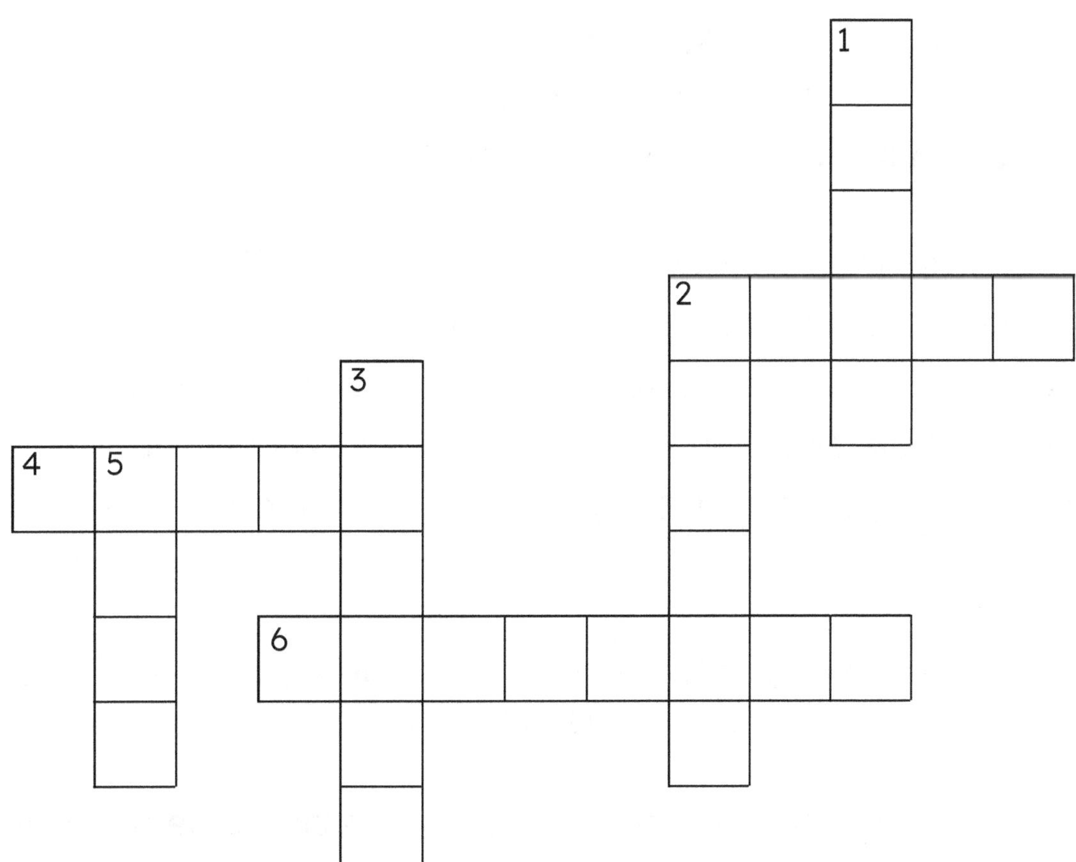

Across

2. Bears _____ to cold weather by growing thick fur.
4. You can _____ all you want, but you still have to do your chores.
6. A map is a helpful _____ if you get lost and need to find your way.

Down

1. My dog is so _____; he waits for me by the door every day.
2. The towel can _____ all the water on the floor.
3. The camera will _____ if someone walks into the room.
5. It is _____ to see a hummingbird in the garden; they hardly ever visit.

Optional Support

Dig Deeper

Want more practice with evaluating summaries?

Time to color code!

Step 1: Read the text below, then use colors to highlight/underline the following in the text.

Main idea: Blue
Supporting details: Green
Extra information/non supporting details: Red

Libraries are important places in many communities. Many libraries have computers and printers that people can use for free. Some libraries run programs for homework help after school. A few even let people borrow tools or games to use at home. Most libraries are quiet places where people are expected to speak softly.

Step 2: Use the same colors to highlight the same parts that have been paraphrased from the original in the summary below.

Libraries help communities in many ways. At libraries, people can use computers and printers without paying for them. Some libraries even have programs that help students with their homework.

Step 3: Compare the original text to the summary using your color coding. Complete the checklist below by circling if the summary follows each rule or not.

Main idea	ALL Supporting details	Paraphrased in own words	No extra information
✓ ✗	✓ ✗	✓ ✗	✓ ✗

Optional Support

Climb Higher

Ready for a challenge
when it comes evaluating summaries?

Let's compare summaries! Read the original text below, then read both summaries.

Libraries are important places in many communities. Many libraries have computers and printers that people can use for free. Some libraries run programs for homework help after school. A few even let people borrow tools or games to use at home. Most libraries are quiet places where people are expected to speak softly.

Summary #1	Summary #2
Libraries are quiet places where people have to speak softly. People can also get homework help or use the printer. Some libraries let people borrow books and tools.	Libraries help communities in many ways. They let people borrow books and tools, use free computers and printers, and attend programs like homework help.

Think about the summaries you read. Which summary do you think is stronger? Why?

____

____

____

How would you fix the summary you thought was weaker?

____

____

____

Day 1

- ❏ Video and Guided Notes
- ❏ Read and Respond
- ❏ Online Practice Levels 1, 2, and 3

Day 2

- ❏ Language Lab
- ❏ Connect and Reflect
- ❏ Online Assessment
- ❏ Optional: Dig Deeper/Climb Higher

Lesson Goal: I can use my skills to make accurate and clear summaries of nonfiction texts.

Record your thoughts: Think of your favorite book, show, or movie. What are the main reasons it is your favorite?

Record your thoughts on the right! →

A Word To Explore:

Distraction

Something that makes it hard to pay attention or focus

Day 1: Guided Notes

Follow along with Bea to complete the guided notes below.

Summary -

a short version of the most important parts of a text

To Write a Summary:

1. Find the main idea and supporting details
2. Paraphrase the important information
3. Check that all the information is there

Sharks have unique features that help them locate and catch prey. Their excellent sense of smell helps them detect prey from far away, and their good vision helps them see in dark water. Sharks can also have around 300 sharp teeth that they lose and regrow often. Some sharks can even grow a new tooth in just 24 hours! That's why many people find shark teeth washed up on the beach!

Underline the main idea of the text or mark it with "MI."

Find two more supporting details and mark them with "SD."

Day 1: Guided Notes

Follow along with Bea to complete the guided notes below.

Sharks have unique features that help them locate and catch prey.

Record your paraphrase of the first sentence, or copy Bea's.

Their excellent sense of smell helps them detect prey from far away, and their good vision helps them see in dark water.

Paraphrase the second sentence.

Sharks can also have around 300 sharp teeth that they lose and regrow often.

Paraphrase the last sentence.

Check your work!

A complete summary:

- ❏ Includes the main idea
- ❏ Includes the supporting details
- ❏ Is paraphrased in the summarizer's own words
- ❏ Includes only the ideas in the original text

Day 1: Read and Respond

Read the text below, or click or scan the QR code to listen. Then, follow the steps to practice writing a summary.

Ants at Work

Ants have important jobs that help their colony survive. Worker ants search for food and carry it back to the nest to feed others. Soldier ants defend the colony from threats, like spiders or other insects. Ants also build tunnels underground so they can travel easily to different places.

Step 1: Highlight/underline the main idea, and mark it with "MI."

Step 2: Highlight/underline two supporting details, and mark them with "SD."

Step 3: Use the organizer on the next page to complete your summary.

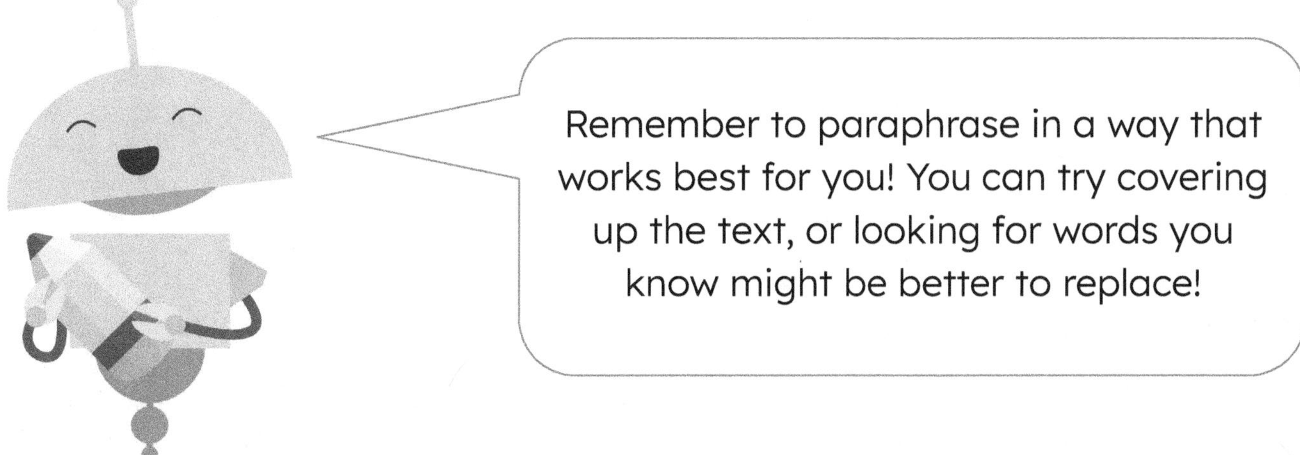

Day 1: Read and Respond

Paraphrase the Main Idea:

Paraphrase Detail 1:

Paraphrase Detail 2:

Put it all together! Write your paraphrased main idea and details.

Check your work! My summary...

- ❏ Has the main idea
- ❏ Has the supporting details
- ❏ Is in my own words
- ❏ Only includes info from the original text

Day 2: Language Lab

Read the mini-lesson. Then, practice the skill in Part 1.

Verbs are words that describe actions.
When the action happens in the future, the verb needs to be in the **future tense**.

To show an action that has not happened yet, we can follow one rule for making the future tense: Add the word "will" before the verb.

Examples:

- I **will** run tomorrow.
- She **will** eat pizza for dinner.
- We **will** go to the store in the morning.
- They **will** talk later.

Part 1: Complete each sentence with the future tense of one of the verbs in the box below. The first one has been done for you as an example.

draw ~~build~~ bake play run read clean

1. We <u>will build</u> a sandcastle at the beach tomorrow.
2. I ______________ soccer at recess this week.
3. Lily ______________ her room since her mom asked her to.
4. Shannon ______________ her book all night.
5. My dad and I ______________ a cake for his birthday.
6. We ______________ a picture of a family.
7. He ______________ quickly in his race on Sunday.

Day 2: Connect and Reflect

Follow the prompts to deepen your understanding of the lesson.

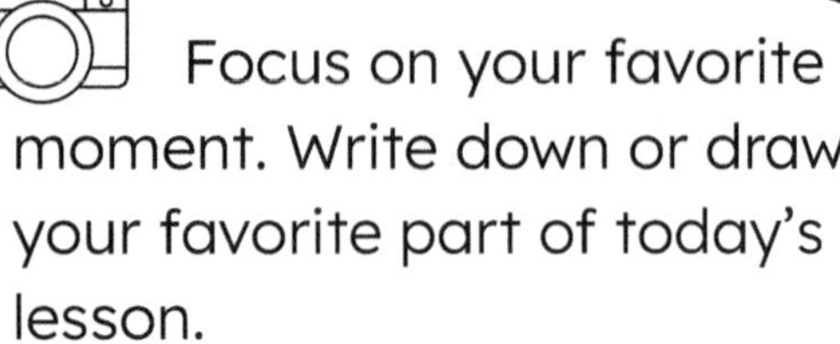

Focus on your favorite moment. Write down or draw your favorite part of today's lesson.

Pack your bags! What's something you learned that you want to take with you and remember later?

Make a real-world connection. How could summarizing help you communicate with friends and family?

Rate how you feel about this week's "Language Lab" skill: I can identify and use future-tense verbs.

Rate how you feel about this week's skill: I can write accurate and clear summaries of nonfiction texts.

Optional Support

Dig Deeper

Want more practice with writing a summary?

Part 1: Read the text below.

Firefighters work to protect people in many ways. They respond quickly when there are fires, car accidents, or other emergencies. To do their job safely, firefighters have to wear heavy gear. Firefighters also educate people on how to prevent fires.

Part 2: Which of the following sentences from the text is the **main idea?** Look for the sentence that mentions the topic and the author's most important point.

a. They respond quickly when there are fires, car accidents, and other emergencies.
b. Firefighters work to protect people in many ways.
c. To do their job safely, firefighters have to wear heavy gear.
d. Firefighters also educate people on how to prevent fires.

Part 3: Put a check mark by the two sentences that explain, describe, or prove **how** firefighters protect people. These are the supporting details.

❏ They respond quickly when there are fires, car accidents, or other emergencies.
❏ To do their job safely, firefighters have to wear heavy gear.
❏ Firefighters also educate people on how to prevent fires.

Optional Support

Dig Deeper: Part 2

Part 4: Practice paraphrasing by matching the original sentences to the paraphrases that make sense. **NOTE:** There are only three sentences and five possible paraphrases, so choose the best one for each sentence.

Original	Paraphrase
Firefighters work to protect people in many ways.	Firefighters are quick to help when there are emergencies.
They respond quickly when there are fires, car accidents, or other emergencies.	Firefighters wear special gear to do their jobs.
Firefighters also educate people on how to prevent fires.	Firefighters help keep people safe in a lot of ways.
	Firefighters are really cool and important.
	Firefighters also teach people how to stop fires from happening.

Part 5: Put it all together! Copy the paraphrases above onto the lines below to create a complete summary. Don't forget to write the main idea and details in the correct order so that the summary makes sense!

Optional Support

Climb Higher

Ready for a challenge
when it comes writing summaries?

Sentence Summary Showdown

Read each text on the left. Using your summarizing skills, write a **one sentence** summary for the text. Try to include the important information, without getting stuck on small details!

Text	Summary
Bridges help people and vehicles cross over water, roads, or valleys. Some bridges are made of metal and concrete, while others are built with wood or stone. Engineers plan bridges carefully so they are strong and safe to use.	→
Musicians perform music for others to enjoy. Some play instruments like guitars or drums, while others sing or write songs. Musicians often practice for hours to improve their skills and perform on stage or in recordings.	→
Rainforests are warm, wet places filled with many different plants and animals. The tall trees create shade, and the leaves help trap moisture. Rainforests are important because they help clean the air and give us oxygen.	→

Unit 2: Find Your Voice: Informational Writing

Day 1

- ❏ Video and Guided Notes
- ❏ Writing Project: Part 1
- ❏ Online Practice Levels 1 and 2

Day 2

- ❏ Language Lab
- ❏ Connect and Reflect
- ❏ Online Practice Levels 3 and 4

Day 3

- ❏ Read and Respond
- ❏ Online Practice Level 5
- ❏ Optional: Dig Deeper/Climb Higher

Lesson Goal: I can identify the structure of an informational paragraph.

Record your thoughts: Is it important to keep your writing organized? Why or why not?

Record your thoughts on the right! →

A Word To Explore:

Graze

To feed on growing grass
OR
to touch lightly

Day 1: Guided Notes

Follow along with Bea to complete the guided notes below.

Informational paragraphs

are written to teach the reader about a certain topic.

Paragraphs

are around three to ________ sentences of writing.

Paragraph structure

is how the sentences in a paragraph are ______________.

Giraffes have many special adaptations. They have long necks that help them reach leaves high up in trees. Giraffes also have long legs that help them run quickly to escape predators. Their spotted patterns help them blend in with the tall grasses. These special features help giraffes survive.

Topic sentence - the first sentence of a paragraph that tells the reader the topic and main idea

Supporting details - explain, describe, or prove the main idea from the topic sentence

Closing sentence - briefly reminds the reader what they learned

Day 1: Guided Notes

Follow along with Bea to complete the guided notes below.

Label the topic sentence, supporting details, and closing sentence in the space on the right of the paragraph.

Lunar New Year is a holiday celebrated in many Asian countries. It marks the beginning of a new year based on the moon's calendar. Families often clean their homes to sweep away bad luck and make room for good luck. People celebrate with fireworks, special foods, and red decorations. Lunar New Year is recognized in many ways to welcome a new year and honor Asian culture.

Today we learned...

Informational paragraphs are written to teach the reader. A paragraph can follow this common structure:

1. Topic sentence
2. Supporting details
3. Closing sentence

Writing Project: Part 1

For this step, you need to **choose your biome**. Remember to choose a topic that you like and want to write about!

Scan or click the QR code to access the slideshow that will help you complete the same step in the writing process as Bea!

The biome I want to write about is the...

Why do you want to write about this biome?
Write and/or draw your response here!

Day 2: Language Lab

Read the mini-lesson. Then, practice the skill in parts 1 and 2.

A **contraction** is formed when two words are combined to make a smaller word that means the same thing. One or more letters get taken out and replaced with an apostrophe. We use contractions to make speaking and writing quicker and to make it sound more conversational.

Example: In this sentence, "I did not like the movie," the words did and not can be combined into a short contraction: didn't.

To make a contraction, the space is removed between two words, and the letters that get removed are replaced with an apostrophe.

Here is a chart you can keep to learn some common contractions:

am Take out the **a**. I am → I'm	is Take out the **i**. he is → he's it is → it's what is → what's that is → that's	are Take out the **a**. you are → you're we are → we're they are → they're
has Take out the **h** and **a**. he has → he's she has → she's who has → who's	not Take out the **o**. can not → can't* do not → don't is not → isn't will not → won't*	have Take out the **h** and **a**. I have → I've you have → you've we have → we've they have → they've
would Take out **w**, **o**, **u**, and **l**. I would → I'd you would → you'd we would → we'd he would → he'd	will Take out the **w** and **i**. I will → I'll you will → you'll we will → we'll she will → she'll	had Take out the **h** and **a**. I had → I'd you had → you'd we had → we'd they had → they'd

* These contractions don't follow the rule exactly.

Day 2: Language Lab

Part 1: Constellation Contractions - Help finish the constellations by combining the two words into their contraction. Remember to look at the chart if you get stuck!

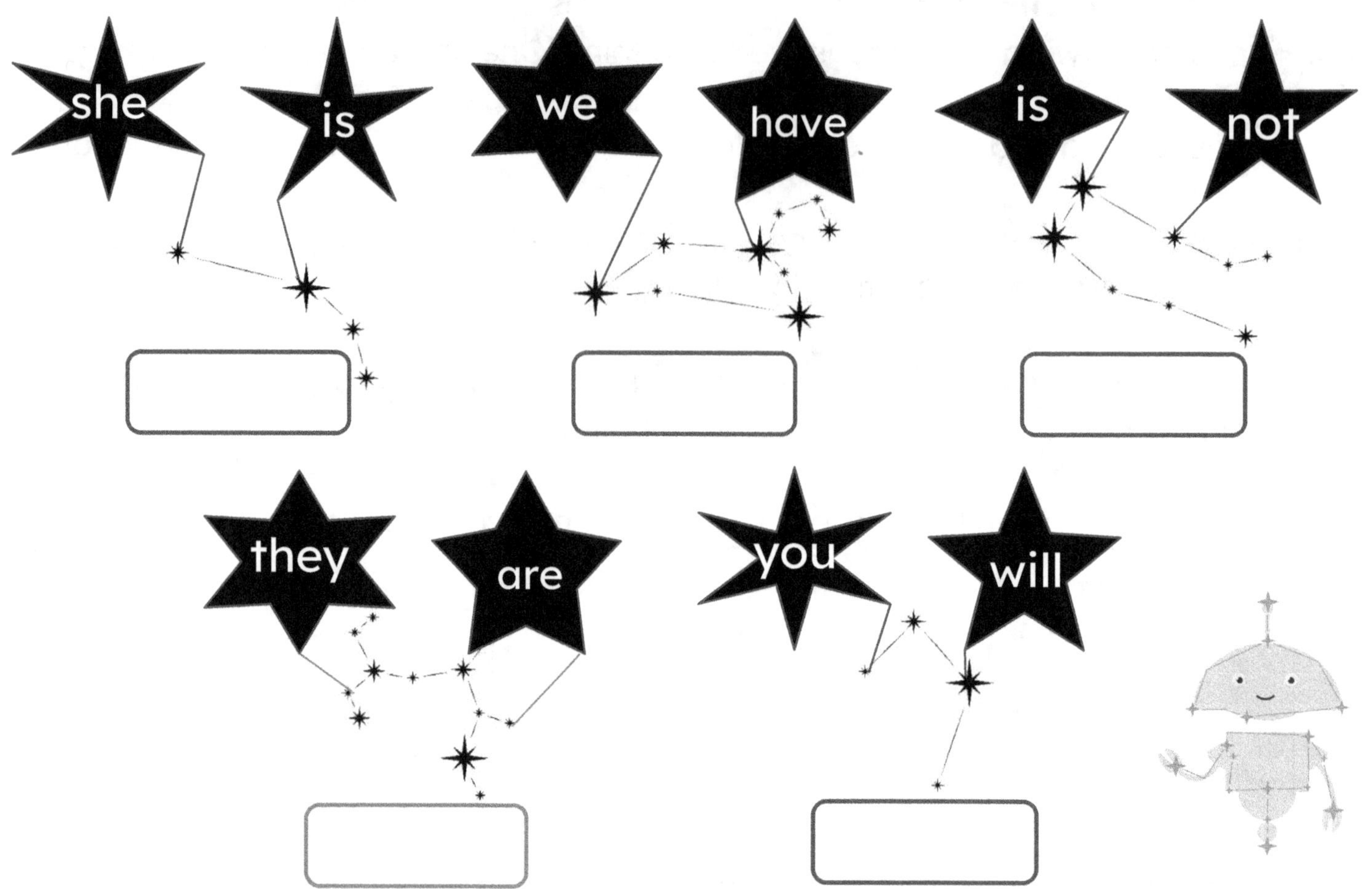

Part 2: Underline the contraction in each sentence and write the two words that made it.

1. She didn't bring a coat even though it was cold.		
2. I'm going to see a movie tomorrow.		
3. Do you know what's for dinner tonight?		
4. You'll be late if you do not get going!		
5. I'd like to go home now.		
6. He's the best pitcher on the baseball team.		
7. They'd better be careful out there!		

Day 2: Connect and Reflect

Follow the prompts to deepen your understanding of the lesson.

Focus on your favorite moment. Write down or draw your favorite part of today's lesson.

Pack your bags! What's something you learned that you want to take with you and remember later?

Make a real-world connection. How might following a routine (like writing follows a structure) make your day easier?

Rate how you feel about this week's "Language Lab" skill: I can define and use common contractions.

Rate how you feel about this week's skill: I can identify the structure of an informational paragraph.

Day 3: Read and Respond

Read the text below, or click or scan the QR code to listen. Then, answer the questions on the next page.

Yellowstone National Park

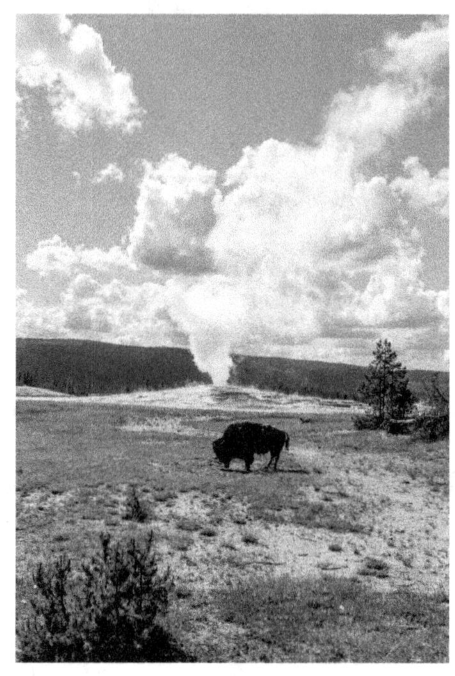

Yellowstone National Park is a place filled with natural wonders and amazing sights. It was the first national park in the world and is known for its forests, rivers, tall mountains, and natural hot springs. Deep below the ground, there is even a giant volcano! One of the most famous sights in the park is Old Faithful, a geyser that shoots hot water and steam high into the air. It sprays like a fountain about every 90 minutes, and visitors from around the world come to see it.

But Yellowstone is not just known for its land; it's also home to many wild animals. If you visit, you might see bison walking across the road, elk grazing in a meadow, or even a bear in the distance. Wolves also live in the park, though they are harder to spot. Park rangers help protect these animals and make sure visitors stay safe. People come to Yellowstone to hike, camp, and explore nature. It's a place full of wild beauty, where people can enjoy nature and learn why it's important to protect it.

Day 3: Read and Respond

Use the text about Yellowstone National Park to answer the questions.

1. What is below the ground at Yellowstone National Park?
   a. Just dirt
   b. A pool of water
   c. A volcano
   d. Wild animals

2. What is Old Faithful?
   a. A waterfall
   b. A geyser
   c. A bear
   d. A mountain

3. What kinds of animals can be found in Yellowstone National Park? List at least three.

____

____

4. What do park rangers do in Yellowstone?

____

____

5. Would you like to visit Yellowstone National Park? Why or why not?

____

____

____

____

Optional Support

Dig Deeper

Want more practice with informational paragraph structure?

The sentences at the bottom of the page all belong in the same paragraph, but they are out of order! Your job is to put the paragraph back in order by following the common paragraph structure you learned in this lesson.

Step 1: Cut out and read each sentence.
Step 2: Use the organizer to put the sentences in the correct order.
Step 3: Check to make sure your answers fit with the definitions of each part of the paragraphs.
Step 4: Paste down your answers into their final spots.

Topic Sentence (tells the reader the topic and what they'll mostly be learning about):
Supporting Details (give the reader facts that explain the topic sentence and main idea):
Closing Sentence (reminds the reader what they learned about; sometimes sounds similar to the topic sentence but usually includes a detail from the text):

Lava flows can burn forests and cover roads and buildings.
Volcanoes are mountains that can erupt with hot lava.
When ash falls from the sky, it can cover the ground.
Volcanoes are powerful natural features that can change the land.
Some eruptions can create new islands and landforms.

Optional Support

Climb Higher

Ready for a challenge when it comes informational paragraph structure?

Below are sentences from two different paragraphs. The problem is that they've been scrambled together! Your job is to separate the sentences into two paragraphs and then put them in the correct order so the paragraphs make sense!

Step 1: Cut out and read the sentences below.
Step 2: Sort the sentences into two paragraphs. (Think about the topics!)
Step 3: Sort each paragraph into the correct structure: topic sentence, supporting details, and closing sentence.
Step 4: Check your work to make sure your paragraphs make sense.
Step 5: Paste your answers onto the next page.

They use their trunks to drink water, pick up food, and spray themselves to cool off.
Dolphins are animals that live in the oceans all around the world.
Elephants are large animals that live on land in places like Africa and Asia.
Dolphins use movement and sound to live and stay safe in the water.
Elephants live in family groups and stay close to each other.
They use sounds and whistles to talk to each other under the water.
Their big ears help them stay cool in hot weather.
Dolphins swim to the surface to breathe through a blowhole.
They jump, play, and swim fast to find food or move through the water.
Elephants have body parts and behaviors that help them live on land with their herd.

Optional Support

Climb Higher Continued

Paragraph 1 Topic: ____________________

Topic Sentence (tells the reader the topic and what they'll mostly be learning about):
Supporting Details (give the reader facts that explain the topic sentence and main idea):
Closing Sentence (reminds the reader what they learned about; sometimes sounds similar to the topic sentence but usually includes a detail from the text):

Paragraph 2 Topic: ____________________

Topic Sentence (tells the reader the topic and what they'll mostly be learning about):
Supporting Details (give the reader facts that explain the topic sentence and main idea):
Closing Sentence (reminds the reader what they learned about; sometimes sounds similar to the topic sentence but usually includes a detail from the text):

Day 1

- ❏ Video and Guided Notes
- ❏ Writing Project: Part 2
- ❏ Online Practice Levels 1 and 2

Day 2

- ❏ Language Lab
- ❏ Connect and Reflect
- ❏ Online Practice Levels 3 and 4
- ❏ Optional: Dig Deeper or Climb Higher

Lesson Goal: I can write clear and focused topic sentences.

Record your thoughts:
What is your favorite way to learn something new?

Record your thoughts on the right! →

A Word To Explore:

Marsh

An area of soft, wet land that usually has a lot of grassy plants

Day 1: Guided Notes

Follow along with Bea to complete the guided notes below.

Topic sentences

tell the reader what the paragraph is mostly about. They include the **topic** and the **main idea**.

We research to find out facts about a topic and understand it better.

Guiding questions help us focus on finding the important information when we research.

Circle the nonfiction books that will teach true facts.

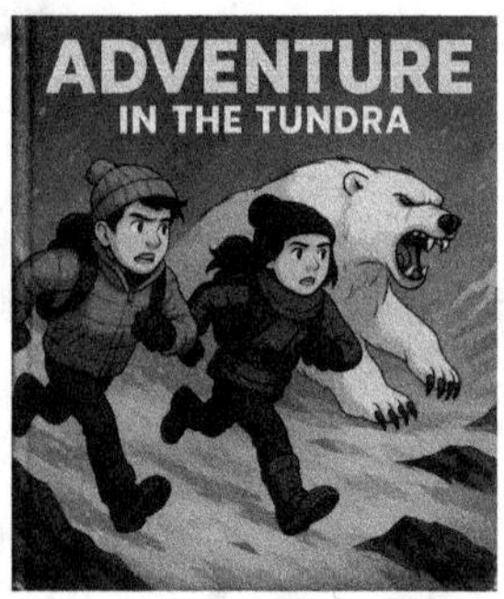

Day 1: Guided Notes

Follow along with Bea to complete the guided notes below.

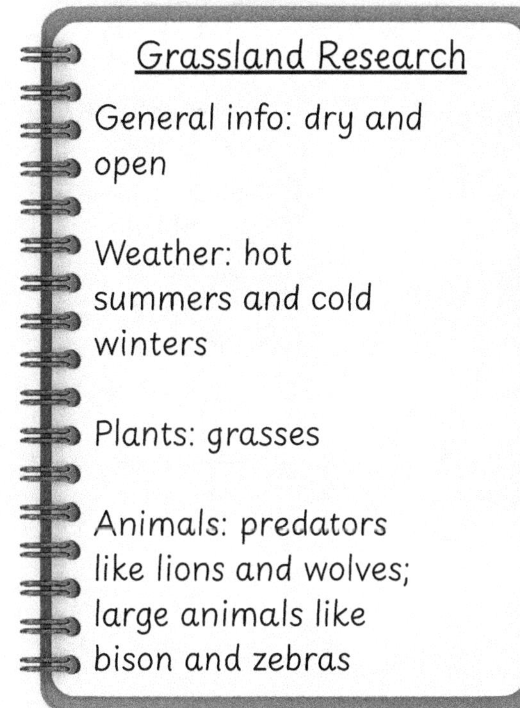

Wetland Research

General info: wet and marshy with standing water

Weather: warm summers and cold winters

Plants: many plants in the water like cattails, reeds, and water lilies

Animals: frogs, turtles, ducks, lots of insects

Use the research to fill in a describing word or two for the grasslands.

The grassland is a ______________ place where animals live and grasses grow.

Create a topic sentence for the wetlands using the sentence frame.

The ____________ is a ______________ place where ________________________
____
____

Today we learned...

Topic sentences are the building blocks of paragraphs that tell readers what the paragraph is about

Research helps us learn more about the topic

Writing Project: Part 2

For this step, you need to **research** and **write your topic sentence**.

Scan or click the QR code to access the slideshow that will help you complete the same step in the writing process as Bea!

Research Notes:

Use the sentence frame and research to write your topic sentence.

The ____________ is a ______________________________ place where

biome / describing word(s)

____

____

main idea

Day 2: Language Lab

Read the mini-lesson. Then, practice the skill in parts 1 and 2.

There, Their, and They're

All three versions of the word sound the same, but they are spelled differently and mean different things. Use this chart to help you remember which is the right word to use!

THERE	Refers to a place *The arrow points over there.* *There is the pencil.*
THEiR	Belongs to someone or something *That is their toy.* *Their trophy is huge!*
THEY'RE (A)	Contraction of the words "they are" *They're my best friends.* *I hope they're having fun.*

Part 1: Fill in the blanks with the correct version of there, their, or they're.

1. ____________ going to the park after lunch to play soccer.
2. The kids left ____________ backpacks at home.
3. Have you been ____________ yet?
4. I think ____________ planning a party for Mia!
5. Look over ____________!
6. The dog barks when ____________ owners get home.

Day 2: Language Lab

Part 2: Cut out the sentences at the bottom of the page. Sort them into the box that shows the correct word that should fill in the blank. Remember to check your work before pasting them down!

There	Their	They're

_____ is a spider on the wall!	The cats are chasing _____ toys.	_____ going to the zoo this weekend.	Please put your shoes over _____ by the door.
The students forgot _____ math books.	_____ are many stars in the sky.	I think _____ playing tag on the playground.	_____ excited about the trip.
Mom said _____ almost ready to leave.	My neighbors are painting _____ fence blue.	The kids rode _____ bikes to the park.	Is _____ any juice left in the fridge?

Day 2: Connect and Reflect

Follow the prompts to deepen your understanding of the lesson.

Focus on your favorite moment. Write down or draw your favorite part of today's lesson.

Pack your bags! What's something you learned that you want to take with you and remember later?

Make a real-world connection. What kind of topic sentence would you use to introduce yourself? Think about how to tell someone what you like to do!

Rate how you feel about this week's "Language Lab" skill: I can use the correct form of there, their, or they're.

Rate how you feel about this week's skill: I can write clear and focused topic sentences.

Optional Support

Dig Deeper

Want more practice with writing topic sentences?

Topic sentences tell the reader the main idea of a paragraph. You'll read some research notes, then use the sentence frame to write your own topic sentence.

Each sentence frame follows this structure:
[Topic] is a [describing word] thing/place/tool that [main idea].

Instructions: Use the facts to figure out the main idea, and fill in the blanks to write a clear topic sentence.

1. Topic: Pencils
Research Notes:
- People use pencils to write and draw.
- Pencils can be erased and used again.
- They are helpful for school and learning.

A ____________ is a ____________ tool that ________________________________
topic describing word

____.
main idea

2. Topic: Libraries
Research Notes:
- Libraries let people borrow books for free.
- They are quiet places.
- Many libraries have computers, story times, and learning events.

A ____________ is a ____________ place that ________________________________
topic describing word

____.
main idea

Optional Support

Climb Higher

Ready for a challenge when it comes to writing topic sentences?

Read the informational paragraphs below. The topic sentences are missing! Use the supporting details and the closing sentence to figure out the main idea, then write a topic sentence that fits each paragraph.

____

____

Slides let you zoom down fast, and swings help you feel like you're flying. Some playgrounds even have climbing walls or spinning equipment. All of these things help kids have fun and stay active.

____

____

They wear heavy gear to protect themselves from heat and smoke. They use special tools and carry hoses that spray water. They even rescue people and animals from dangerous situations. Firefighters are trained to help during emergencies.

____

____

They happen when the Earth's plates move suddenly. Sometimes, they can shake buildings and roads. People who live in areas with earthquakes often have safety plans. Earthquakes can cause damage, but people can prepare for them.

Day 1

- ❑ Video and Guided Notes
- ❑ Writing Project: Part 3
- ❑ Online Practice Levels 1 and 2

Day 2

- ❑ Language Lab
- ❑ Connect and Reflect
- ❑ Online Practice Levels 3 and 4

Day 3

- ❑ Read and Respond
- ❑ Online Assessment
- ❑ Optional: Dig Deeper/ Climb Higher

Lesson Goal: I can develop supporting details to add depth to informational writing.

Record your thoughts: Have you ever had to explain something to someone? How did you help them learn?

Record your thoughts on the right! →

A Word To Explore:

Grasp

To hold onto something

Day 1: Guided Notes

Follow along with Bea to complete the guided notes below.

Supporting details

explain, describe, or prove the main idea.

In the tundra, temperatures often drop far below freezing, and snow covers the ground most of the year.

Paraphrase this fact about the tundra's weather.

____

____

The ground of the tundra is frozen all year. Plants like trees and flowers with larger root systems can't survive since their roots can't grow in frozen soil. Because of this, only smaller plants that live on the surface of the ground or rocks can grow.

Underline the information you think is most important.

Finish the sentence with the information you think should come next.

Because the ground is frozen, ____________________________

____

Day 1: Guided Notes

Follow along with Bea to complete the guided notes below.

 Lemming

 Gull

 Penguin

 Snowy Owl

 Polar Bear

 Lynx

 Arctic Fox

 Caribou

Record a supporting detail that will help readers learn about the types of animals in the tundra. Then, record why you chose those animals.

Some of the animals that can live in the tundra are ______________________

____

I chose these animals because ______________________________

____

Today we learned...

We write supporting details to explain more about our main idea to our readers

After doing more research, we can paraphrase or summarize what we learn to create supporting details

Writing Project: Part 3

Look back at your notes from Part 2 to find your topic sentence.
Remember to save this page for next time!

For this step, you need to **research** further if needed and **write your supporting details**.

Scan or click the QR code to access the slideshow that will help you complete the same step in the writing process as Bea!

Supporting Detail 1: What is the weather like in your biome?

Supporting Detail 2: What kinds of plants grow there?

Supporting Detail 3: What kinds of animals live there?

Day 2: Language Lab

Read the mini-lesson. Then, practice the skill in parts 1 and 2.

Your and You’re

Both versions of this word sound the same, but they are spelled differently and have different meanings. Use this chart to help you remember which is the right word to use.

YOUR	Shows that something belongs to you *That is your pizza.* *Go get your coat.*
A YOU’RE	Is a contraction of the words “you” and “are” *You’re a great friend.* *You’re so kind!*

Part 1: Fill in the blanks with the correct version of your or you’re.

1. Is that ____________ backpack on the floor?
2. Can I have a bite of ____________ sandwich?
3. I think ____________ going to love this movie!
4. ____________ drawing looks great!
5. ____________ the best friend ever.
6. If ____________ hungry, we can eat dinner early.
7. This might be ____________ seat.

Day 2: Language Lab

Part 2: Crack the secret message! Read each sentence and decide if "your" or "you're" belongs in the blank. Circle the correct word. Then, find the letter next to your answer and write that letter in the matching number space at the bottom. The first one is done for you!

1. Is that _____ pencil on the floor?		**2.** I think _____ going to like this book.		**3.** Don't forget to brush _____ teeth.	
your (A)	you're (R)	your (A)	you're (O)	your (R)	you're (T)

4. Please take off _____ shoes.		**5.** _____ doing a great job!		**6.** I know _____ going to win.	
your (Y)	you're (B)	Your (D)	You're (M)	your (C)	you're (S)

7. Can I borrow _____ coat?		**8.** Is that _____ cat on the porch?		**9.** _____ coming with me to the park, right?	
your (E)	you're (T)	your (U)	you're (I)	Your (L)	You're (W)

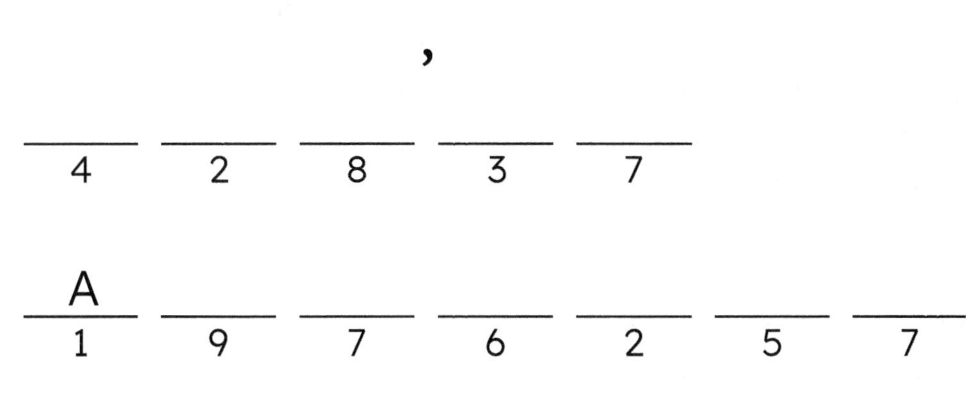

___ ___ ___ , ___ ___
4 2 8 3 7

A ___ ___ ___ ___ ___ ___
1 9 7 6 2 5 7

Day 2: Connect and Reflect

Follow the prompts to deepen your understanding of the lesson.

Focus on your favorite moment. Write down or draw your favorite part of today's lesson.

Pack your bags! What's something you learned that you want to take with you and remember later?

Make a real-world connection. In what ways have you ever felt supported by your friends and family?

Rate how you feel about this week's "Language Lab" skill: I can identify and use the correct version of "your" or "you're."

Rate how you feel about this week's skill: I can develop supporting details to add depth to informational writing.

Day 3: Read and Respond

Read the text below, or listen to it by clicking or scanning the QR code. Then, answer the questions on the next page.

Green Tree Pythons

Green tree pythons are bright green snakes that live in tropical rainforests. They spend most of their time in the trees. Their green color helps them blend in with the leaves so other animals can't see them.

These snakes are quiet hunters. Instead of chasing their food, green tree pythons stay still and wait. They wrap their long bodies around tree branches and hold on tight. When a bird or small animal comes close, the python strikes quickly to catch it.

Green tree pythons have special bodies that help them live in the trees. Their tails can twist and grab like an extra hand. This helps them stay balanced on thin branches. They can also curl up in a spiral shape with their head in the middle so they are ready to move fast if they see food nearby.

Even though they look scary, green tree pythons are not dangerous to humans. They use their strength to catch food, not to hurt people. These sneaky snakes are some of the quietest hunters in the rainforest!

Day 3: Read and Respond

Use the text about green tree pythons to answer the questions.

1. Why are green tree pythons hard to see?
   a. They move very fast.
   b. They are the same color as the leaves.
   c. They hide under rocks.
   d. They only come out at night.

2. Where do green tree pythons live?
   a. In the desert
   b. On the forest floor
   c. In the trees of rainforests
   d. In underground tunnels

3. Why do green tree pythons curl up in a spiral with their head in the middle?

___

___

___

4. Why are green tree pythons known as quiet hunters?

___

___

___

5. If you saw a green tree python in the wild, what would you do? Why?

___

___

___

___

___

Optional Support

Dig Deeper

Want more practice with writing supporting details?

Part 1: On the left, there are three guiding questions about research on playgrounds. On the right, there are four facts that were found through research.

Step 1: Match each fact to the guiding question it answers.

Step 2: Cross out the fact that doesn't answer a question.

A. What things can you play on at the playground?

B. How do playgrounds keep kids safe?

C. What activities can kids do at playgrounds?

___. Soft ground materials, like rubber, help protect kids if they fall.

___. Slides, swings, and monkey bars are found on most playgrounds.

___. Playgrounds can be many different colors.

___. Kids climb, swing, run, and play games together on the playground.

Part 2: Use the sentence starters below to help you put the researched facts into your own words.

A. On most playgrounds, you can play on ______________________________

____

B. Playgrounds help keep kids safe by ______________________________

____

C. At playgrounds, kids can ______________________________

____

Optional Support

Climb Higher

Ready for a challenge when it comes to writing supporting details?

Silly Support!

Each topic sentence is silly and untrue, and the made-up facts below are written to sound like real research. Choose one fact and write it as a supporting detail **in your own words**. Make sure your sentence supports the topic clearly.

Topic Sentence #1: Living in a house made of cheese is a good idea for many reasons.

Research Facts:

- Cheese is soft and squishy, so it can make a fall less painful.
- Mice will help clean up crumbs, which keeps the house tidy.
- In cold weather, cheese holds in heat better than wood.

Your supporting detail: ____

____

Topic Sentence #2: Snails are excellent mail carriers.

Research Facts:

- Snails can carry light objects, like paper, without damaging them.
- They leave slime trails, which make it easy to track deliveries.
- They always move in one direction, which helps them stay on route.

Your supporting detail: ____

____

Optional Support

Climb Higher, continued

Topic Sentence #3: Banana peels can be used to make fast boats.

Research Facts:

- Banana peels are light and can float easily on water.
- When shaped correctly, banana peels can move quickly with the current.
- Banana peel boats are strong enough to carry small animals.

Your supporting detail: ______________________________

____

Topic Sentence #4: Pizza crust is used to make strong fences on farms.

Research Facts:

- Hard, stale pizza crust is tough enough to make fence posts.
- Crusts can be stacked tightly to block animals from getting out.
- Pizza crust fences are lightweight and easy to move.

Your supporting detail: ______________________________

____

Day 1

- ❏ Video and Guided Notes
- ❏ Writing Project: Part 4
- ❏ Online Practice Levels 1 and 2

Day 2

- ❏ Language Lab
- ❏ Connect and Reflect
- ❏ Online Practice Levels 3 and 4
- ❏ Optional: Dig Deeper or Climb Higher

Lesson Goal: I can use examples and explanations to clarify information.

Record your thoughts: Have you ever tried something again to get better at it? What happened?

Record your thoughts on the right! →

A Word To Explore:

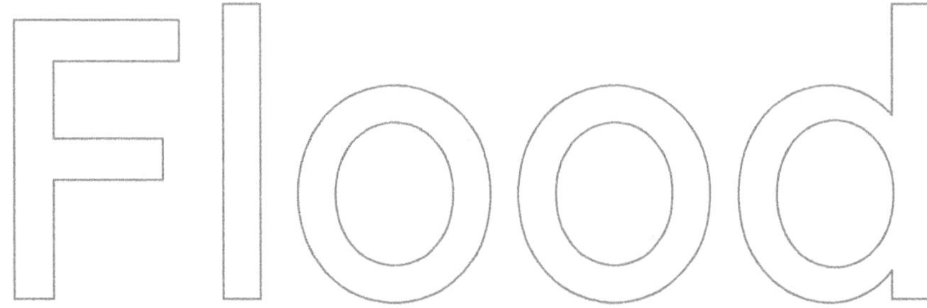

A sudden, strong flow of water into an area OR to overfill something with water

Day 1: Guided Notes

Follow along with Bea to complete the guided notes below.

changing or ___________ to writing to make it stronger

We use **examples** and **explanations** to make details clear.

Examples - details that help the reader picture and understand the idea

Explanations - details that tell WHY something matters or HOW something works

Some animals that can live in the tundra are polar bears, arctic foxes, and snowy owls.

Explanation: Animals survive with thick layers of fur or feathers to keep them warm.

Rewrite Bea's supporting detail using the word "because" and the explanation.

____

____

____

Day 1: Guided Notes

Follow along with Bea to complete the guided notes below.

Do not add examples or explanations if they will confuse the reader.

Use these questions to help decide if examples and explanations are needed.

- Would examples make this idea clearer?
- Did I include the WHY or HOW?
- Is the information I want to add going to help my reader?

Today we learned...

There's always something we can improve — and that's a good thing

Examples help readers picture and understand an idea

Explanations help teach readers WHY or HOW something works

Writing Project: Part 4

Look back at your notes from Part 3 to find your supporting details.
Remember to save this page for next time!

For this step, you need to **edit** your details to include **examples and explanations** as needed.

Scan or click the QR code to access the slideshow that will help you complete the same step in the writing process as Bea!

Review each of your supporting details. Circle if each one already has examples, an explanation, or neither. Then, decide what you can add to each one to make it stronger.

Supporting Detail 1

This detail **has**...	This **needs**...
Examples Explanation	Examples Explanation
I can add...	

Supporting Detail 2

This detail **has**...	This **needs**...
Examples Explanation	Examples Explanation
I can add...	

Writing Project: Part 4 continued

Supporting Detail 3

This detail **has**... Examples Explanation	This **needs**... Examples Explanation
I can add...	

Rewrite each of your supporting details with the added examples and/or explanations.

New Supporting Detail 1: What is the weather like in your biome? Use examples and an explanation if needed.

New Supporting Detail 2: What kinds of plants grow there? Use examples and an explanation if needed.

New Supporting Detail 3: What kinds of animals live there? Use examples and an explanation if needed.

Day 2: Language Lab

Read the mini-lesson. Then, practice the skill in parts 1 through 3.

A **comma** is a punctuation mark that has many uses in writing. One use is to separate items in a **list** or series. A comma looks like this: **,**

When you make a list of three or more things, commas are used to separate them from each other.
Example: My favorite colors are blue, green, and yellow.

Commas should come after the listed terms and before the word "and."
A comma does NOT come after the last item after the word "and."
Example: I like to play hockey, read books, run outside, and watch movies.

If you are only talking about two things, commas are not needed.
Example: Her favorite foods are tacos and hamburgers.

Part 1: Circle whether or not the following sentences need commas.

I went to the beach and the mountains last summer.	YES or NO
John wanted vanilla chocolate and strawberry ice cream.	YES or NO
The shirt was purple green and yellow.	YES or NO
She has two dogs and one cat.	YES or NO

Part 2: Add commas to the sentences to make them correct.

1. I like to play softball tennis and football.
2. We saw lions tigers and bears at the zoo.
3. Mia wanted to go outside play in the snow and make a snowman.
4. I want peppers onions ham and bacon on my pizza.

Day 2: Language Lab

Part 3: Sort the sentences based on whether they correctly use commas or not.

1. Cut out each sentence below along the dotted lines.
2. Read each sentence and decide if the items are listed correctly.
3. Sort the sentences into the columns based on whether they are **correct** or **incorrect**.
4. Before pasting them down, reread and check your answers!

Correct ☑	Incorrect ✕

Sarah went with her dad, uncle, and sister to the game.	I want to eat cake pizza and ice cream on my birthday.	He plays with cars and trucks.
Can I have, a cat dog, and, parrot as a pet?	Her favorite animals are frogs, bears, cats, and dolphins.	The restaurant serves burgers milkshakes fries, and hot dogs.

Day 2: Connect and Reflect

Follow the prompts to deepen your understanding of the lesson.

Focus on your favorite moment. Write down or draw your favorite part of today's lesson.

Pack your bags! What's something you learned that you want to take with you and remember later?

Make a real-world connection. Why do you think it's important to become a better writer?

Rate how you feel about this week's "Language Lab" skill: I can use commas when making a list.

Rate how you feel about this week's skill: I can use examples and explanations to clarify information.

Optional Support

Dig Deeper

Want more practice with examples and explanations?

Some sentences already include an example or an explanation, but great writers check to see what's missing.

In this activity, you'll read each sentence, decide what it already includes, and choose the best phrase to add.

- Circle whether the supporting detail already has an example or explanation.
- Circle what the sentence is missing.
- Choose the option that has the best information to add to the sentence based on what's missing.

Fruits, like strawberries and grapes, are sweet.	
This sentence **has**... Examples OR Explanation	This sentence **needs**... Examples OR Explanation
a) They contain natural sugars that taste sweet. b) Pineapples and mangoes are sweet. c) Some fruits are red or green.	

Rain gear helps keep people dry because it is waterproof.	
This sentence **has**... Examples OR Explanation	This sentence **needs**... Examples OR Explanation
a) Most people don't like getting wet when it rains. b) Waterproof means water can't soak through the fabric. c) People use gear like rain boots and an umbrella.	

Optional Support

Dig Deeper continued

Many cities have tall buildings, like skyscrapers and office towers.	
This sentence **has**... Examples OR Explanation	This sentence **needs**... Examples OR Explanation
a) Cities have a lot of buses and cars. b) Cities have a lot of people but not a lot of space to build. c) Some people are afraid of heights in tall buildings.	

Musical instruments, like guitars, violins, and pianos, make different sounds.	
This sentence **has**... Examples OR Explanation	This sentence **needs**... Examples OR Explanation
a) Instruments make sounds based on what they are made of. b) Many people like to listen to music. c) Instruments like flutes and bells are made out of metal.	

Optional Support

Climb Higher

Ready for a challenge when it comes to examples and explanations?

Sometimes a fact is true, but it's not very helpful to a reader on its own. Your job is to fix each fact by making it clearer and more complete!

For each sentence below...

1. Add at least one example to help your reader picture what you mean
2. Add an explanation to help your reader understand **why** or **how** it works
3. You can use what you already know or ask a parent for help if you want to do some quick research

Example:

Original Fact: People wear shoes.

Fixed Fact: People wear shoes, like sneakers or boots, because they protect their feet from getting hurt.

1. People eat fast food.

____

____

2. Many animals live on farms.

____

____

3. Birds build nests.

____

____

4. Kids play games.

____

____

Day 1	Day 2	Day 3
❑ Video and Guided Notes	❑ Language Lab	❑ Read and Respond
❑ Writing Project: Part 5	❑ Connect and Reflect	❑ Online Practice Level 5
❑ Online Practice Levels 1 and 2	❑ Online Practice Levels 3 and 4	❑ Optional: Dig Deeper/ Climb Higher

Lesson Goal: I can add text features, like a title, illustration, and caption, to my work for clarity.

Record your thoughts:
Do you like reading nonfiction texts?
Why or why not?

Record your thoughts on the right! →

A Word To Explore:

Several

More than a few but less than a lot

Day 1: Guided Notes

Follow along with Bea to complete the guided notes below.

Text features

are items in or around a text that ___________ or ___________ important information and help readers understand the text.

Title - tells what the paragraph is generally about

Illustration - a drawing that shows what a term or idea looks like

Animals in Winter

As the weather gets colder, many animals prepare for winter. Squirrels collect nuts and hide them underground so they can eat later. Bears eat a lot of food before finding a cozy den to hibernate. Some birds fly south where it's warmer and there's more food to find. These changes help animals survive when it's cold and food is hard to find.

Squirrels, bears, and birds all prepare for winter in different ways, like gathering food, hibernating, or flying south.

Caption - the words under or next to an illustration or photo that explain what is shown

Record a title for your biome paragraph on the line below.

____

Day 1: Guided Notes

Circle the illustration that is strongest and explain why below.

Draw a quick sketch of what you want to include in your final illustration.

Record a one-sentence caption that describes your illustration.

Today we learned...

Text features help your reader know what to expect, understand your ideas better, and enjoy your writing even more

Writing Project: Part 5

Look back at your notes from all previous lessons AND your guided notes to use for this part.

For this step, you need to **create text features** that go along with your informational paragraph.

Scan or click the QR code to access the slideshow that will help you complete the same step in the writing process as Bea!

Step 1: Look back on your previous work and **rewrite** your topic sentence and supporting details together in order to create one full paragraph. Don't worry about the concluding sentence yet!

Writing Project: Part 5

Step 2: Create a title for your paragraph. You can use the one you created during the lesson video! Record it on the line below.

____

Step 3: Create an illustration that helps your readers understand more about your paragraph.

Step 4: Create a caption that describes the illustration you made in Step 3.

____

____

Day 2: Language Lab

Read the mini-lesson. Then, practice the skill in parts 1 and 2.

A **singular noun** is a word that describes **one** person, place, or thing. A **plural noun** is a word that describes **more than one** person, place, or thing.

Examples: Cats, trees, friends, lakes, boxes

Usually, to make a plural noun, we add -s to the end of the singular noun.

Example: dog → dogs

Some words do not follow the rule of adding -s to the end of the word. Here is a chart you can keep that shows the rules for creating a plural noun.

Spelling Rules	Examples
Most common nouns Add -s.	chair → chairs pencil → pencils
Noun ends in ch, sh, s, or x Add -es.	brush → brushes fox → foxes
Noun ends in vowel + y Add -s.	boy → boys key → keys
Noun ends in consonant + y Change the y to i and add -es.	lady → ladies city → cities
Noun ends in f or fe Change the f or fe to v and add -es.	leaf → leaves life → lives
Noun ends in vowel + o Add -s.	video → videos studio → studios
Noun ends in consonant + o Add -es.	potato → potatoes hero → heroes

Day 2: Language Lab

Some of the nouns in the story below are written in the singular form, but they should be plural. Your job is to find and fix them! Use clues like numbers and words such as "some" or "many" to help you decide which nouns should be changed.

Part 1: Read the silly story carefully. As you read, highlight or underline each noun that should be plural.

This morning, Farmer Mia found three pitchfork stuck in a hay bale. She set them aside and grabbed two box of corn from the shed. Five puppy were running in circles around the ducks, chasing after a few toy. In the garden, Mia picked up several leaf and tossed them into a bucket. Then, she noticed that all of the tomato she planted last week had grown into shapes that looked just like pigs! Her favorite part of the day was watching the baby goats try to wear dish as hats.

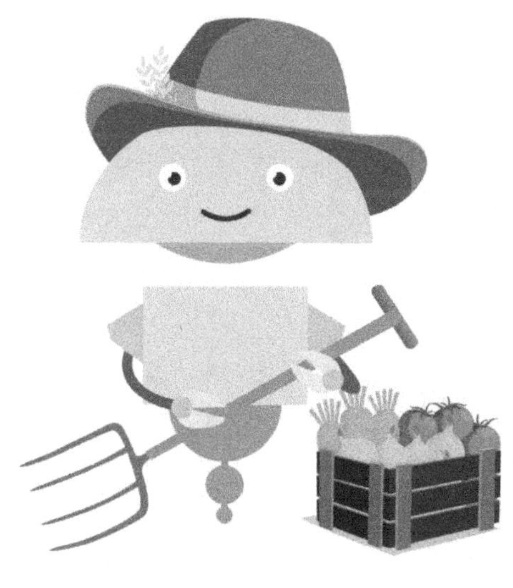

Part 2: On the **left**, record the **nouns you found in the story** that need to be made plural. On the **right**, record the **correct plural form** of each. Remember to look back at the chart to check your work!

__________ → __________

__________ → __________

__________ → __________

__________ → __________

__________ → __________

__________ → __________

__________ → __________

Day 2: Connect and Reflect

Follow the prompts to deepen your understanding of the lesson.

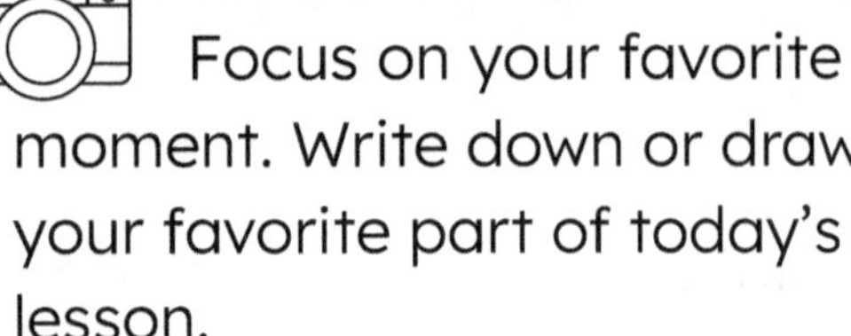

Focus on your favorite moment. Write down or draw your favorite part of today's lesson.

Pack your bags! What's something you learned that you want to take with you and remember later?

Make a real-world connection. Have you ever seen things that look like text features in everyday life? Where?

Rate how you feel about this week's "Language Lab" skill: I can identify and use plural nouns.

Rate how you feel about this week's skill: I can add text features like titles, illustrations, and captions to my writing.

Day 3: Words To Explore (Unit 2)

Explore and review the words to explore from this unit. Add in your own picture to help you remember what the word means.

Word	Definition/Example	Picture
Graze	- To feed on growing grass OR to touch lightly *I watched the cows graze in the field.*	
Marsh	- An area of soft, wet land that usually has a lot of grassy plants *There were a lot of frogs living in the marsh.*	
Grasp	- To hold onto something *I had to grasp my bag tightly so I didn't drop it.*	
Flood	- A sudden, strong flow of water into an area OR to overfill something with water *A flood of water poured out of the bathtub.*	
Several	- More than a few but less than a lot *I saw several dogs while I was on my walk.*	

Day 3: Words To Explore (Unit 2)

Fill in the blanks below with the words to explore you've learned so far in this unit.

1. The soap was slippery so Jake had to ________________ it tightly.
2. Carter picked out ________________ books from the library because he wanted to read more than one.
3. The heavy rain caused a ________________ in the streets.
4. When deer are hungry, they ________________ in the forest.
5. We wore boots while walking through the wet, squishy grass of the ________________.

Find your vocabulary words in the word search below!

F	R	I	J	G	E	C	D
L	T	M	A	R	S	H	Q
O	F	W	P	O	L	N	T
O	T	L	P	O	F	G	E
D	U	S	V	B	T	R	Y
P	S	E	V	E	R	A	L
N	L	K	T	H	E	Z	P
E	G	R	A	S	P	E	S

Optional Support

Dig Deeper

Want more practice with adding text features?

Part 1: Match each text feature in the boxes at the top with its name on the bottom.

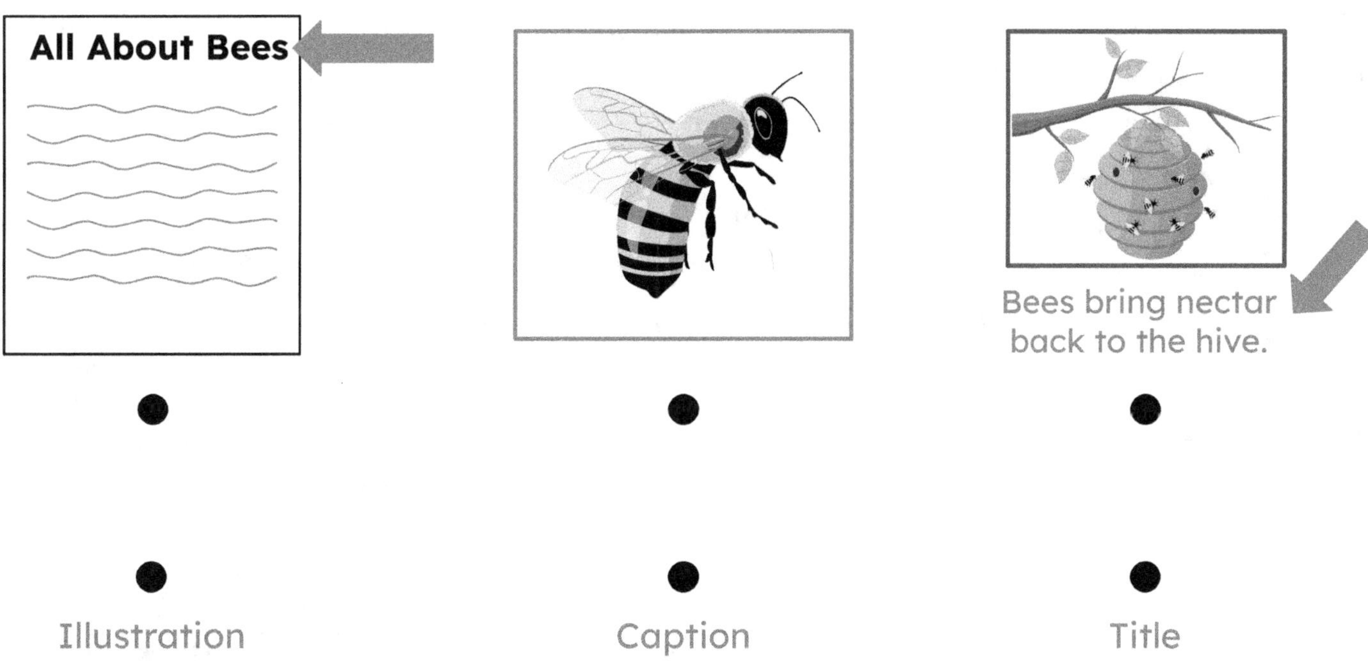

Illustration

Caption

Title

Part 2: Read the text below, or listen to it by clicking or scanning the QR code. Then, make a **title**, **illustration**, and **caption** that help make the writing clearer.

Title

Butterflies do more than just fly around; they help plants grow. As a butterfly drinks nectar from a flower, pollen sticks to its body. When it visits the next flower, some of the pollen rubs off. This helps the plant make seeds and grow new flowers. Without pollinators like butterflies, many plants could not survive.

Illustration

Caption:

Optional Support

Climb Higher

Ready for a challenge when it comes to adding text features?

Below are two texts about monkeys. One is part of a fictional story, and the other is a nonfiction text. Read each text and observe the text features, then answer the questions on the next page.

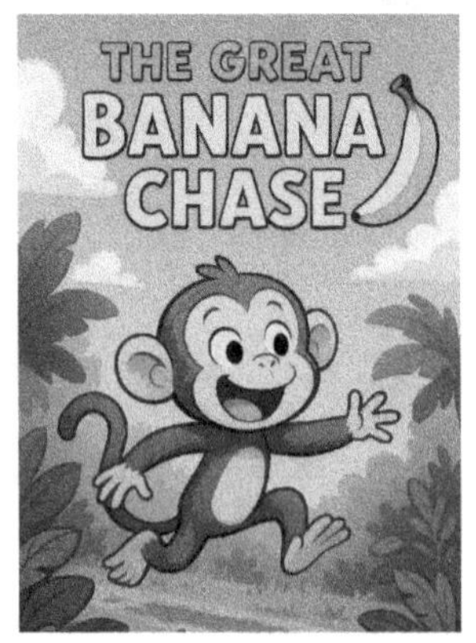

Book cover

Max, the monkey, loved bananas more than anything. One day, he saw a strange banana flying through the air with a note that said "Catch me if you can!" Max jumped into the trees and swung through the jungle, chasing the banana from branch to branch. Every time he got close, the banana zoomed away. Max was determined to catch it — he had never let a banana win before!

Monkey Tails

Many monkeys have strong, flexible tails. These tails help them swing from tree to tree and keep their balance. Some monkeys can even use their tails to grab onto branches like a hand. This is called a prehensile tail. It helps monkeys move quickly through the forest and stay safe from predators.

A monkey uses its tail to keep balance while swinging.

Optional Support

Climb Higher continued

Answer the questions to compare how the text features work in each kind of text.

1. Which had more text features, the fiction or the nonfiction text?

2. How did the illustration in the fiction text help you understand the story?

3. How did the illustration in the nonfiction text help you understand the supporting details?

4. Why do you think illustrations in fictional texts don't usually have captions?

5. Which text feature do you think is the most helpful (title, illustration, or caption)? Why?

Day 1

- ❏ Video and Guided Notes
- ❏ Writing Project: Part 6
- ❏ Online Practice Levels 1-3

Day 2

- ❏ Language Lab
- ❏ Connect and Reflect
- ❏ Online Assessment
- ❏ Optional: Dig Deeper or Climb Higher

Lesson Goal: I can write clear and focused closing sentences. I can revise and refine my writing.

Record your thoughts: How are you feeling about your biome writing project? Explain how you think it's going so far!

Record your thoughts on the right! ⟶

A Word To Explore:

Unite

To join together or combine

Day 1: Guided Notes

Follow along with Bea to complete the guided notes below.

The closing sentence

is the ______________ sentence in a paragraph that

________________ the reader of what they read.

To make a closing sentence, **paraphrase the main idea**.

Bea's topic sentence:

The Arctic tundra is a freezing place where only some plants and animals can survive.

Paraphrase Bea's main idea.

____

____

____

____

Circle which closing sentence you think is strongest.

Wetlands are wet, usually warm places where many plants and animals live. Animals that like wet places, like frogs, alligators, and fish, live there. Those animals are so cool looking! Plants like cattails and water lilies are helpful. Wetlands stay wet and humid for most of the year.

- Now you know about the wetlands.
- The wetlands are home to many animals and plants that are important to the biome.
- Wetlands are muddy and full of water.
- I think wetlands are the most helpful biome in the world.

Day 1: Guided Notes

Revising - looking at your writing as a whole to decide how to make it clearer and more organized

Revise with ARMS

❑ **A**dd ✚

Are there any sentences or words we need to add to make this writing better?

❑ **R**emove

Is there anything you think that is not needed and should be taken out?

❑ **M**ove

Does the order of my ideas make sense?

❑ **S**ubstitute

Are there any words I should replace with new ones?

Wetlands are wet, usually warm places where many animals and plants live. Animals that like wet places, like frogs, alligators, and fish, live there. Those animals are so cool looking! Plants like cattails and water lilies are helpful. ✚ Wetlands stay wet and humid for most of the year. The wetlands are home to many animals and plants that are important to the biome.

✚ This sentence is missing an explanation of HOW the plants are helpful.

— This sentence shows an opinion, not a fact, so it needs to be removed.

□ This sentence should be moved to before the animal detail to match the order of the topic sentence.

○ The word "wet" is repeated a lot. To avoid this, it can be replaced with other synonyms.

Today we learned...

Closing sentences end the paragraph and remind the reader of what they learned

We revise to make our work clear and organized for our readers

Writing Project: Part 6

Look back at your notes from all previous lessons AND your guided notes to use for this part.

For this step, you need to **write the closing sentence** and **revise** your final paragraph.

Scan or click the QR code to access the slideshow that will help you complete the same step in the writing process as Bea!

Step 1: Reread your current paragraph. Then, create a closing sentence to add to the end.

Step 2: Revise your paragraph using the ARMS checklist below. Mark off each step as you go. You can make changes on a separate paper or write on your paragraph from the last step.

- ❑ **ADD:** Is there anything I should add to my writing to make it clearer?
- ❑ **REMOVE:** Is there anything that needs to be taken out of my writing?
- ❑ **MOVE:** Is there anything that should be moved around to make my writing clearer?
- ❑ **SUBSTITUTE:** Are there any words or parts that need to be replaced?

Writing Project: Part 6

Step 3: Look for any mistakes in spelling or structure. Here are some tips to help you with the final steps.

- ❑ Read your paragraph and circle any words that you are **not completely sure** are spelled correctly. Look up the correct spelling, or ask a grown-up for help.
- ❑ Make sure each sentence starts with a capital letter and ends with a period.
- ❑ Read your paragraph out loud or listen to someone else read it. Keep an ear out for anything that does not sound as you expected.
- ❑ Revise your work as many times as you like until you are happy with the result!

Step 4: Create your final paragraph with a title, illustration, and caption on the next page. Your illustration and caption can be cut and pasted from the previous lesson if you do not wish to redo them. The image below shows where each part of your project should be placed.

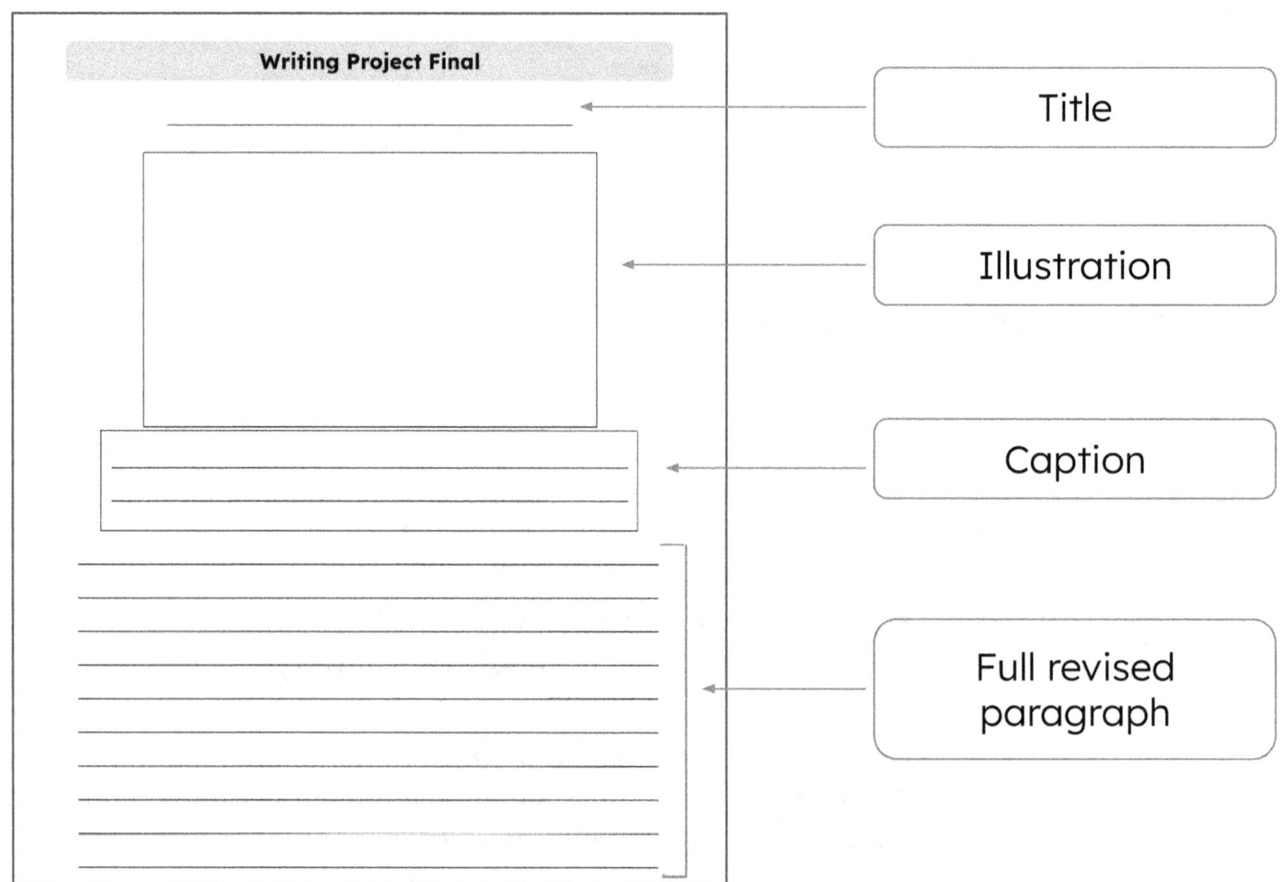

Writing Project Final

Day 2: Language Lab

Read the mini-lesson. Then, practice the skill in parts 1 through 2

Nouns describe a person, place, or thing.
Plural nouns describe a group of two or more nouns.
Examples: Cats, berries, foxes, leaves

Irregular plural nouns are nouns that don't follow any rules when they are made plural. They are plurals that you just have to learn and remember. Some nouns change completely:

Examples: man → men, child → children, tooth → teeth.

Other plural nouns are the same word as their singular form:

Examples: sheep, deer, fish

When thinking about how to make an irregular plural noun. Trust what sounds right, and ask for help if needed!

Part 1: Use the word bank to fill in the blank with the correct plural form of the word in parentheses.

mice	women	teeth	people	deer	feet	cacti

1. I've lost three of my baby ______________. (tooth)
2. There's a family of ______________ living under the stairs. (mouse)
3. A lot of ______________ came to see the show. (person)
4. Did you see all of the baby ______________ in the forest? (deer)
5. The ______________ meet for book club every week. (woman)
6. My ______________ hurt from walking in my new shoes. (foot)
7. There are many types of ______________ in the desert. (cactus)

Day 2: Language Lab

Part 2: Play a matching game with the cards below and on the next page! (To make sure the cards aren't see-through, print them on cardstock or glue them onto construction paper before cutting.)

Step 1: Cut out all of the cards on the dotted lines.
Step 2: Turn all of the cards face down and mix them up.
Step 3: Arrange the cards on a flat surface.
Step 4: Take turns with another player flipping over two cards at a time. Try to flip over two cards that have matching singular and plural nouns. Each time you flip a card, read the words aloud.
Step 5: If your cards match, keep the pair! If they don't, put them back down on the table where you picked them up from.
Step 6: After all of the pairs have been matched, the player with the most pairs wins.

This game can also be played with one player! Grab a timer, and see how long it takes you to find all of the correct matches!

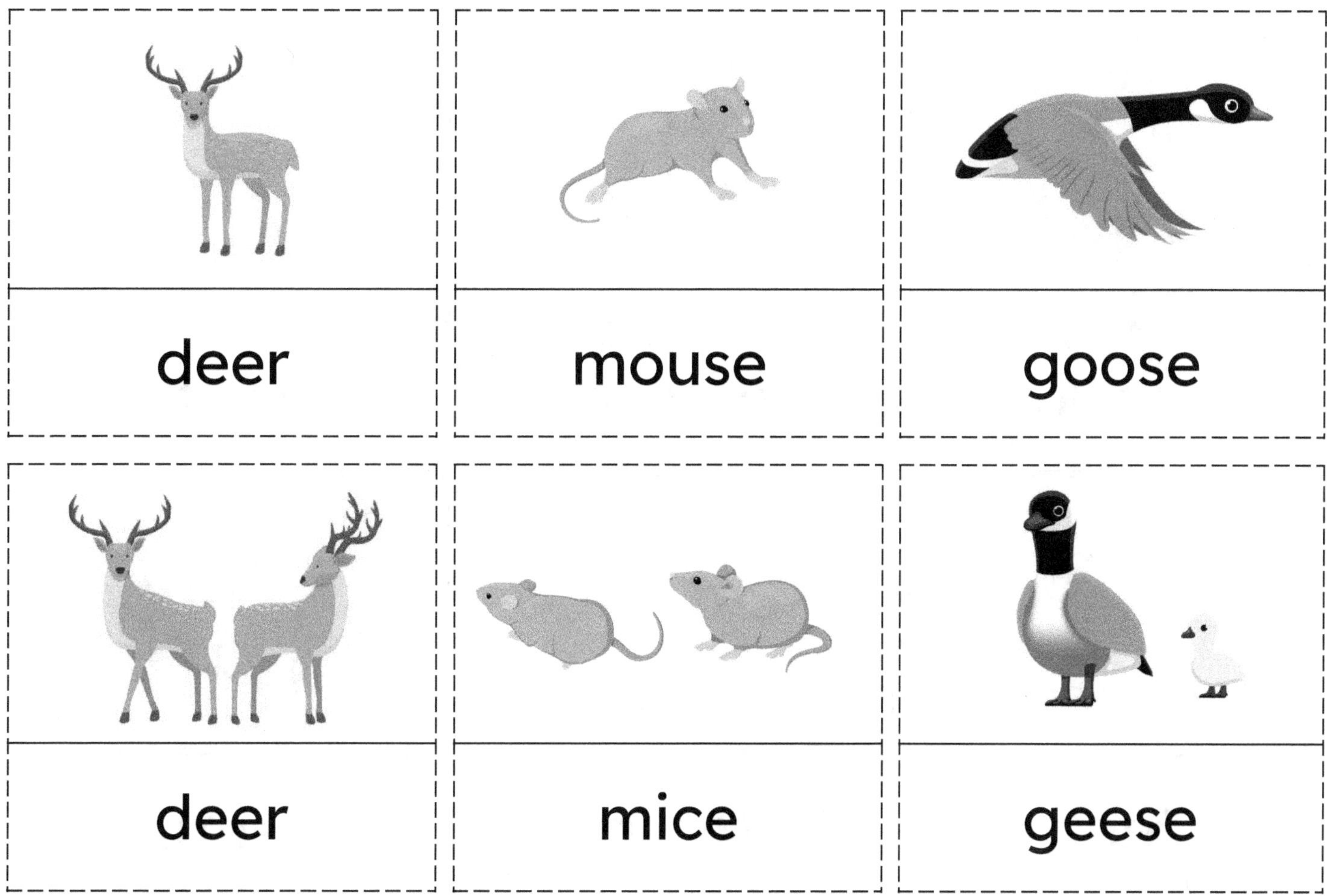

Day 2: Language Lab

child	children	man
men	sheep	sheep
octopus	octopi	foot
feet	tooth	teeth

Day 2: Connect and Reflect

Follow the prompts to deepen your understanding of the lesson.

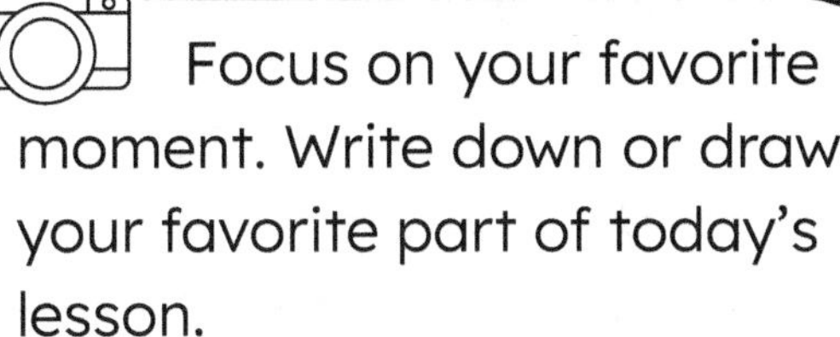

Focus on your favorite moment. Write down or draw your favorite part of today's lesson.

Pack your bags! What's something you learned that you want to take with you and remember later?

Make a real-world connection. When might it be helpful to say something in a new way?

Rate how you feel about this week's "Language Lab" skill: I can identify and use irregular plural nouns.

Rate how you feel about this week's skills: I can create closing sentences, and I can revise my writing.

Optional Support

Dig Deeper

Want more practice with closing sentences and revising?

Part 1: Practice writing closing sentences. Read each topic sentence, then practice paraphrasing it using the sentence frame. Remember to use some different words from the original.

1. **Topic sentence:** Dogs are great pets because they are playful, friendly, and easy to train.

Closing sentence: Dogs make ______________________________ because they ________________________________ and are ______________________________.

2. **Topic sentence:** Fall is a season when the weather gets cooler and the leaves begin to drop from the trees.

Closing sentence: In the fall, ____, and ____ as the season changes.

3. **Topic sentence:** Pancakes are a popular breakfast food because they are easy to make and taste good.

Closing sentence: Many people like pancakes because they ____ and taste __________________.

Continue

Part 2: Read the paragraph, or listen to it by clicking or scanning the QR code. Then, answer the questions from the ARMS checklist to figure out what should be revised.

Bird feeders help birds by giving them food and a place to rest. Some bird feeders have a small perch. I think bird feeders are the coolest things! Bird feeders are usually filled with small nuts or seeds that birds like to eat. Bird feeders are helpful to birds in many ways.

1. **ADD:** What should be added to the underlined sentence to make it clearer?
   a. Examples of types and colors of bird feeders
   b. More details about other parts of the bird feeder
   c. An explanation of how a perch helps birds rest

2. **REMOVE:** Cross out the sentence that does not belong in the informational paragraph.

3. **MOVE:** Circle a sentence you think needs to be moved, then draw an arrow showing where you would move it to. Make the order of the details match the order in the topic sentence.

4. **SUBSTITUTE:** Which of the following would help the paragraph sound less repetitive?
   a. Replace the word "food" with the word "meal."
   b. Replace some of the repetitions of "bird feeders" with words like "they" or "some feeders."
   c. Cut out the word bird since it is said more than once.

Optional Support

Climb Higher

Ready for a challenge when it comes to creating closing sentences and revising?

Part 1: Read the paragraph below, or listen to it by clicking or scanning the QR code. Then, write a closing sentence that restates the main idea in a new way.

Venus flytraps are unusual plants that have special leaves, trap bugs, and live in wet places. The leaves of a Venus flytrap can open and close like a mouth. Venus flytraps grow well in warm, humid biomes because of nutrients in the muddy soil. The fly traps eat many types of bugs by closing their leaves on them. I think Venus flytraps are the coolest plants in the world.

____

____

____

Part 2: Use the ARMS checklist to revise the paragraph.

ADD: I would add ____

because ____

REMOVE: I would remove ____________________________________

because ____

MOVE: I would move ______________________________________

because ____

SUBSTITUTE: I would replace ________________________________

because ____

Unit 3: What Authors Write: Stories

Day 1

- ❏ Video and Guided Notes
- ❏ Read and Respond
- ❏ Online Practice Levels 1 and 2

Day 2

- ❏ Language Lab
- ❏ Connect and Reflect
- ❏ Online Practice Levels 3 and 4

Day 3

- ❏ Extend Your Skills
- ❏ Online Practice Level 5
- ❏ Optional: Dig Deeper or Climb Higher

Lesson Goal:
I can identify the characteristics of different genres.

Record your thoughts:
When you choose a book to read or movie to watch, how do you choose one that you think you'll like?

Record your thoughts on the right! →

A Word To Explore:

Sprouted

Started to grow or come out, like when a seed grows into a little plant

Day 1: Guided Notes

Follow along with Bea to complete the guided notes below.

are groups of ______________ stories, usually sorted by how they're written, what they're about, or what happens in them.

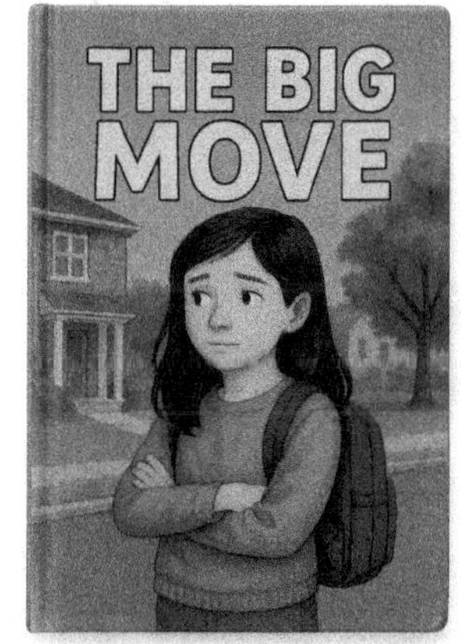

Realistic fiction - stories about people, places, and problems that could exist in ______________ life

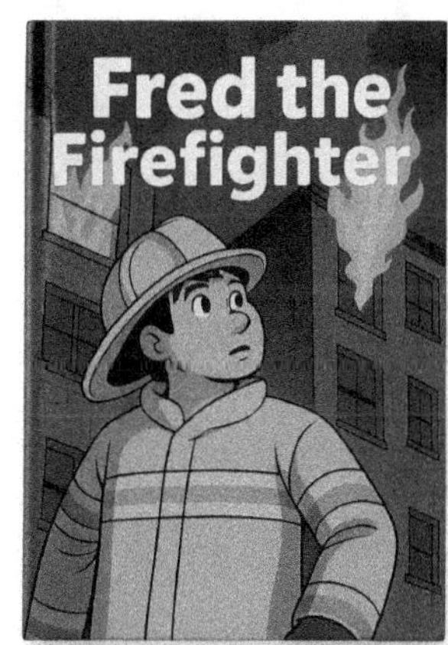

Action - stories that are fast-paced and exciting with brave characters who face dangerous situations

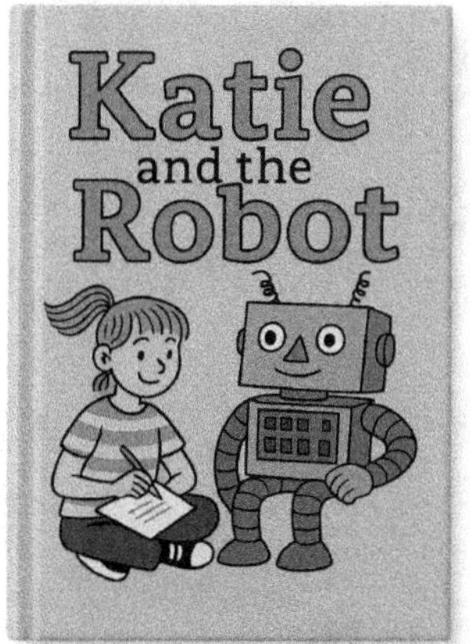

Science fiction - stories about what could happen in the future, like new technology and space travel

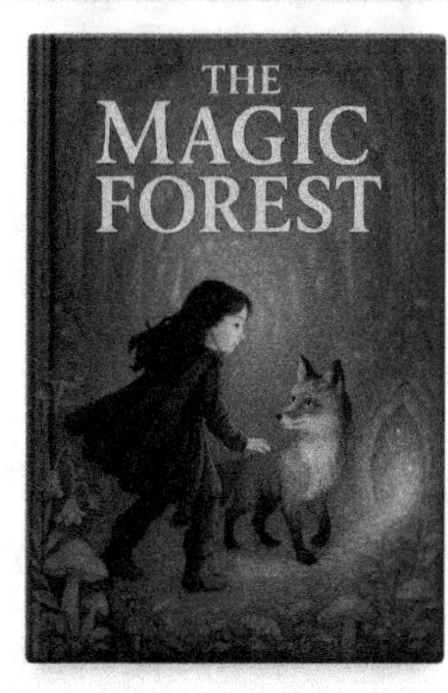

Fantasy - stories full of ____________, talking creatures, and things that couldn't happen in real life

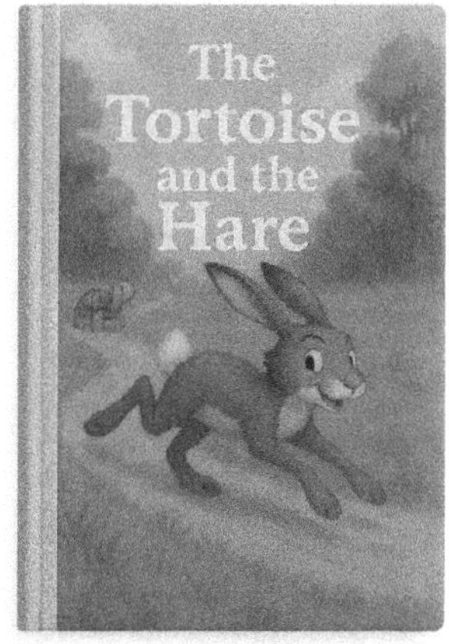

Fables - stories that often include talking animals and teach ______________

Record which genre you like the most and explain why.

____

____

____

____

Day 1: Guided Notes

Read or **listen along to** the story summary below with Bea.

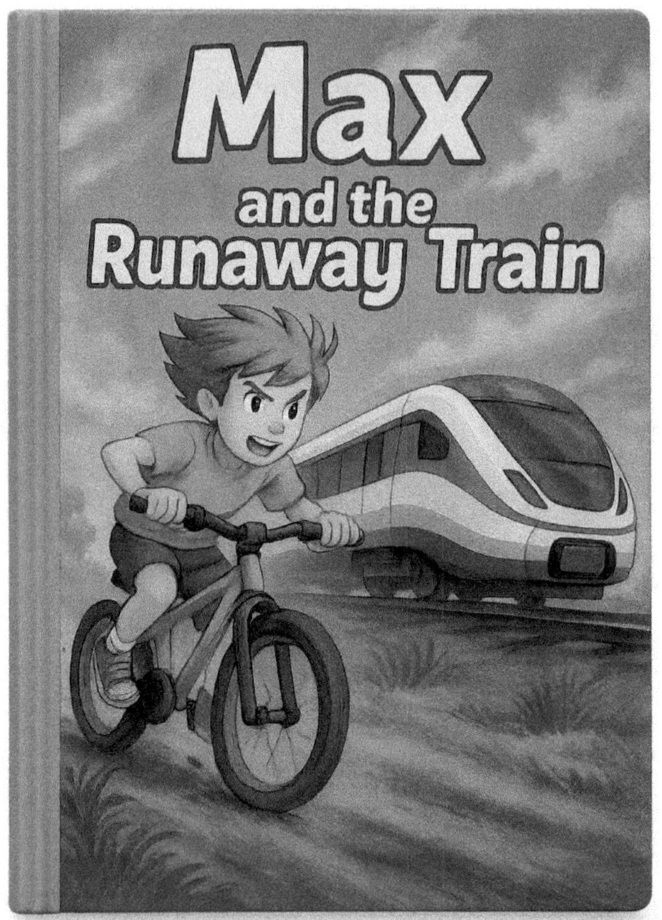

When 9-year-old Max visits his uncle who works at the train station, he never expects to face a real emergency. But when a train without a driver starts rolling down the tracks, Max jumps into action! He races alongside it on his bike, dodging traffic, then jumps on board. With help from his uncle and a trusty walkie-talkie, will Max find a way to stop the runaway train?

- **Realistic fiction:** Could this story really happen? **Yes**
- **Fantasy:** Are there any magical elements or talking animals? **No**
- **Fable:** Does the story teach a lesson? **No**
- **Action:** Are there any dangerous or fast-paced events? **Yes**
- **Sci-fi:** Does it take place in the future or use futuristic technology? **No**

The genre of this story is **action**.

Day 1: Guided Notes

Read or **listen along to** the story summary below with Bea.

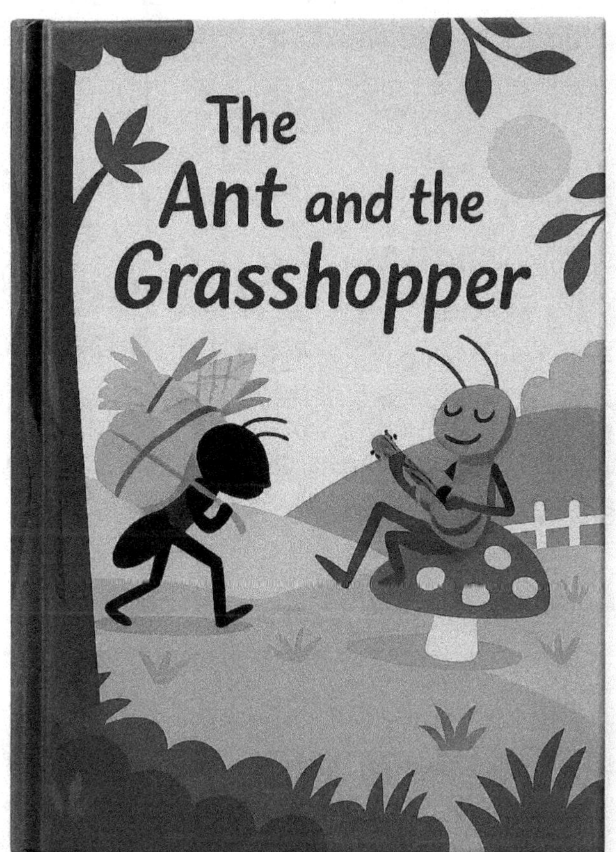

There was a hardworking ant and a playful grasshopper who lived in the same field. While the ant spent summer gathering food and getting ready for winter, the grasshopper sang and played all day. When winter came, the ant was ready, but the grasshopper had nothing. The grasshopper learned that it's important to plan ahead and work hard before it's too late!

Use the questions below to help you figure out the genre of the story above.

- **Action:** Are there any dangerous or fast-paced events? ______
- **Sci-fi:** Does it take place in the future or use futuristic technology? ______
- **Realistic fiction:** Could this story really happen? ______
- **Fantasy:** Are there any magical elements or talking animals? ______
- **Fable:** Does the story teach a lesson? ______

The genre of this story is ____________________.

Today we learned...

We can figure out the genre of stories by looking for clues about how they're written, what they're about, and what happens in them

Day 1: Read and Respond

Step 1: Read each story summary below, or click or scan the QR codes to listen to them. Record what genre you think each story is. Then, highlight the words that helped you figure out the genre. **Tip:** Use the questions on the previous page to help you choose the genre!

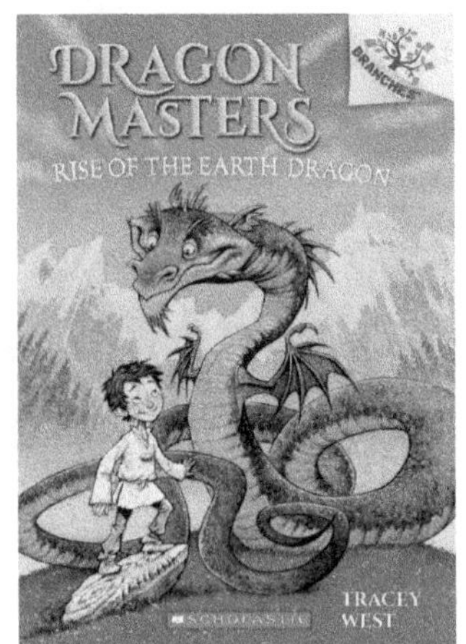

Eight-year-old Drake lives in a world filled with magic, dragons, wizards, and kings! One day, Drake's taken away to King Roland's castle, where he learns he's been chosen to train dragons! But there's more to these dragons than meets the eye. Each one has a secret power that must be discovered! Does Drake have what it takes to become a Dragon Master?

The genre is: ____________________________

Image: West, Tracey. *Dragon Masters: Rise of the Earth Dragon.* Scholastic Inc, 2014.

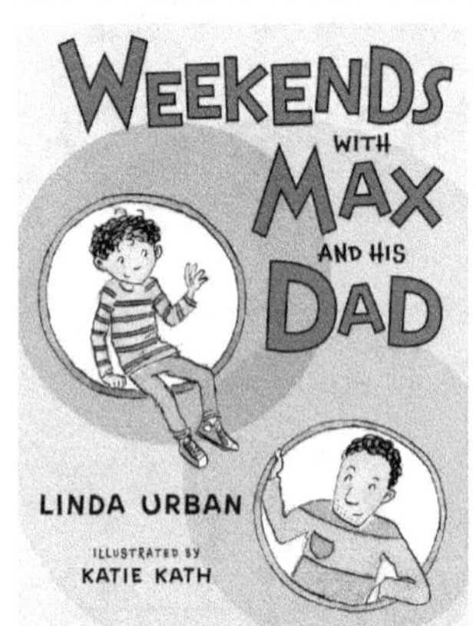

Max loves his weekends with his dad. They're always packed with pizza, games, school projects, dog walking, and even surprising the neighbors! Each weekend brings a new adventure as Max learns about his dad's new neighborhood and discovers new ideas about what home really means.

The genre is: ____________________________

Image: Urban, Linda. *Weekend with Max and His Dad.* Houghton Mifflin Harcourt, 2016.

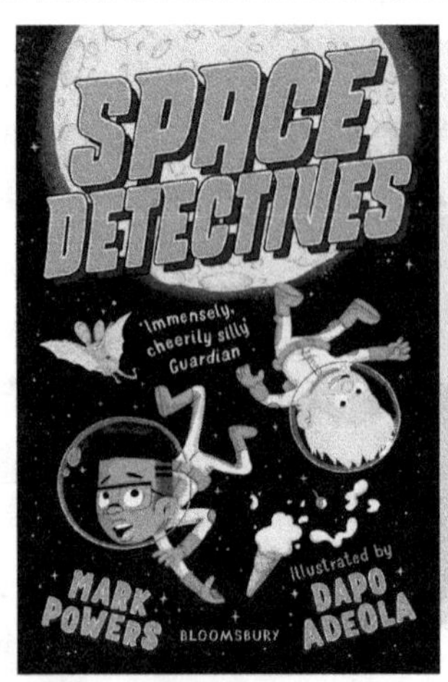

Sprouted an extra head and have no clue why? Dog disappeared in space? Call in the Space Detectives! Connor and Ethan are spending their summer vacation on Starville, the world's first orbiting city. When they discover Starville is speeding straight for the moon, they decide to help! Can Connor and Ethan crack the case and save Starville from disaster?

The genre is: ____________________________

Image: Powers, Mark. Space Detectives. Bloomsbury Publishing PLC, 2021.

Day 2: Language Lab

Read the mini-lesson. Then, practice the skill in parts 1 and 2.

Some words can have **multiple meanings**. One word can mean different things depending on how it's used in a sentence.

For example, the word "light" can mean something that's not heavy, or it can mean brightness that helps us see.

A useful way to figure out the meaning of a word is to look at details around it.

Part 1: Read the sentences below. For each one, circle the correct meaning of the underlined word. Remember to look at details around the word to help you decide.

1. Alice loved the gold ring her friend gave her.

   a) The sound a phone or bell makes

   b) A piece of jewelry you wear on your finger

2. The bat flew out of the dark cave and into the night sky.

   a) A small, flying animal

   b) A wooden stick used to hit balls in sports

3. To reach the train station, go straight, then turn right.

   a) When something is correct

   b) The opposite direction of left

4. My friend's puppies bark when they're scared.

   a) The outer covering of a tree

   b) The sound a dog makes

5. Fran ducked under the water when he saw a big wave coming.

   a) A moving bump of water in the sea

   b) When you move your hand to say hello or goodbye

Day 2: Language Lab

Part 2: Fill out the table below by writing the correct words from the word bank next to their multiple meanings.

seal	rock	hard	fly	trip	park	spring	nail	duck

Note: There are two words that you won't use, so choose carefully!

Word	Meaning 1	Meaning 2
	The season before summer	To jump up or move quickly
	An animal with flippers	To close something tightly
	A small piece of metal used to join things together	The hard part on the tip of your finger and toe
	A bird that lives near water	To move down quickly to avoid something
	A tiny insect with wings	To move through the air
	A place with trees and grass where people play	To stop and leave your car in a spot
	Something that's solid and not soft	Something that's difficult to do

Day 2: Connect and Reflect

Follow the prompts to deepen your understanding of the lesson.

Focus on your favorite moment. Write down or draw your favorite part of today's lesson.

Pack your bags! What's something you learned that you want to take with you and remember later?

Make a real-world connection. Imagine you're telling a friend about your favorite story. What would you tell or show them to help them understand what genre it is?

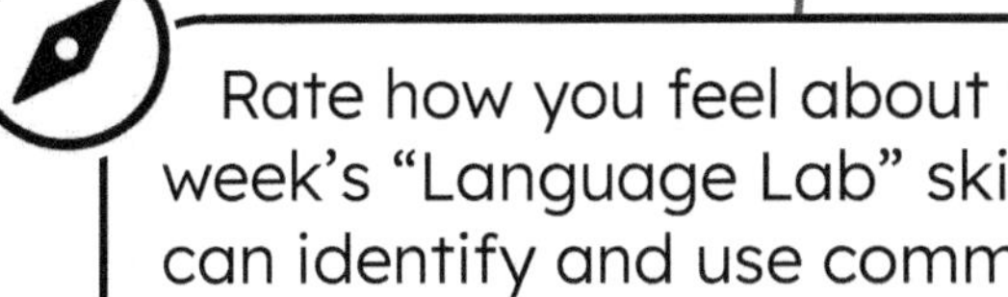

Rate how you feel about this week's "Language Lab" skill: I can identify and use common words with multiple meanings.

Rate how you feel about this week's skill: I can identify the characteristics of different fictional genres.

Day 3: Extend Your Skills

Step 1: Read the characters in the box and decide the genres they belong to. Some may fit in more than one genre, so add them to all genres that make sense. For example, a talking cat can be a fantasy or fable, so you can add it to both.

Kid inventor | Talking tree | Friendly neighbor | Robot pet | Fairy
Monkey teacher | Jungle explorer | Sneaky fox | Quick-thinking spy
Brave police officer | Quiet grandma | Space explorer | Clever owl

Realistic Fiction	Action

Fantasy	Fable	Sci-fi

Step 2: Think of characters you know from books and movies, or invent your own. Then, add them to the genre you think they belong to. You can write or draw!

Optional Support

Dig Deeper

Want more practice with genres?

Choose any activity you'd like to do from this page!

Genre Clue Hunt
Find a short story or picture book. As you read, look for clues (like talking animals or robots) that help you figure out what genre the story is. Make a list or draw pictures of each clue. When you finish reading, look back at the notes you made to figure out the genre!

Genre Picture Scene
Draw a scene that clearly shows a genre. For example, you could draw a girl chasing after a bank robber for action or a talking mouse with magical powers for fantasy. You can also add labels and words to your picture. Then, show it to someone to see if they can guess the genre.

My Favorite Genre
Choose your favorite genre! Write a few sentences about why you like it and give an example of a story, book, or movie that fits this genre. You can also draw a picture to show what makes this genre special for you.

Design a Book Cover
Imagine you're an artist! Your job is to make a book cover that shows which genre a story belongs to. Read the details below, then create a book cover based on the information:

- **Genre:** Action
- **Title:** The Lost Treasure
- **Summary:** Adventurous Amanda races through a dark cave full of traps to find the lost treasure — before anyone else gets to it first!

Optional Support

Climb Higher

Ready for a challenge when it comes to genres?

Find books at home, in the library, or online (with the permission of an adult) that fit each genre below. For each book, write the title, draw a picture of the cover, and write two to three details explaining why it belongs in that genre.

	Book Title and Picture	Why It Fits This Genre
Realistic Fiction		
Fantasy		
Action		
Fable		
Science Fiction		

Day 1

- ❑ Video and Guided Notes
- ❑ Read and Respond
- ❑ Online Practice Levels 1 and 2

Day 2

- ❑ Language Lab
- ❑ Connect and Reflect
- ❑ Online Practice Levels 3 and 4
- ❑ Optional: Dig Deeper or Climb Higher

Lesson Goal: I can identify the setting in a story and describe the effect a setting can have on a story.

Record your thoughts:
Think of a memorable event from your past. How could you describe the place and time of that event?

Record your thoughts on the right! →

A Word To Explore:

Cautiously

To act in a slow and careful way because you want to be safe

Day 1: Guided Notes

Follow along with Bea to complete the guided notes below.

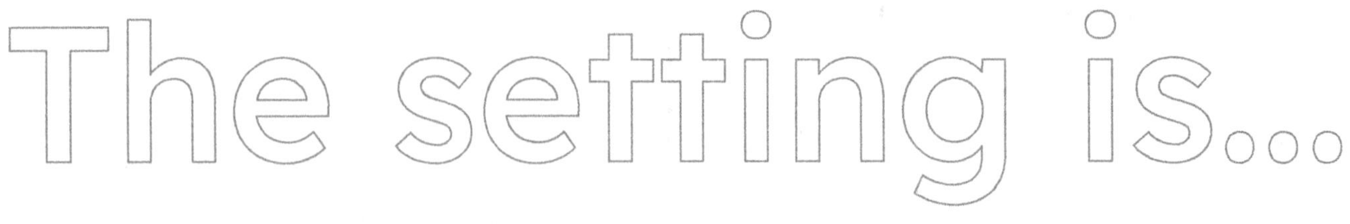

__________ and __________ a story takes place.

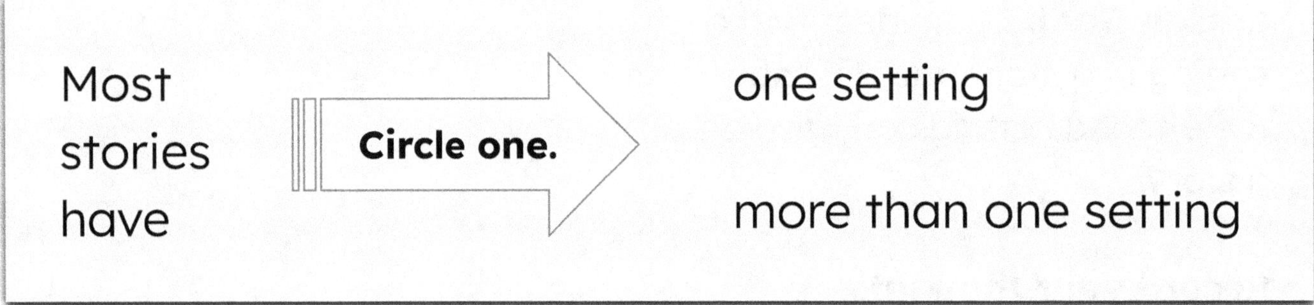

Underline clues for the setting in the passage, then write the setting.

"The metal doors slid open with a hiss, and Kara stepped cautiously into a dark hallway. Through a window, she noticed a streak of light cut through the stars. Was it another spaceship or just a shooting star? Kara saw the lights of a robot slowly moving toward her when she heard a scream from far away."

The setting in this passage is ______________.

Day 1: Guided Notes

Follow along with Bea to complete the guided notes below.

Record whether each event would take place in an ocean or a spaceship setting.

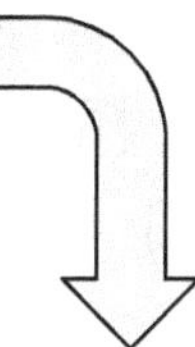

Event	
Getting chased by a robot	______________
Losing a paddle	______________
Getting locked in a room	______________
Seeing a big sea creature	______________

Today we learned...

The **setting** is where and when a story takes place

The setting can affect what happens in a story, what challenges the characters face, and what actions the characters take

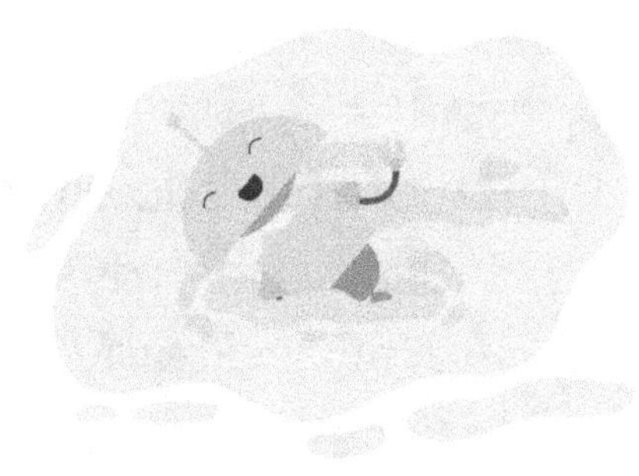

Day 1: Read and Respond

Read the passage below and answer the questions that follow.

Canceled Plans

Maya pressed her nose against the window, which had rain pouring down the other side of it. "I was planning on playing soccer today," she said with a sigh. "Now, I can't do anything fun." Maya didn't feel like playing inside. The whole house felt boring and quiet. She flopped onto the couch. "This is the worst day," she mumbled.

Just then, her mom walked into the room holding some rain boots. She spoke with a smile, "Come on. Let's go outside."

Maya sat up. "In the rain?"

Mom nodded. "You'll see."

Outside was foggy and a bit cold. Maya stepped carefully onto the sidewalk and saw her mom jump into a big puddle! Water flew everywhere. Maya laughed. She jumped into the next puddle and then another. Soon, they were both splashing, stomping, and laughing in the rain. Maya looked up at the gray sky and grinned. "This is even better than soccer!"

1. Underline three words or phrases in the story that give you a clue about the setting at the beginning.

2. Which of the following best describes this first setting?
   a. Scary and mysterious
   b. Wet and rainy
   c. Quiet and uneventful
   d. Fun and exciting

Day 1: Read and Respond

Use the “Canceled Plans” passage to answer the questions.

3. What is the first setting in this story?

    ____

4. Circle three words or phrases in the story that give you a clue about the setting at the end of the story.

5. Which event could only happen in this second setting of the story?
    a. Maya looks out the window at the rain.
    b. Maya puts on rain boots.
    c. Maya enjoys her day.
    d. Maya splashes through some puddles.

6. What is the second setting in this story?

    ____

Day 2: Language Lab

Read the mini-lesson. Then, practice the skill in parts 1 and 2.

Remember what a noun is? A **noun** is a person, place or a thing.

- Examples: boy, mom, doctor, library, table, tree, cat

Pronouns are words that take the place of a noun.

- Examples: I, he, she, him, her, them, us, it

Pronouns are used so we don't have to keep saying the name of a noun over and over. Here's how pronouns can be used in a sentence:

Greg was feeling tired, so **he** got ready for bed.

Greg → Noun   he → **Pronoun**

The leaf fluttered down until **it** hit the ground.

leaf → Noun   it → **Pronoun**

Part 1: Fill in each blank with the correct pronoun from the word bank.

us	he	it	she	I	them

1. Jenna took her coat so ____________ would not be cold.
2. Max said that ____________ could walk to the store himself.
3. My family was excited when the waiter gave ____________ our food.
4. All the snacks looked delicious. I wanted to try some of ____________.
5. Sarah took the basketball and threw ____________ toward the basket.
6. They told me to hurry up, so ____________ started to run.

Day 2: Language Lab

Part 2: Play "Pronoun Pile-up!"

Setup:

1. Cut out all of the cards on the next page.
2. Spread the green cards out on the table or floor so everyone can see them.
3. Divide the blue cards with pronouns evenly between all the players.

Play the game:

1. When it's your turn, pick one of your blue pronoun cards.
2. Try to drop or toss the card on top of a green card that matches what the pronoun could describe. For example, you could try to throw the blue card with the pronoun "he" onto a green card, like "Dad."
3. If the cards are touching and make a correct match, you get a point!
4. There could be more than one correct answer for each pronoun.
5. Keep playing until all of the blue cards have been used.
6. The player with the most points at the end wins!

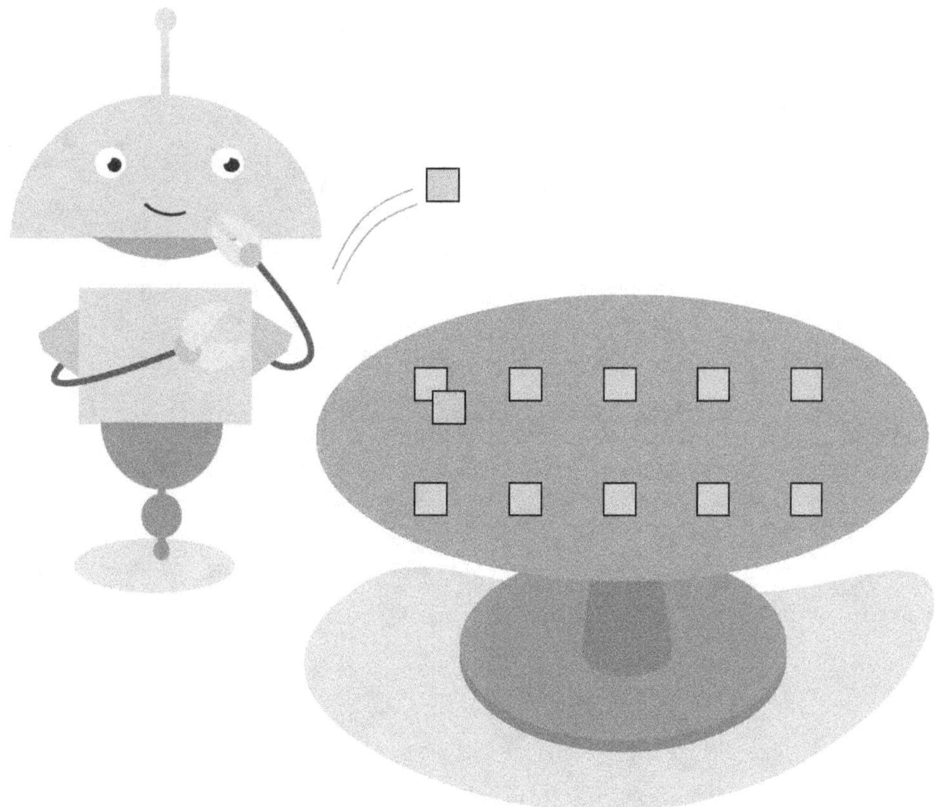

Day 2: Language Lab

Cut out these cards to play the "pronoun pile-up" game outlined on the previous page.

John	Mary	he	she
My brother	My sister	him	her
Sam, Matt, and myself	My family and I	we	us
The group of kids	The team	they	them
The book	Dad	it	you

Day 2: Connect and Reflect

Follow the prompts to deepen your understanding of the lesson.

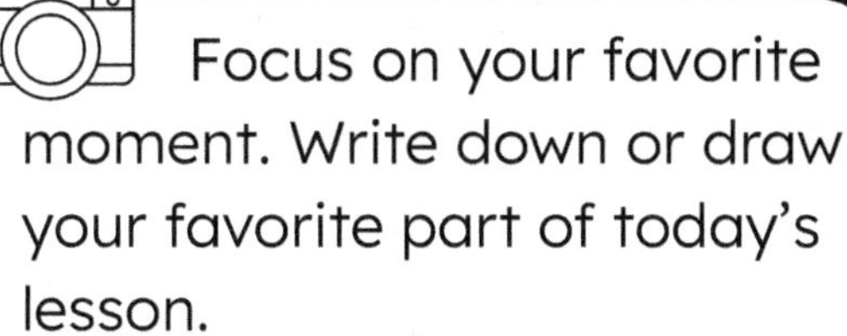

Focus on your favorite moment. Write down or draw your favorite part of today's lesson.

Pack your bags! What's something you learned that you want to take with you and remember later?

Make a real-world connection. What does the setting look like in your life?

Rate how you feel about this week's "Language Lab" skill: I can identify and use pronouns.

Rate how you feel about this week's skill: I can identify the setting in a story and describe the effect a setting can have on a story.

Optional Support

Dig Deeper

Want more practice with setting?

Cars zoomed past Leila as she walked along the sidewalk. Tall buildings stretched into the sky and reflected the afternoon sun. The honking of horns mixed with the chatter of people heading home from work.

As she passed a bus stop, Leila spotted a tiny kitten curled up under a bench. The kitten looked lost and afraid. Leila knelt down and held out her hand. The kitten slowly crawled toward Leila.

Think about where this story takes place. Underline some words in the story that give clues to what the setting is, then write the setting here.

____

Draw the setting for this story below. The underlined words can help give you ideas for what to draw.

Optional Support

Climb Higher

Ready for a challenge when it comes to setting?

Read each story event and write a setting that would make sense for it.

Some characters make a fire to stay warm. → Setting ______________________

A character needs help finding her lost dog. → Setting ______________________

A group of characters find an alien city filled with strange creatures. → Setting ______________________

Write out an event that could happen in the setting of a backyard treehouse.

____

____

Write something a character could do if the setting of the story were a magical kingdom in the sky.

____

____

Day 1

- ❏ Video and Guided Notes
- ❏ Read and Respond
- ❏ Online Practice Levels 1 and 2

Day 2

- ❏ Language Lab
- ❏ Connect and Reflect
- ❏ Online Practice Levels 3 and 4

Day 3

- ❏ Extend Your Skills
- ❏ Online Practice Level 5
- ❏ Optional: Dig Deeper or Climb Higher

Lesson Goal:
I can identify characters' external traits and actions to understand their roles in stories.

Record your thoughts:
Think about a character from a book, movie, or show that you love. How would you describe what they look like and the things they do?

Record your thoughts on the right! →

A Word To Explore:

Chuckle

To laugh quietly

Day 1: Guided Notes

Follow along with Bea to complete the guided notes below.

The outer world of characters

refers to the things we can see or ___________ about characters from the outside.

External trait - describes a character's ___________ appearance	**Actions -** refers to what characters ___________ or how they behave	**Role -** the part a character ___________ in the story, like their job or purpose

External traits

Actions

Jasper was a little gray cat with a torn ear and dusty fur who called the alleyway his home. When big dogs chased the kittens, Jasper stepped in. He arched his back, hissed loudly, and stood firm until the bullies backed off.

Jasper's role: He saves others and stands up for what's right, like a hero.

Day 1: Guided Notes

Read or **listen along to** the first part of the story below with Bea.

Everyone on Milton Lane kept an eye on Mr. Luton. He was tall, skinny, and always dressed in a black-and-white suit. As he stomped through the neighborhood, his black boots clicked loudly on the pavement. He took letters from mailboxes, stole packages from doorsteps, and snipped flowers from gardens. He only ever smiled when he was causing trouble.

Across the lane lived Miss Jenkins. She was small and round, with rosy cheeks and a soft voice. Her clothes were always cheerful, from bright sweaters and rainbow scarves to frilly skirts. Miss Jenkins never left the house without a basket filled with things like bandages, biscuits, and buttons, just in case someone needed help. She smiled and greeted everyone as they walked by, even grumpy people like Mr. Luton!

Highlight three external traits that describe Miss Jenkins in the text above.

Underline at least one action that Miss Jenkins does in the text above.

Put a check mark next to the role you think Miss Jenkins plays, then write one to two sentences explaining why on the lines underneath.

☐ *Plays funny tricks on others*   ☐ *Takes care of others*   ☐ *Saves others from danger*

____

____

Today we learned...

Authors help us understand characters by showing us their **external traits** and **actions**. This also helps us figure out the **roles** they have in stories.

Day 1: Read and Respond

Step 1: Read the text below about a character called Professor Puddlewick, or listen to it by clicking or scanning the QR code. Then, take a moment to imagine what he's like.

There was a little shop in Wellington with the sign: *Professor Puddlewick's Puzzling Potions.* Inside was Professor Puddlewick himself. He was an old man with a messy gray beard and a long purple coat. His potions worked, but not in the way you'd expect. That's because what he liked most in the world was playing pranks on people.

He would giggle as he gave customers "Hair-Growth Medicine" that made their socks longer. He would laugh when he sold customers "Snore-No-More Potion" that gave them the hiccups all night. Once, he even sold a bottle of "Invisibility Mist" that only made people's hats disappear. When angry customers came back to complain, Professor Puddlewick would just chuckle and say, "Well, I did say my potions were puzzling!"

Step 2: Highlight three external traits that describe Professor Puddlewick in the text above.

Step 3: Underline two actions that Professor Puddlewick does in the text above.

Step 4: Based on the information you have about Professor Puddlewick, describe the role you think he has and explain why on the lines below, then draw a picture of him in the box.

____

____

____

____

____

____

Day 1: Read and Respond

Step 5: Adjectives are words that describe nouns (people, places, or things). In this activity, you need to identify adjectives and nouns in the sentences below that were taken from the text.

- First, circle all the adjectives you find.
- Next, underline the nouns that the adjectives describe.

There are eight adjectives and six nouns in total that you need to find!

1. There was a little shop in Wellington with the sign.
2. He was an old man with a messy gray beard and a long purple coat.
3. When angry customers came back to complain, Professor Puddlewick would just chuckle and say, “Well, I did say my potions were puzzling!”

Step 6: Copy five of the adjectives you found in the table below. For each one, write your own sentence that includes the adjective. Your sentences can be about anything, so be creative!

Adjective	Sentence

Day 2: Language Lab

Read the mini-lesson. Then, practice the skill in parts 1 and 2.

A **noun** is a word that names a person, place, thing, or idea. We'll learn about two types of nouns in this lesson.

1. **Common nouns** name general people, places, things, or ideas. We don't capitalize common nouns unless they begin a sentence. Here are some examples:

    - **People** (like job titles or family members, not people's names)
      Examples: teacher, sister, firefighter
    - **General places**
      Examples: city, country, park
    - **Things**
      Examples: book, pencil, chair
    - **Ideas**
      Examples: love, happiness, freedom

2. **Proper nouns** name specific people, places, things, or ideas. Proper nouns always begin with a capital letter, no matter where they are in a sentence. Here are some examples:

    - **People's names**
      Examples: Emily, Mr. Chen, Paul
    - **Names of specific places** (like cities, countries, and addresses)
      Examples: Chicago, France, Walmart, Whitmore Street
    - **Days, months, and holidays**
      Monday, February, Thanksgiving
    - **Titles** (like titles of books, movies, shows)
      Charlotte's Web, Frozen, Finding Nemo

Day 2: Language Lab

Part 1: Color the common nouns blue and the proper nouns yellow.

Benjamin	town	Penny Avenue
cousin	April	girl
England	Christmas	snake
castle	Saturday	Mrs. Benson

Part 2: In each sentence below, look for a noun that's capitalized when it shouldn't be or not capitalized when it should be. Circle the mistakes, then rewrite the nouns correctly on the lines next to the sentences. The first one's been done for you!

Remember, proper nouns always begin with a capital letter, while common nouns only do at the start of a sentence!

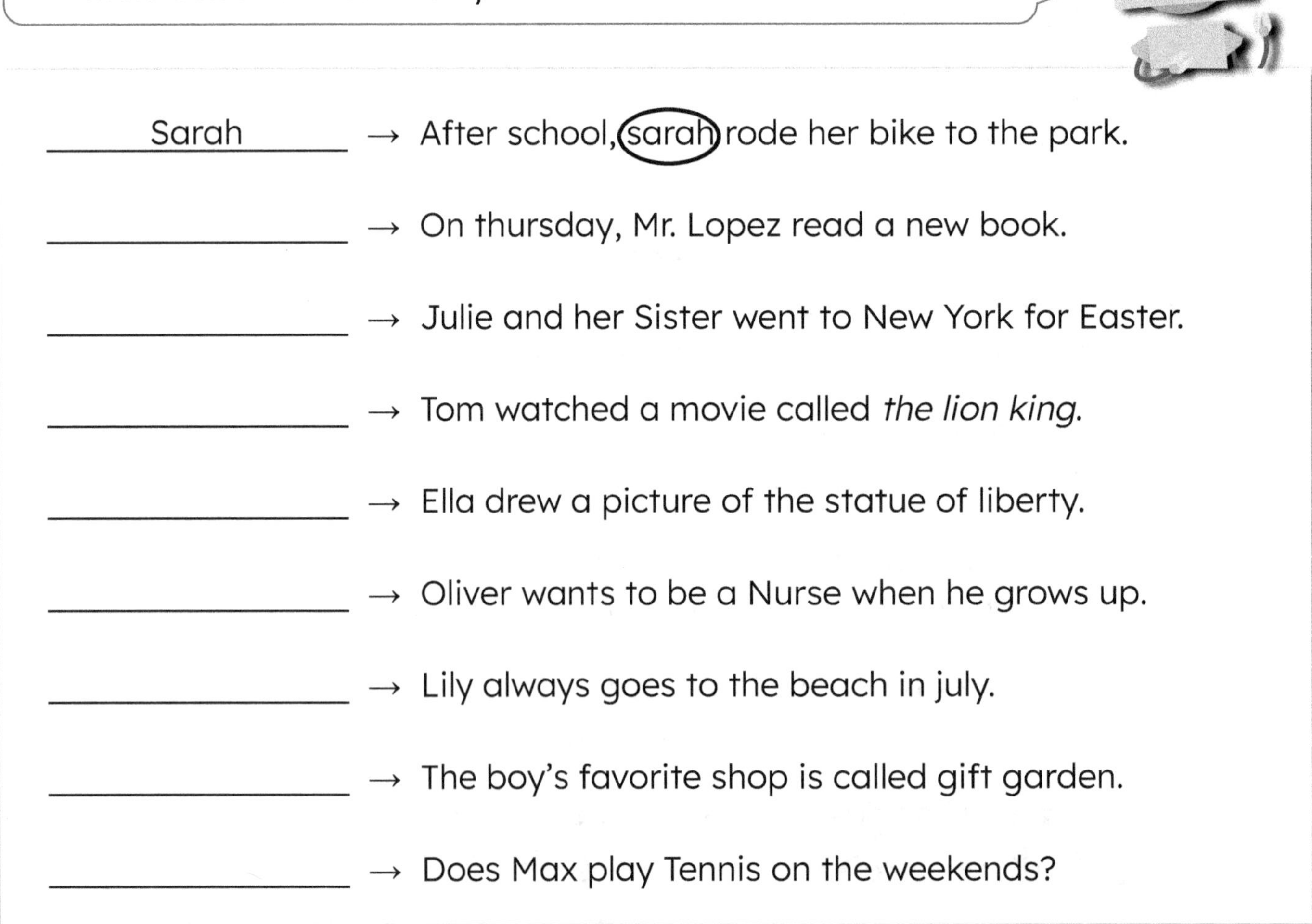

Sarah → After school, sarah rode her bike to the park.

__________ → On thursday, Mr. Lopez read a new book.

__________ → Julie and her Sister went to New York for Easter.

__________ → Tom watched a movie called *the lion king.*

__________ → Ella drew a picture of the statue of liberty.

__________ → Oliver wants to be a Nurse when he grows up.

__________ → Lily always goes to the beach in july.

__________ → The boy's favorite shop is called gift garden.

__________ → Does Max play Tennis on the weekends?

Day 2: Connect and Reflect

Follow the prompts to deepen your understanding of the lesson.

Focus on your favorite moment. Write down or draw your favorite part of today's lesson.

Pack your bags! What's something you learned that you want to take with you and remember later?

Make a real-world connection. Think about people in real life. How does focusing on what they do help you understand what they're like?

Rate how you feel about this week's "Language Lab" skill: I can identify and use proper nouns.

Rate how you feel about this week's skill: I can identify characters' external traits and actions to understand their roles in stories.

Day 3: Extend Your Skills

A Real-Life Character Study

You will use the skills you learned today to describe a family member or friend from real life! Use the template on the next page to do the steps below.

Step 1: Think of someone in your life whom you see often.
This could be a family member, like a grandparent, or it could be a friend.

For example: My Aunt Maggie

Step 2: Draw a picture of your person. Around your drawing, label at least three external traits, like their hairstyle, eye color, clothes, or height.

For example: Curly brown hair, neat blue suit, tall

Step 3: Below your drawing, list three nice things this person does. These actions can be things they do with you or others (like fun activities, tasks, favors, etc.).

For example: My dad cooks dinner, tells jokes, and checks my homework.

Step 4: Choose a role that best fits the person based on what they do.
You can choose from the list below or invent a new one.

- Helper - helps others
- Organizer - keeps things neat and tidy
- Leader - guides people and sets a good example
- Entertainer - brings fun and joy
- Peacemaker - helps solve conflicts between people
- Teacher - explains how to do things
- Fixer - repairs things or solves problems
- Explorer - tries new things or goes to new places
- Chef - prepares delicious food

Day 3: Extend Your Skills

Extend Your Skills, continued

My Person: ____

What They Look Like:

Three Nice Things They Do:

____

____

____

____

Their Role: ____

Optional Support

Dig Deeper

Want more practice identifying external traits, actions, and roles?

Step 1: Read the character descriptions below and circle the external traits that help you picture the characters. Then, draw the characters in the spaces below.

Alice walked down the hidden path with a backpack and red boots.	Grandma Lee, who loves to knit, has silver hair and round glasses.	Mike the Magician had a long, thin nose and wore a tall, black hat.

Step 2: The following sentences describe things that the characters above do. Based on each action, decide which role the character might play in a story.

1. Alice goes on adventures to find places no one has ever been before.

☐ She's someone who saves the day. ☐ She's someone who goes exploring. ☐ She's someone who helps others.

2. Grandma Lee gives all the clothes she knits to people who need them.

☐ She's someone who helps others. ☐ She's someone who causes problems. ☐ She's someone who tricks others.

3. Mike swapped a person's drink with slime and left before they noticed.

☐ He's someone who saves the day. ☐ He's someone who helps others. ☐ He's someone who tricks others.

Optional Support

Climb Higher

Ready for a challenge when it comes to the outer world of characters?

Below is a text like the one you read about Professor Puddlewick. In the original, he's an old man who plays tricks on people. Now, imagine Professor Puddlewick is a young boy who helps others instead! Think about how the story would change.

Step 1: Fill in the blanks with external traits and actions that match Professor Puddlewick's new description. Use the clues under the blanks to help you add details. The first one has been done for you!

There was a little shop in Wellington with the sign: *Professor Puddlewick's Puzzling Potions.* Inside was Professor Puddlewick himself. He was

_____a young boy_____ with ____________________ and
an external trait

____________________. His potions worked. That's because what he liked
an external trait

most in the world was ____________________.
something he likes doing

He would ____________________.
an action

He would also ____________________.
an action

When he spoke to ____________________ customers, Professor Puddlewick
an adjective

would chuckle and say, "My potions are ____________________!"
an adjective

Step 2: Read the text again. How did changing Puddlewick's appearance and actions impact his role and the story's events? Write one to three sentences.

____

____

____

Day 1

- ❏ Video and Guided Notes
- ❏ Read and Respond
- ❏ Online Practice Levels 1 and 2

Day 2

- ❏ Language Lab
- ❏ Connect and Reflect
- ❏ Online Practice Levels 3 and 4
- ❏ Optional: Dig Deeper or Climb Higher

Lesson Goal:
I can identify characters' internal traits, thoughts, and feelings and describe how they impact their actions.

Record your thoughts:
Think about a character you like. How would you describe their personality or what they're like deep down?

Record your thoughts on the right! →

A Word To Explore:

Pounding

Hitting again and again with force or making a loud, repeated sound

Day 1: Guided Notes

Follow along with Bea to complete the guided notes below.

The inner world of characters

refers to the things that happen on the ___________, which we can't always see or observe. It includes what characters think, how they feel, and what they're like deep down.

Internal trait - a characteristic that describes someone's ______________

Ruby noticed Matt sitting alone on the playground bench. *He probably doesn't have anyone to play with,* Ruby thought. She felt sad for him, so she walked over with a smile and asked him to play soccer with them. When he nodded, they went to the field where Ruby passed him the ball first.

Thought

Feeling

Actions

Ruby's internal trait is **kindness**.

Day 1: Guided Notes

Read or **listen along to** the the first text below with Bea.

Liam stood near the doorway at Jacinda's birthday party. His heart was pounding. *What if no one talks to me? Or worse... I do something embarrassing and everyone laughs?* he thought. "Are you OK?" Jacinda asked him. "I'm fine!" Liam said with a big smile. It was a lie. He felt nervous and wished he could just disappear. When Jacinda waved him over to join a game, Liam stayed by the snacks, pretending to act busy so he didn't have to talk to new people.

Highlight Liam's thoughts in the text above.

Record a word that describes how Liam feels in the text above.

____

Decide if Liam is brave, shy, or jealous by checking one of the boxes below.

☐ *Brave* ☐ *Shy* ☐ *Jealous*

Today we learned...

We can understand characters better by figuring out their thoughts, feelings, and internal traits

A character's inner world helps us understand their actions on the outside

Day 1: Read and Respond

Step 1: Read the text below, or click or scan the QR code to listen. Then, take a moment to imagine what Jessica is like.

Jessica stood tall in a green jacket and leather boots, tucking her long red hair behind her ears. She focused her blue eyes on the cave ahead where the Shadow Beast was hiding. She'd been sent to defeat it because it had been scaring people and stealing food. *No matter how scary the beast is, I can do this!* Jessica thought. She felt excited and confident. When she heard the beast growl, she marched into the cave and called out, "I'm not afraid!" As the beast came closer, Jessica ran toward it. She was ready to fight.

Remember, the inner world includes their thoughts, feelings, and internal traits, while the outer world includes their external traits, actions, and roles.

Step 2: Show Jessica's inner and outer world by filling out the boxes below about her. In the middle, draw a picture of what she looks like.

Inner World:	**Picture:**	**Outer World:**
Thoughts:		External Traits:
Feelings:		Actions:
Internal Traits:		Role:

Day 2: Language Lab

Read the mini-lesson. Then, practice the skill in parts 1 and 2.

A **compound word** is a word that combines two smaller words. The combination creates a new word with its own meaning.

For example: jelly + fish = jellyfish.

Part 1: Make compound words by combining the names of the pictures below. You can draw pictures and/or write words. The first one has been done for you.

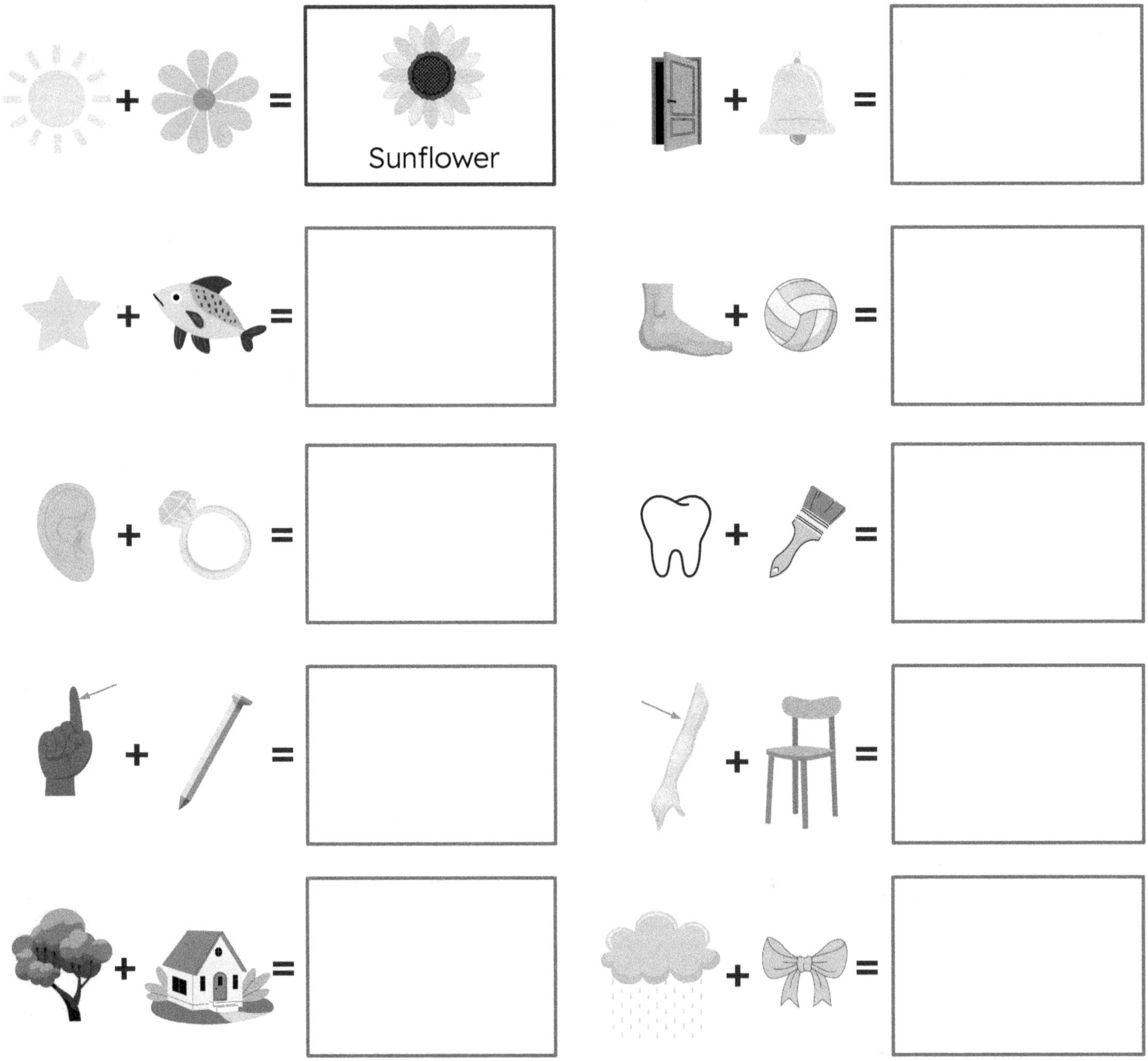

+ = Sunflower

+ =

+ =

+ =

+ =

+ =

+ =

+ =

+ =

+ =

Day 2: Language Lab

Part 2: Copy the 10 compound words you made in Part 1 on the lines below. Then, find and circle all the hidden words in the puzzle. Words might be placed horizontally, vertically, or diagonally. Check off each word as you find it.

____________________	____________________
____________________	____________________
____________________	____________________
____________________	____________________
____________________	____________________

D	T	O	O	T	H	B	R	U	S	H	R	H	F
J	F	R	J	L	P	T	D	I	H	X	E	I	I
S	T	A	C	B	T	D	M	V	J	L	O	I	N
T	U	I	M	S	R	D	O	I	N	D	I	R	G
A	R	N	E	O	E	I	O	O	A	E	R	E	E
R	F	B	F	P	E	G	P	T	R	G	R	F	R
F	E	O	L	L	H	E	Q	N	M	B	U	U	N
I	R	W	C	H	O	N	A	A	C	C	E	J	A
S	M	O	O	F	U	W	W	M	H	J	R	L	I
H	I	O	T	E	S	U	E	T	A	A	E	E	L
O	N	G	A	B	E	A	R	R	I	N	G	D	N
D	A	M	T	I	N	R	F	N	R	T	A	E	R
F	O	O	T	B	A	L	L	R	O	A	T	L	P

Day 2: Connect and Reflect

Follow the prompts to deepen your understanding of the lesson.

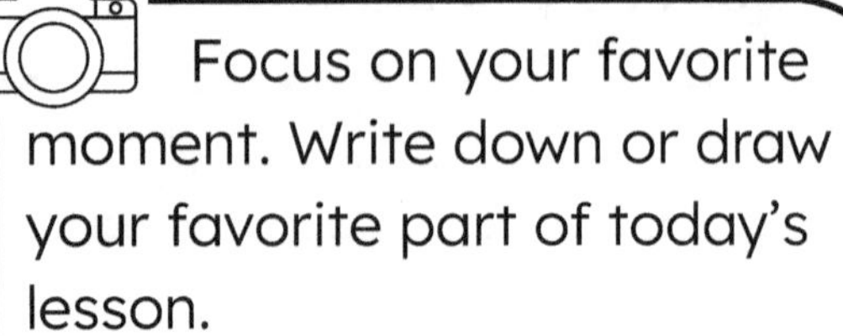

Focus on your favorite moment. Write down or draw your favorite part of today's lesson.

Pack your bags! What's something you learned that you want to take with you and remember later?

Make a real-world connection. Think about people in real life. Why is it important to try to understand how they feel?

Rate how you feel about this week's "Language Lab" skill: I can identify and use compound words.

Rate how you feel about this week's skill: I can identify characters' internal traits, thoughts, and feelings, and describe how they impact their actions.

Optional Support

Dig Deeper

Want more practice identifying thoughts, feelings, and internal traits?

Read the sentences, then cut, sort, and paste them into the correct category: thoughts, feelings, and internal traits.

Thoughts	Feelings	Internal Traits

Adam was scared.	Pedro felt frustrated.	The dog is feeling tired today.
I can't believe it! Andy thought.	The girl is intelligent.	Patrick is an honest man.
Where did he go? wondered Julie.	Lesley is a very helpful person.	*I wish I had a pony,* thought George.
Luis is a kind boy.	*I've got homework to do!* Ben remembered.	I'm angry at you!

Optional Support

Climb Higher

Ready for a challenge when it comes to the inner and outer world of characters?

These characters have internal traits but are missing the rest of their descriptions! Complete the descriptions by writing thoughts, feelings, and actions that match their internal traits.

Allie the Alien

Internal trait: Hardworking

Thoughts: ______________________________

____

Feelings: ______________________________

Actions: ______________________________

____

Pete the Pirate

Internal trait: Adventurous

Thoughts: ______________________________

____

Feelings: ______________________________

Actions: ______________________________

____

Walt the Wizard

Internal trait: Funny

Thoughts: ______________________________

____

Feelings: ______________________________

Actions: ______________________________

____

Day 1

- ❏ Video and Guided Notes
- ❏ Read and Respond
- ❏ Online Practice Levels 1 and 2

Day 2

- ❏ Language Lab
- ❏ Connect and Reflect
- ❏ Online Practice Levels 3 and 4

Day 3

- ❏ Extend Your Skills
- ❏ Online Practice Level 5
- ❏ Optional: Dig Deeper or Climb Higher

Lesson Goal:
I can identify the story's conflict and resolution and their impact on the story's events.

Record your thoughts:
Think about a story you like where the character faces a problem. What happened? How did they handle it?

Record your thoughts on the right! →

A Word To Explore:

Smirk

Smile in a mean or sneaky way

Day 1: Guided Notes

Follow along with Bea to complete the guided notes below.

Conflict is the ____________ or struggle that the main character faces in a story.

Resolution is how the problem is ____________.

Read or **listen along to** the story below with Bea.

Skye wasn't like the other squirrels. While her friends loved to leap through tall trees, Skye stayed on the ground. She wished she was brave enough to climb up high, but she was terrified of heights. Still, she worked hard. She helped gather acorns for winter and placed them at the bottom of the Grand Oak, the tallest tree in the forest. Skye felt sad watching the others carry acorns to the top to keep them safe.

A conflict Skye faces is her fear of heights.

One afternoon, disaster struck. Skye noticed a crackling sound echoing in the forest, followed by smoke. "Fire! Head for the creek!" called the squirrels. They ran, leaves crumbling under their paws and fiery branches crashing down behind them. Finally, they reached the creek. "We're safe here," said one squirrel. But Skye gasped, "Our acorns are still in the Grand Oak!" The squirrels knew they would go hungry this winter without their acorn supply. "It's too dangerous to go back," said one squirrel.

Record the conflict Skye faces in the second part of the story above.

Day 1: Guided Notes

Read or **listen along to** the last part of the story below with Bea.

Skye looked toward the smoke. "I'll go," she said softly. "But Skye... it's not safe," one squirrel whispered. Without saying a word, Skye ran into the forest, her heart pounding as she dodged flames. Luckily, when she reached the Grand Oak, the fire hadn't touched it yet.

Skye took a deep breath and started climbing, one paw at a time. At the top, she grabbed the bag of acorns. She climbed down quickly and raced back through the forest to the creek. "You did it!" called one squirrel. "You're so brave!" exclaimed another.

Skye smiled as they all cheered around her. She had faced her biggest fear, and now, she wasn't afraid anymore. That winter, no one went hungry. The squirrels had all the food they needed — all thanks to Skye's bravery.

Describe the resolution in one to two sentences.

Imagine the conflict was different. Instead of a fire, imagine the acorns were stolen by a raccoon. Describe how you think the story might change.

Day 1: Read and Respond

Step 1: Read the first part of "The Sweetest Steal," or click or scan the QR code to listen.

Our family ran Bramble's Jam Shop for as long as I could remember. It was a beautiful store filled with the smell of sweet fruit and rows of shiny jars with labels like "Strawberry Swirl" and "Blueberry Bliss." Our jam was so famous that people would travel miles just to taste it.

Hidden behind the shelves was an old book full of our top-secret jam recipes, which I checked every day to see if it was still there. But one morning, the book was gone! My family panicked, but I knew exactly who took it. It was Mr. Pockle, the greediest man in town. He had a candy store but couldn't stand that our jam was more popular than his candy. I'd often see him sneaking around our shop, which must've been when he saw the book.

Step 2: Describe the conflict in the first part of the story in one to two sentences.

Step 3: Identify whether you think the conflict is on the inside or the outside of the character.

The conflict is on...

☐ The inside ☐ The outside

Day 1: Read and Respond

Step 3: Read the last part of "The Sweetest Steal," or click or scan the QR code to listen.

That night, I hatched a plan. I was going to steal the book back and leave behind a fake one with silly recipes like "Burnt Broccoli" and "Sour Spinach." At midnight, I crept to Mr. Pockle's candy shop and peeked through the dusty window. He was smirking and stirring a pot of jam with the book beside him. I slipped in through the back door and hid behind a shelf. When he turned to gather more ingredients, I swapped the real book for the fake one and ran out the door as quick as a flash.

The next day, my family cheered when they saw the book, and we celebrated by making a fresh batch of strawberry jam. Across town, Mr. Pockle's shelves were stacked with his own jam, but customers said it was awful. From that day on, I kept our recipe book locked away, and Mr. Pockle never bothered us again!

Step 4: Describe the resolution in the last part of the story in one to two sentences.

Step 5: The conflict in the story is Mr. Pockle stealing the recipe book. Now, imagine that instead of stealing it, he destroys it! How would the story change? List three new, different things you think would happen with this conflict.

1. ______________________________
2. ______________________________
3. ______________________________

Day 2: Language Lab

Read the mini-lesson. Then, practice the skill in parts 1 through 3.

An **abbreviation** is a short way to write a word to help us save time when we write and read. They usually start with a capital letter and end with a period.

Here are some different types of abbreviations:

Titles of people
Senior → Sr.
Mister → Mr.
Missus → Mrs.
Doctor → Dr.
Captain → Capt.

Addresses
Street → St.
Road → Rd.
Avenue → Ave.
Lane → Ln.
Drive → Dr.

Measurements
Minute → min.
Second → sec.
Hour → hr.
Foot → ft.
Inch → in.

Months
January → Jan.
February → Feb.
March → Mar.
April → Apr.
May → May
June → June
July → July
— No abbreviations
August → Aug.
September → Sept.
October → Oct.
November → Nov.
December → Dec.

Days
Monday → Mon.
Tuesday → Tues.
Wednesday → Wed.
Thursday → Thurs.
Friday → Fri.
Saturday → Sat.
Sunday → Sun.

Part 1: Circle the abbreviation you find in each sentence below.

1. I visited Dr. Lee at his office for my annual checkup.
2. The new house on Oak Ave. has a big backyard.
3. Mrs. Brown, who teaches science, is my favorite teacher.
4. Dad's note said, "Remember to buy tickets to the show in Oct."
5. Naomi lives next to a lovely lady called Mrs. García.

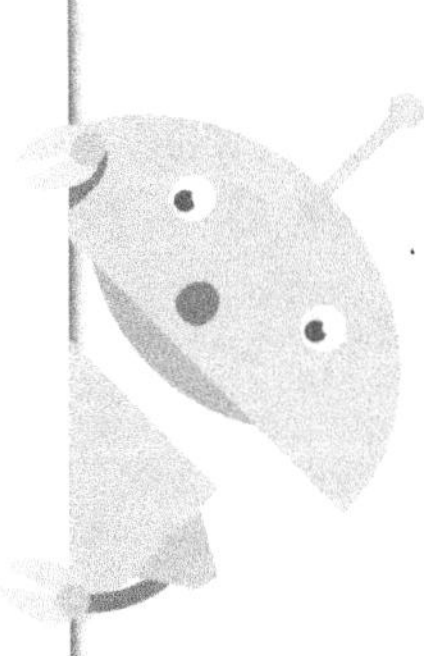

Day 2: Language Lab

Part 2: Write abbreviations of the words below.

1.	Captain - __________	5.	Sunday - __________
2.	Hour - __________	6.	Second - __________
3.	Street - __________	7.	Foot - __________
4.	Friday - __________	8.	October - __________

Part 3: Ready to play bingo? Find two more people then follow the steps below!

1. Cut out the abbreviation cards below and give them to players 1 and 2.
2. Give Player 3 the previous page with the different types of abbreviations.
3. Player 3 must call out random full words (for example, doctor).
4. Players 1 and 2 must listen carefully and cross out the matching abbreviation if it's on their card (for example, Dr.).
5. The first player to cross out all their abbreviations and shout "bingo!" wins!
6. When someone wins, switch players and use different cards to play again!

Dr.	Ln.	in.
Sept.	ft.	May.
Capt.	Rd.	Dec.

min.	Oct.	Sr.
Ln.	Fri.	Aug.
Sun.	Dr.	Rd.

ft.	Ave.	Aug.
Dr.	Sept.	Mr.
Rd.	min.	sec.

Sat.	ft.	Wed.
Feb.	Ave.	Mrs.
in.	St.	min.

Mrs.	hr.	Tues.
Apr.	Capt.	Jan.
sec.	Mr.	Wed.

Mrs.	May.	Feb.
Dec.	hr.	St.
Rd.	Sr.	Fri.

Day 2: Connect and Reflect

Follow the prompts to deepen your understanding of the lesson.

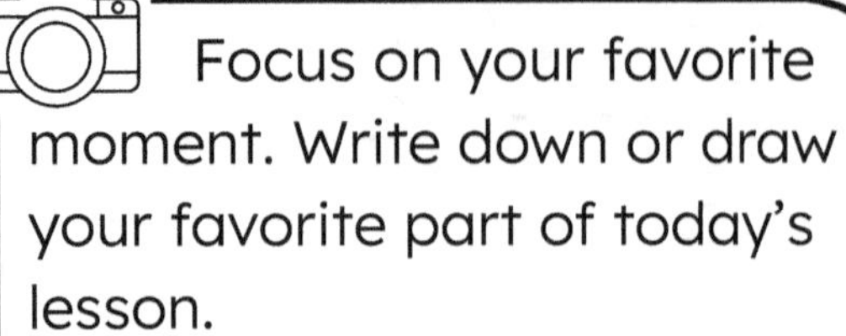

Focus on your favorite moment. Write down or draw your favorite part of today's lesson.

Pack your bags! What's something you learned that you want to take with you and remember later?

Make a real-world connection. Think about a real-life conflict you faced recently. What happened and what was the resolution?

Rate how you feel about this week's "Language Lab" skill: I can identify and use abbreviations.

Rate how you feel about this week's skill: I can identify the story's conflict and resolution and their impact on the story's events.

Day 3: Extend Your Skills

Create your own comic!

Think of a story you know that you love, or make up a story of your own.

Box 1: Draw and write about the setting and the main characters.
Box 2: Draw and write about the problem.
Box 3: Draw and write about what the character does to try to solve the problem.
Box 4: Draw and write about the resolution.

1.	**2.**
____________ ____________ ____________ ____________	____________ ____________ ____________ ____________
3.	**4.**
____________ ____________ ____________ ____________	____________ ____________ ____________ ____________

Optional Support

Dig Deeper

Want more practice exploring conflict and resolution in stories?

Step 1: Look at the picture and read about the conflict the character is facing.
Step 2: In the boxes below, write one to two sentences or draw a picture showing how the character might solve the problem.

Conflict: Ed has to fight the fierce dragon to protect the queen's castle.

Resolution:

Conflict: Erika is scared to speak in front of a big audience.

Resolution:

Conflict: Buddy is lost and can't find his way to his family's home.

Resolution:

Conflict: Tommy feels sad because he's getting teased in class.

Resolution:

Optional Support

Climb Higher

Ready for a challenge when it comes to conflict and resolution?

Step 1: Reread the start of the story "The Sweetest Steal" below.

Our family has run Bramble's Jam Shop for as long as I can remember. It was a beautiful store filled with the smell of sweet fruit and rows of shiny jars with labels like "Strawberry Swirl" and "Blueberry Bliss." Our jam was so famous that people would travel miles just to taste it. Hidden behind the shelves was an old book full of our top-secret jam recipes.

Step 2: The conflict in the original story was Mr. Pockle stealing the recipe book. Now, imagine there's a different conflict! Put a check next to the conflict you want the story to have.

- ☐ The labels on the jam jars get mixed up.
- ☐ Jam is accidentally spilled on the recipe book.
- ☐ Squirrels steal the shop's fruit, so the family doesn't have enough for jam.

Step 3: Finish writing the story with your new conflict. Remember to include a new resolution!

____

____

____

____

____

____

____

____

____

Day 1

- ❏ Video and Guided Notes
- ❏ Read and Respond
- ❏ Online Practice Levels 1 and 2

Day 2

- ❏ Language Lab
- ❏ Connect and Reflect
- ❏ Online Practice Levels 3 and 4
- ❏ Optional: Dig Deeper or Climb Higher

Lesson Goal:
I can describe how the inner and outer worlds of characters may change with the conflict and resolution of a story.

Record your thoughts:
Have you ever read a story where a character changed by the end? How and why did they change?

Record your thoughts on the right! →

A Word To Explore:

Stunned

Very surprised or shocked

Day 1: Guided Notes

Follow along with Bea to complete the guided notes below.

How conflict changes characters:

Conflict and resolution affect characters' inner and outer worlds.

Outer world - includes what they look like and what they ____________	**Inner world -** includes what they ____________, feel, and who they are deep down

Read or **listen along to** "The Tortoise and the Hare" to see how the hare changes.

Once, there was a hare who loved to talk about how fast he was and often made fun of the slow-moving tortoise. One day, the tortoise got tired of the hare's teasing and asked the hare for a race. When the race began, the hare zoomed ahead! He was so far in front that he took a nap.

What the hare was like **at the beginning**.

Meanwhile, the tortoise kept moving slowly. When the hare woke up, he was too far behind to catch up. The tortoise won the race, and the hare felt like a fool! The hare learned that slow and steady wins the race, and from that day on, he never teased the tortoise again.

What the hare was like **after the conflict**.

Day 1: Guided Notes

Read or **listen along to** "The Lion and the Mouse" to see how the lion changes.

One day, a mouse ran across a sleeping lion's paw and woke him up. The lion grabbed the mouse and growled, ready to eat her. "Please let me go," begged the mouse. "Maybe someday I can help you!" The lion laughed at her. He thought an animal this small couldn't possibly be useful.

 Highlight what the lion was thinking in the text above.

The lion got bored of tormenting the mouse and let her go. A few days later, the lion got caught in a hunter's net and couldn't escape. The mouse heard the lion's roar and rushed over to help. She chewed through the ropes to set him free. The lion felt surprised and thankful and realized that even small friends could be a big help.

Use what you know to complete the two sentences below.

Because the mouse helped the lion, the lion learned ______________________

____

At the end, the lion felt ______________________________

____

Today we learned...

 **Conflict and resolution** help characters learn and grow, because characters usually change in some way when they're faced with a problem

 Characters change so that the story is **more interesting and realistic**

Day 1: Read and Respond

Step 1: Read the story below, or click or scan the QR code to listen to it, and notice how Ralph, the dog, changes.

Once, there was a greedy dog with an old brown collar called Ralph. One day, he was sniffing around the park trying to find food. He often went there just to see what he could find, even when he wasn't hungry! This time, he found a big, juicy bone. But as he picked it up, he was already thinking about the next thing he could find. He always felt unsatisfied.

As Ralph crossed over the park bridge, he glanced down and saw what looked like another dog holding an even bigger, tastier bone! Ralph opened his mouth to grab the other bone, but his own bone fell into the river and disappeared.

Ralph was stunned! He realized the dog was his reflection. As he walked away with nothing, he thought, *I need to be less greedy!* From that day on, he only went to the park to play with the other dogs. Soon, the park-keeper noticed Ralph's new attitude and gave him a beautiful red collar. Ralph finally felt happy and learned the important lesson of being thankful for what you already have.

Step 2: In the table below, record what Ralph was like **at the beginning**. One has been added for you already!

Inner world: Thoughts, feelings, and internal traits	**Outer world:** Actions and external traits
He was greedy.	

Step 3: Describe the conflict that Ralph faced in one to two sentences below.

Day 1: Read and Respond

Step 4: In the table below, record what Ralph was like **after the conflict**. One has been added for you already!

Inner world: Thoughts, feelings, and internal traits	**Outer world:** Actions and external traits
He was stunned.	

Step 5: Genres are groups of similar stories, usually sorted by how they're written, what they're about, or what happens in them.

Look at the story about Ralph again. Next, figure out the genre by answering "yes" or "no" to the questions below. Then, write what you think the genre is.

- **Action:** Are there any dangerous or fast-paced events? _______
- **Sci-fi:** Does it take place in the future or use futuristic technology? _______
- **Realistic fiction:** Could this story really happen? _______
- **Fantasy:** Are there any magical elements or animals that act or think like people? _______
- **Fable:** Does the story teach a lesson? _______

The genre of this story is ________________________.

Day 2: Language Lab

Read the mini-lesson. Then, practice the skill in parts 1 through 3.

Synonyms are words with similar meanings.

For example, "quick" and "fast" are synonyms because they both describe something that moves at high speed.

Part 1: Color the pairs of synonyms green and the pairs that aren't red.

friend / buddy	smooth / rough	happy / glad
neat / messy	smart / clever	blanket / bed
error / mistake	scary / frightening	start / middle

Part 2: Match the words on the left to their synonyms on the right.

Strange	Powerful
Energetic	Grin
Strong	Present
Gift	Unusual
Smile	Leap
Jump	Lively

Day 2: Language Lab

Part 3: Look at the underlined words in the sentences below. Find a synonym for each underlined word in the box and write it next to the sentence.

Note: There are two words from the box that you **won't** use, so choose carefully!

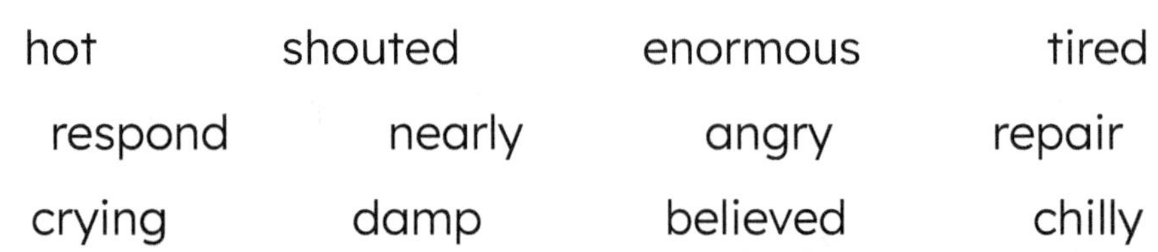

hot	shouted	enormous	tired
respond	nearly	angry	repair
crying	damp	believed	chilly

1. Elephants have big ears and long trunks. → ______________
2. Ren yelled for help because he was lost in the woods. → ______________
3. Pete was exhausted because he didn't sleep well. → ______________
4. I asked a question, but Sam didn't answer right away. → ______________
5. The monster was furious that we woke it up. → ______________
6. Brenda wore a jacket because it felt cold outside. → ______________
7. Aunt Kelly will fix the wobbly chair before dinner. → ______________
8. My top got wet when I accidentally spilled juice on it. → ______________
9. Julia was so sad that she couldn't stop sobbing. → ______________
10. Amy was so nervous that he almost dropped the cup. → ______________

Day 2: Connect and Reflect

Follow the prompts to deepen your understanding of the lesson.

Focus on your favorite moment. Write down or draw your favorite part of today's lesson.

Pack your bags! What's something you learned that you want to take with you and remember later?

Make a real-world connection. Think about real people. How can going through a challenge or problem help someone change or grow?

Rate how you feel about this week's "Language Lab" skill: I can identify and use synonyms.

Rate how you feel about this week's skill: I can describe how the inner and outer world of characters may change with the conflict and resolution of a story.

Optional Support

Dig Deeper

Want more practice identifying thoughts, feelings, and internal traits?

Choose any of the following activities you'd like to do!

Before and After Character Sketch
Choose a story you know well or use one from today's lesson. Draw the main character two times: once at the beginning of the story and once at the end. Under each drawing, write a few words or a sentence to show how the character looked, acted, or felt at that point in the story.

Dear Diary
Choose a story you love. Imagine you're the main character, and the conflict has just been solved. Write a diary entry as the character. In three to five sentences, describe how you feel, what you're thinking, and how you've changed. You can also draw a picture to show the changes using speech and thought bubbles!

Climb Higher

Ready for a challenge when it comes to the inner and outer world of characters?

Choose any of the following activities you'd like to do!

Character Interview
Pick a main character from a story. Imagine you're interviewing them at the end of the story about how they've changed. First, write five to 10 questions, like "How did you feel at the start of the story?" and "What did you learn from the problem you faced?" Then, record your answers as the character!

Conflict Comic Strip
Choose a story you know well. Create a comic strip that shows the main character before, during, and after a conflict. Use speech and thought bubbles to show how the character's feelings and actions change because of the conflict.

Day 1

- ❏ Video and Guided Notes
- ❏ Read and Respond
- ❏ Online Practice Levels 1 and 2

Day 2

- ❏ Language Lab
- ❏ Connect and Reflect
- ❏ Online Practice Levels 3 and 4

Day 3

- ❏ Extend Your Skills
- ❏ Online Practice Level 5
- ❏ Optional: Dig Deeper or Climb Higher

Lesson Goal:
I can use sequence words to retell the main events of a story and create a plot map.

Record your thoughts:
Think of a story you like. Then, imagine you're telling a friend about it. What events and details would you include to help them understand the story?

Record your thoughts on the right! →

A Word To Explore:

Sequence

The order that things happen in

Day 1: Guided Notes

Follow along with Bea to complete the guided notes below.

Sequencing events in a plot

Plot - what ______________ in order, with each event connecting to the next to help the story make sense

Retell a story - say what happened from ______________ to end using our own words

Read or **listen along to** the last part of the story below with Bea.

Once upon a time, there was an emperor who cared greatly about his appearance. He loved spending money on expensive clothes and was always looking to buy more.

One day, two tricksters came to the palace, saying they could weave special fabric that only intelligent people could see. The emperor was too greedy to notice their lies and hired them to make clothes.

They requested gold thread and the finest silk, which they smuggled into their bags to sell later. For days, they pretended to weave the fabric. When the emperor and his advisors checked on them, they couldn't see any fabric but were too afraid to admit it. "The clothes are beautiful!" they said. After several days, the thieves announced the clothes were finished.

Day 1: Guided Notes

The next day, the emperor showed off his new clothes in a parade. As he marched through the streets, the public praised his outfit because they were too scared to tell the truth. Suddenly, a boy shouted, "But he's not wearing anything!" The crowd gasped, then one by one, began laughing. The emperor blushed but continued walking, too proud to admit his mistake. Meanwhile, the tricksters had vanished with the thread and silk, leaving the emperor with nothing but his pride.

Plot map - a tool that helps us _______________ the most important parts of a story

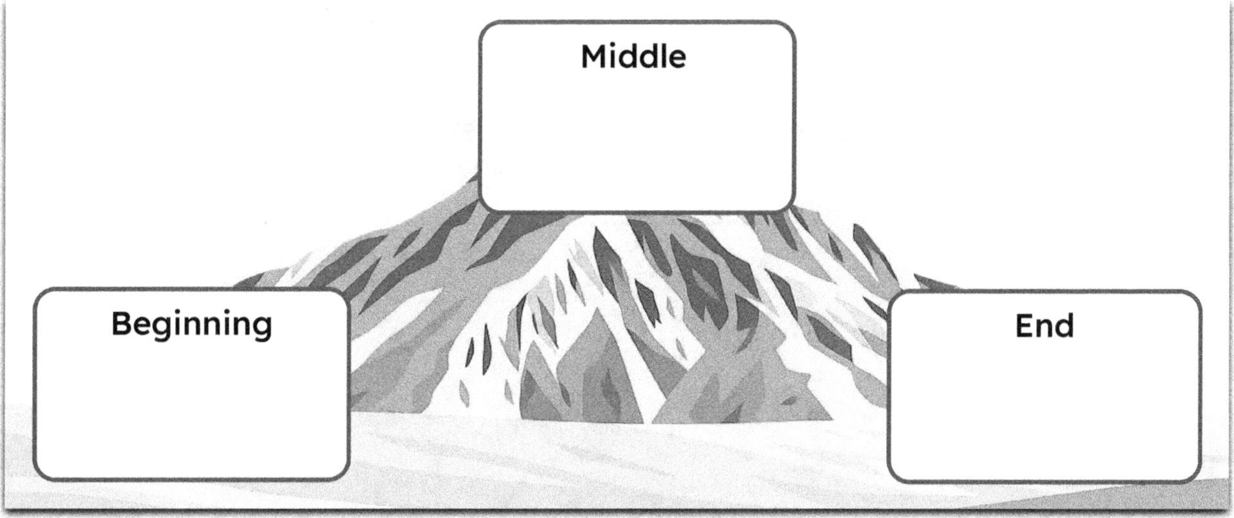

Follow along with Bea to fill out the beginning, middle, and end of the plot map below and on the next page.

Beginning

First, there was an emperor who cared a lot about what he looked like and loved fancy clothes. He always wanted to buy more.

Next, two tricksters came along and lied about being able to make magical fabric that only smart people could see. The emperor hired them.

Day 1: Guided Notes

Decide which retelling is better for the middle of the plot map by putting a check mark in one of the boxes below.

Middle ☐

Then, the tricksters asked for gold thread and fine silk, which they hid to sell later. They pretended to weave for many days. When the emperor and his helpers came to check, they were too scared to say they couldn't see any fabric. After a few days, the clothes were ready.

Middle ☐

Then, the tricksters got some gold thread and fine silk and pretended to weave for many days. The emperor and his helpers checked the clothes and said they were beautiful. After a few days, the clothes were ready.

Retell the last part in three to four sentences starting with the sequence word "last."

End

Today we learned...

- We **retell a story** by explaining what happened from beginning to end using our own words
- We can use **sequence words**, like "first," "then," "next," and "last," to help retell a story
- A good retelling includes the **plot**, characters, conflict, and resolution

Day 1: Read and Respond

Step 1: Read the story below called "Ollie's New Home," or listen to it by clicking or scanning the QR code.

One day, Ruby's mum brought home a kitten called Ollie. Everyone was excited — except Ruby. "He's so cute!" said her brother. "It's just what our family needs!" said her dad. But Ruby didn't think so. She thought Ollie was annoying.

Every time she opened her bedroom door, Ollie would slip in like a furry little ninja. He played with things on her desk, chased her shoelaces, and left orange fur everywhere. He even scratched her rug! And wherever Ruby went, Ollie would follow. Ruby's mom thought it was adorable. "He just wants to be your friend," she said. "You should be nicer to him." Ruby frowned. "He's *too* friendly!"

One night, Ruby went into her room and found Ollie curled up on her bed. "Fine," she sighed. "I guess we could be friends." She reached out and patted him, and Ollie instantly started purring — a deep, rumbling, happy purr. Ruby smiled, just a little. That night, Ruby let Ollie sleep on her bed. After that, they became friends. Ollie still followed Ruby everywhere, but now, she didn't mind.

Day 1: Read and Respond

Turn the paper to read the instructions and do the activity!

Step 2: Retell the story on the previous page by filling out the plot map below. Explain what happened in the beginning, middle, and end in your own words. Use the sequence words "first" at the start and "last" at the end. Anywhere in between, use the sequence words "next" and "then."

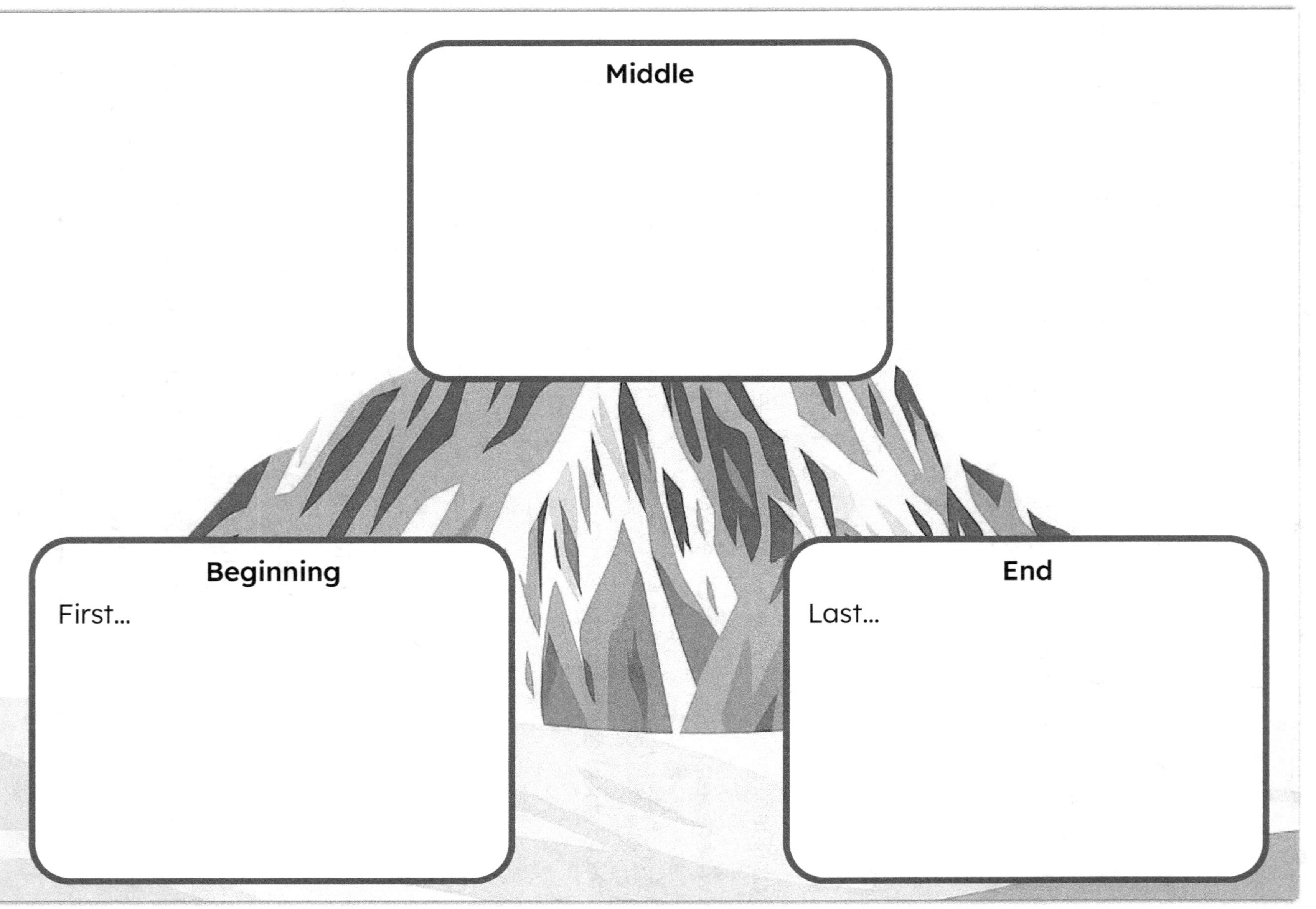

Day 2: Language Lab

Read the mini-lesson. Then, practice the skill in parts 1 through 3.

Antonyms are words with opposite meanings.

For example, "happy" and "sad" are antonyms because they describe opposite feelings.

Part 1: Circle the pairs of antonyms.

damp / dry	smart / foolish	construct / build
short / small	honest / truthful	smooth / rough
poor / rich	travel / bike	huge / gigantic

Part 2: Match the words on the left to their antonyms on the right.

Strong	Neat
Speedy	Boiling
Messy	Listen
Speak	Weak
Freezing	Remember
Forget	Slow

Day 2: Language Lab

Part 3: Complete the crossword puzzle below by reading the numbered words and writing the antonyms in the squares provided.

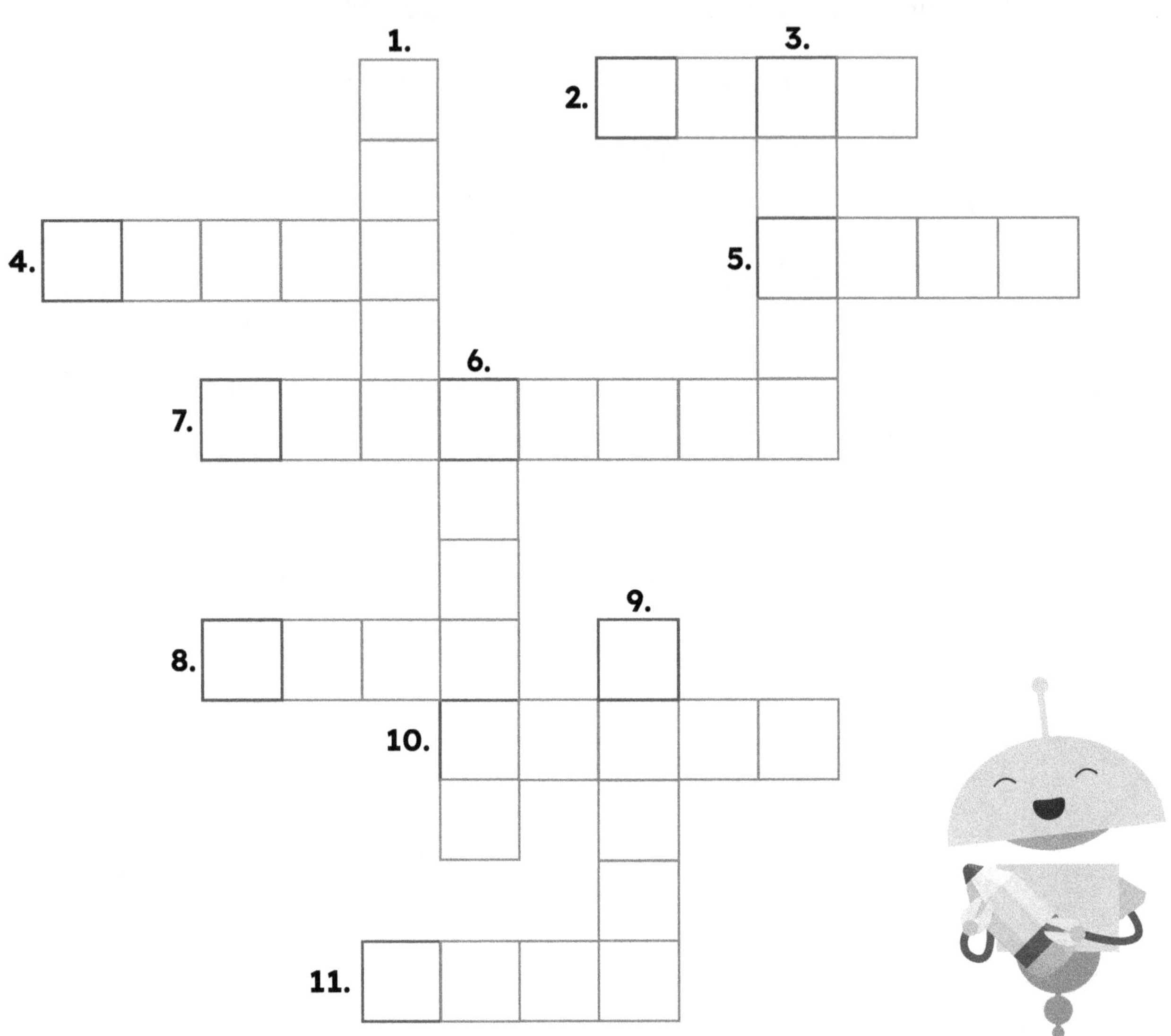

ACROSS

2. Empty

4. Loud

5. Take

7. Curly

8. Dangerous

10. Late

11. Up

DOWN

1. Before

3. Dark

6. Awake

9. Smile

Day 2: Connect and Reflect

Follow the prompts to deepen your understanding of the lesson.

Focus on your favorite moment. Write down or draw your favorite part of today's lesson.

Pack your bags! What's something you learned that you want to take with you and remember later?

Make a real-world connection. If you were telling a friend about something that happened to you recently, how would you retell it?

Rate how you feel about this week's "Language Lab" skill: I can identify and use antonyms.

Rate how you feel about this week's skill: I can use sequence words to retell the main events of a story in the correct order and create a plot map.

Day 3: Extend Your Skills

Step 1: Read the fairy tale "Little Red Riding Hood."

Once, there lived a girl named Little Red Riding Hood in a peaceful village. One day, her mother asked her to take a basket of fresh bread to her grandma, who lived in a cottage in the forest. Little Red Riding Hood set off on her bike and decided to take a different path. Suddenly, she encountered a wolf. "Where are you going?" the wolf asked. "My grandma's cottage," she said. The wolf grinned and vanished into the trees.

When she arrived, the door was open. "Come in," a voice called. Little Red Riding Hood entered to find her grandma in bed wearing a nightcap covering most of her face. "What big ears you have!" Little Red Riding Hood exclaimed. "All the better to hear you with," came the reply. "What big teeth you have!" Little Red Riding Hood said. "All the better to eat you with!" The wolf revealed himself with a growl and leaped out of bed.

Little Red Riding Hood screamed. A woodcutter, who had been working nearby, heard the scream. He rushed over with his axe and scared the wolf away, rescuing her grandma hiding in a closet and Little Red Riding Hood. She was so thankful to the woodcutter, and from that day on, she learned to stay on the same path in the forest!

Step 2: Cut out the plot cards below. Paste them on the plot map on the next page in order. Notice the sequence words "first," "next," "then," and "last" to help you!

Then, she biked to her grandma's house on a new path. She met a wolf and told him she was going to her grandma's house. He ran off.

A woodcutter was working near the cottage. He came in with an axe just in time and scared the wolf away.

First, there was a girl called Little Red Riding Hood. One day, her mom asked her to bring bread to her grandma, who lived in the forest.

When Little Red Riding Hood got to the cottage, the door was open. A voice told her to come in. She saw her grandma in bed with a nightcap.

Last, Little Red Riding Hood and her grandma were safe. Little Red Riding Hood promised to stay on the path next time!

Next, she noticed her grandma's big ears and teeth, but it was actually the wolf! Suddenly, the wolf jumped out of bed and tried to catch her.

Day 3: Extend Your Skills

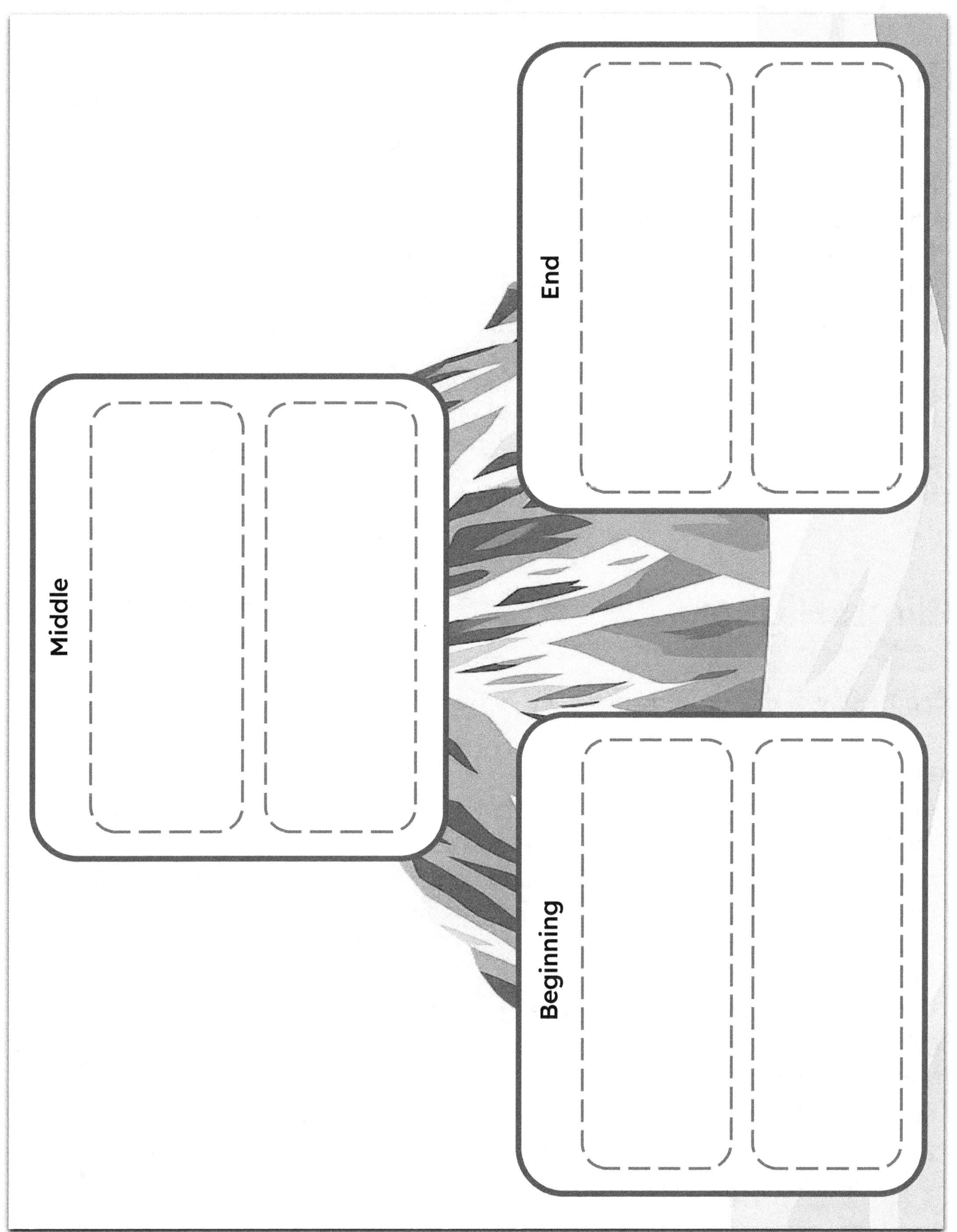

Optional Support

Dig Deeper

Want more practice retelling the main events of a story?

Picture Story Retell
Choose a story you know well or use one from today's lesson. Draw three boxes for the beginning, middle, and end. Instead of retelling the story using words, draw one picture in each section instead. If you'd like, you can draw two pictures in each section to include more detail.

Now, share it with someone! Use your pictures to help you retell the story out loud to someone else. Be sure to tell the events in order and use sequence words, like "first," "next," "then," and "last," to guide you through the story.

Climb Higher

Ready for a challenge when it comes to retelling the main events of a story?

Choose any of the following activities you'd like to do!

Plot Map Upgrade
Create a plot map by drawing a mountain and three boxes titled beginning, middle, and end. Choose a story you know well and retell it by writing on the plot map. Then, show off your knowledge of story elements by circling all the characters, highlighting the conflict, and underlining the resolution.

Retell Theater
Choose a story you know well or use one from today's lesson. With a partner or group, act out the story by retelling the main events in order using sequence words, like "first," "next," "then," and "last." One person must be the narrator, who is the person telling the story, and the others must act out what's happening by playing the different characters.

Day 1

- ❏ Video and Guided Notes
- ❏ Read and Respond
- ❏ Online Practice Levels 1 and 2

Day 2

- ❏ Language Lab
- ❏ Connect and Reflect
- ❏ Online Practice Levels 3 and 4
- ❏ Optional: Dig Deeper or Climb Higher

Lesson Goal:
I can summarize a story by describing the main events, conflict, and resolution.

Record your thoughts:
Think about a story you read recently. Imagine you have to tell someone only the most important parts in two to four sentences. What would you include?

Record your thoughts on the right! →

A Word To Explore:

Relieved

Feeling happy and calm after being worried

Day 1: Guided Notes

Follow along with Bea to complete the guided notes below.

Summarizing stories

is using your own words to tell the most _______________ parts, in a much _______________ way, without all the tiny details.

Read or **listen along to** "The Show-and-Tell Mystery."

Today was Ben's turn for show-and-tell, and he'd brought his grandmother's lucky coin. It was shiny, old, and had traveled through ten countries. Ben stood in front of the class and reached into his bag. He froze. "It's gone!" Ben gasped.

"Are you sure?" Ms. Carter asked. Just then, Ben noticed something strange on the floor — a sparkly trail of glitter leading out of the classroom. "I'll be right back!" Ben said. He followed the trail past the art room and gym, and finally to the janitor's closet.

Inside, something squeaked. It was Buttons, the classroom hamster. Buttons had escaped from her cage and was sitting next to a pile of treasures. There was a gold earring, a foil candy wrapper, paper clips, and a whole lot of glitter. And right on top was Ben's coin.

Ben picked up Buttons and the pile of shiny things and then headed back to class. Ms. Carter looked surprised. "Looks like Buttons has a thing for sparkly stuff," she laughed. With the mystery solved, Ben finally got to show the class his coin!

Day 1: Guided Notes

Somebody Who is the main character?	Ben
Wanted What did they want?	Ben wanted to show his grandmother's special coin to the class for show-and-tell.
But What was the conflict?	**Option 1:** But the coin went missing. **Option 2:** But Ben realized the coin was missing, and Ms. Carter asked if he was sure.
So What did they do to solve it?	
Then How did it all end?	Then, Ben brought Buttons and the treasures back to class and finally got to show his coin.

Circle the best summary in the "But" part.

Summarize the "So" part in a sentence.

Bea's final summary:
Ben wanted to show his grandmother's special coin to the class for show-and-tell, but the coin went missing. So he followed a trail of glitter and found Buttons the class hamster with lots of shiny objects, including his coin. Then, Ben brought Buttons and the treasures back to class and finally got to show his coin.

Today we learned...

Summarizing is different from retelling. When we summarize, we only say the most important parts in a **shorter** way.

Day 1: Read and Respond

Step 1: Read the story below, or listen to it by clicking or scanning the QR code. As you read, try noticing the conflict the main character faces and the resolution.

Mikey was walking home from tennis practice when dark clouds began rolling in. *Oh, no! It looks like a storm's coming! I'd better get home before it starts,* he thought.

When he reached Maple Alley, he stopped in his tracks. A giant tree had fallen across it, completely blocking his usual path home! The sky was getting darker, and he could hear thunder in the distance. He had to find another way and fast.

Mikey glanced around and spotted a trail leading into the woods. He stepped onto the dirt path. At first, it seemed fine. But soon, rain started pouring down. His clothes got soaked, and the trail grew muddy and hard to follow. "Great," he muttered. "Now I'm wet and lost."

Just then, he spotted a red barn roof through the trees. He ran toward it and found a small farmhouse. A kind old lady opened the door and smiled. "Oh, dear, come in and dry off! I'll call your parents right away."

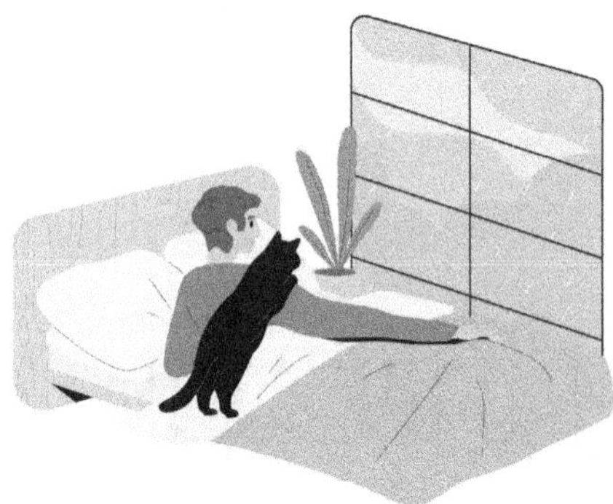

Soon, Mikey's parents arrived, relieved and thankful that he was OK. That night, Mikey listened to the rain from his cozy bed, happy to be safe and warm at last. *No more shortcuts for me,* he thought. *Next time, I'll just call home!*

Day 1: Read and Respond

Step 2: Fill out the "Somebody–Wanted–But–So–Then" table below with details from the story you just read. Remember to keep your sentences short and clear!

Somebody Who is the main character?	
Wanted What did they want?	
But What was the conflict?	
So What did they do to solve it?	
Then How did it all end?	

Step 3: Using the information you wrote in the table above, write a summary of the story in three to five sentences. You can add or remove any details if you need to!

____

____

____

____

____

____

Day 2: Language Lab

Read the mini-lesson. Then, practice the skill in parts 1 through 3.

Concrete nouns are words that name things you can see, hear, smell, taste, or touch. For example, "apple" and "dog" are concrete nouns because you can see and touch them.

Abstract nouns are words that name things you can't see or touch, like feelings, ideas, or qualities. For example, "happiness" is an abstract noun because you can feel it, but you can't touch it.

Part 1: Color the concrete nouns green and the abstract nouns orange.

bravery	book	truth
window	hospital	love
kindness	robot	chocolate

Part 2: Circle one abstract noun in each sentence below.

1. I could feel my anger growing when I saw the broken toy.
2. Fred and Mandy have a great friendship.
3. The loud laughter was coming from the playground.
4. Leo's imagination makes his stories fun to read.
5. Amber loves to draw because she has a lot of creativity.
6. The boy tried to show respect by listening carefully.

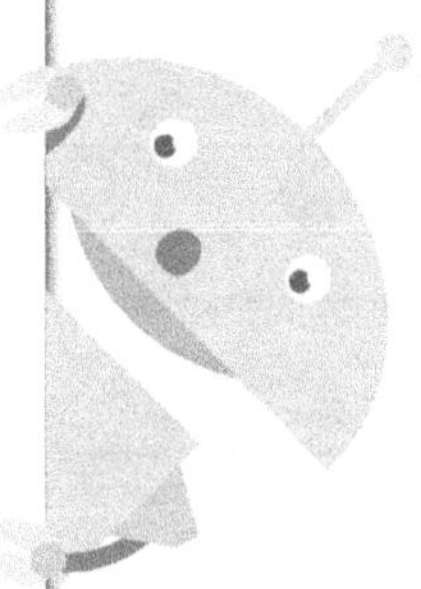

Day 2: Language Lab

Part 3: Find and circle all the hidden words in the puzzle. Words might be placed horizontally, vertically, or diagonally. Check off each word as you find it.

beauty	sadness	knowledge	joy
importance	life	progress	strength
jealousy	peace	health	motivation

D	E	I	O	T	H	B	R	F	X	H	R	H	F
K	F	M	J	L	P	T	I	S	I	M	P	Y	R
S	N	P	C	J	T	D	I	H	E	A	L	T	H
W	U	O	M	E	R	D	V	J	L	O	I	H	F
L	R	R	W	A	E	I	B	N	D	I	F	G	D
E	F	T	F	L	E	G	P	E	A	C	E	N	E
F	E	A	L	O	E	E	R	R	A	R	F	B	S
H	R	N	C	U	O	D	O	M	B	U	S	L	T
G	M	C	O	S	U	W	G	R	J	R	T	Y	R
H	I	E	T	Y	S	U	R	E	A	E	E	Y	E
O	N	G	F	B	E	A	E	D	N	J	L	N	N
D	A	S	A	D	N	E	S	S	T	A	O	R	G
F	Q	R	E	A	D	L	S	R	A	T	T	Y	T
M	O	T	I	V	A	T	I	O	N	R	Y	T	H

Day 2: Connect and Reflect

Follow the prompts to deepen your understanding of the lesson.

Focus on your favorite moment. Write down or draw your favorite part of today's lesson.

Pack your bags! What's something you learned that you want to take with you and remember later?

Make a real-world connection. Think about something fun you've done recently, like a trip or party. Imagine you need to summarize it in two to four sentences. What would you say?

Rate how you feel about this week's "Language Lab" skill: I can identify abstract nouns.

Rate how you feel about this week's skill: I can summarize a story by describing the main events, conflict, and resolution.

Optional Support

Dig Deeper

Want more practice summarizing stories?

Step 1: Read "The Three Little Pigs" below.

Once upon a time, three little pigs decided to build houses. The first pig made his out of straw, the second pig built his house out of sticks, and the third pig worked hard to build a strong house made of bricks.

One day, a Big Bad Wolf came along. He was very hungry and wanted to eat the pigs. He went to the first pig's house and huffed and puffed until he blew it down. The first pig ran to his brother's stick house, but the wolf followed. He took a deep breath and blew it down too, so the two pigs ran to their brother's brick house.

The wolf huffed and puffed at the brick house, but he couldn't blow it down. Soon, he gave up and ran away. The pigs were safe, and they lived happily ever after.

Step 2: Summarize "The Three Little Pigs" by completing the sentences below.

Somebody: Who are the main characters?	The three little pigs
Wanted: What did they want?	They wanted to ______________________________.
But: What was the conflict?	But the Big Bad Wolf wanted to eat, so he blew down ______________________________.
So: What did they do to solve it?	So the two brothers ______________________________ ______________________________.
Then: How did it all end?	Then, the wolf couldn't blow the brick house down, so he ______________, and the pigs ______________.

Step 3: (Optional) On a new sheet of paper, use the details above to write your final summary. You can add or remove details and draw pictures if you want!

Optional Support

Climb Higher

Ready for a challenge when it comes to summarizing stories?

Choose any of the following activities you'd like to do!

Movie Trailer Challenge

Pick a movie you know well. Pretend you're making a dramatic movie trailer for it by writing an exciting two- to three-sentence summary. Create a poster or video about the movie, or record yourself reading your summary out loud in a dramatic movie voice, like a real movie trailer! You can make your voice deep and serious, silly and fun, spooky and mysterious, or whatever fits your story best!

New Summary Method

There are many different ways to summarize a story. Choose a story you know well, then pick a new way to summarize it from these options:

- Tell the story in just three sentences. Write one for the beginning, one for the middle, and one for the end!
- Challenge yourself to write a one-sentence summary that describes the story in a super simple way.
- Create a comic strip summary. Draw three to four boxes, then draw pictures that show the important parts of the story. You can use speech bubbles, too!

Speedy Summarizing

Pick a story and get ready to summarize it as quickly as possible! First, find a partner and a timer. Next, read the short story together. When you've finished reading, ask your partner to set the timer for 30-60 seconds while you summarize the story aloud. Make sure you say who the main character is, what they wanted, the conflict, and the resolution. Your partner will listen and give a thumbs-up if you included all the important parts.

Day 1

- ❏ Video and Guided Notes
- ❏ Read and Respond
- ❏ Online Practice Levels 1 and 2

Day 2

- ❏ Language Lab
- ❏ Connect and Reflect
- ❏ Online Practice Levels 3 and 4

Day 3

- ❏ Words To Explore
- ❏ Online Assessment
- ❏ Optional: Dig Deeper or Climb Higher

Lesson Goal:
I can compare and contrast two stories using my knowledge of the setting, characters, and plot.

Record your thoughts:
Think about two stories you've read recently. What things were similar? What things were different?

Record your thoughts on the right! →

A Word To Explore:

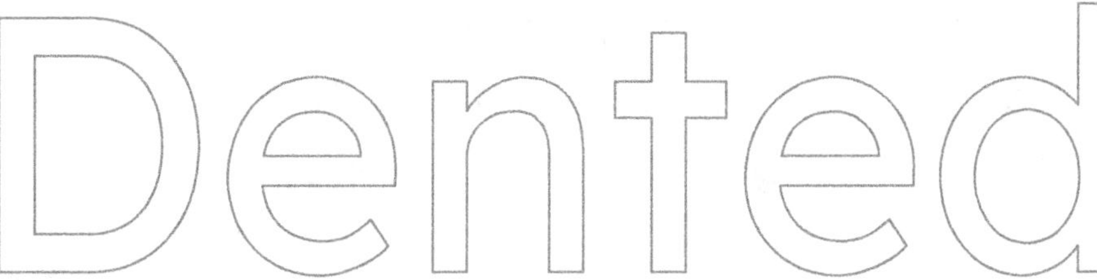

Bent or pushed in, usually from being hit or bumped

Day 1: Guided Notes

Follow along with Bea to complete the guided notes below.

Comparing and contrasting

When we **compare**, we look for what's the ____________ or similar between two or more things.

When we **contrast**, we look for what's ______________ between two or more things.

Read or **listen along to** "How the Tiger Got Its Stripes."

Long ago, in a jungle in Vietnam, there lived a strong, powerful tiger without any stripes. One day, he wandered to the edge of the jungle and saw a buffalo working alongside a man in the rice fields.

Confused, the tiger asked the buffalo, "Why do you let that man boss you around?" "Because he has something called wisdom," the buffalo replied. The tiger was curious. He wanted wisdom too, so he approached the man and asked for some.

The man felt frightened, so he came up with a plan to trap him. "I'll go home to get it. But first, I'll tie you to this tree so that the villagers aren't scared of you while I'm gone."

The man tied him to a tree, but instead of going home, he lit a fire around the tiger. Panicked, the tiger pulled on the ropes as the flames grew higher. He finally got free and ran away, but the fire left black marks on his fur. From that day on, tigers always had stripes as a reminder of that tiger's mistake.

Day 1: Guided Notes

Read or **listen along to** "The Rabbit and the Lion."

Once, in East Africa, there was a lion who was the king of the jungle. He was big and strong and bullied the smaller animals into bringing him food.

One day, it was the rabbit's turn, but he had a clever plan to trick the lion instead. The rabbit arrived late and told the lion, "Another lion took the food and said he's the real king!"

"Where is he?!" The lion roared. The rabbit led him to a deep well and pointed at the water. "He's in there!"

The lion saw his own reflection and thought it was another lion. He jumped in to fight and got stuck in the well. From then on, the animals lived happily, free from the lion's rule.

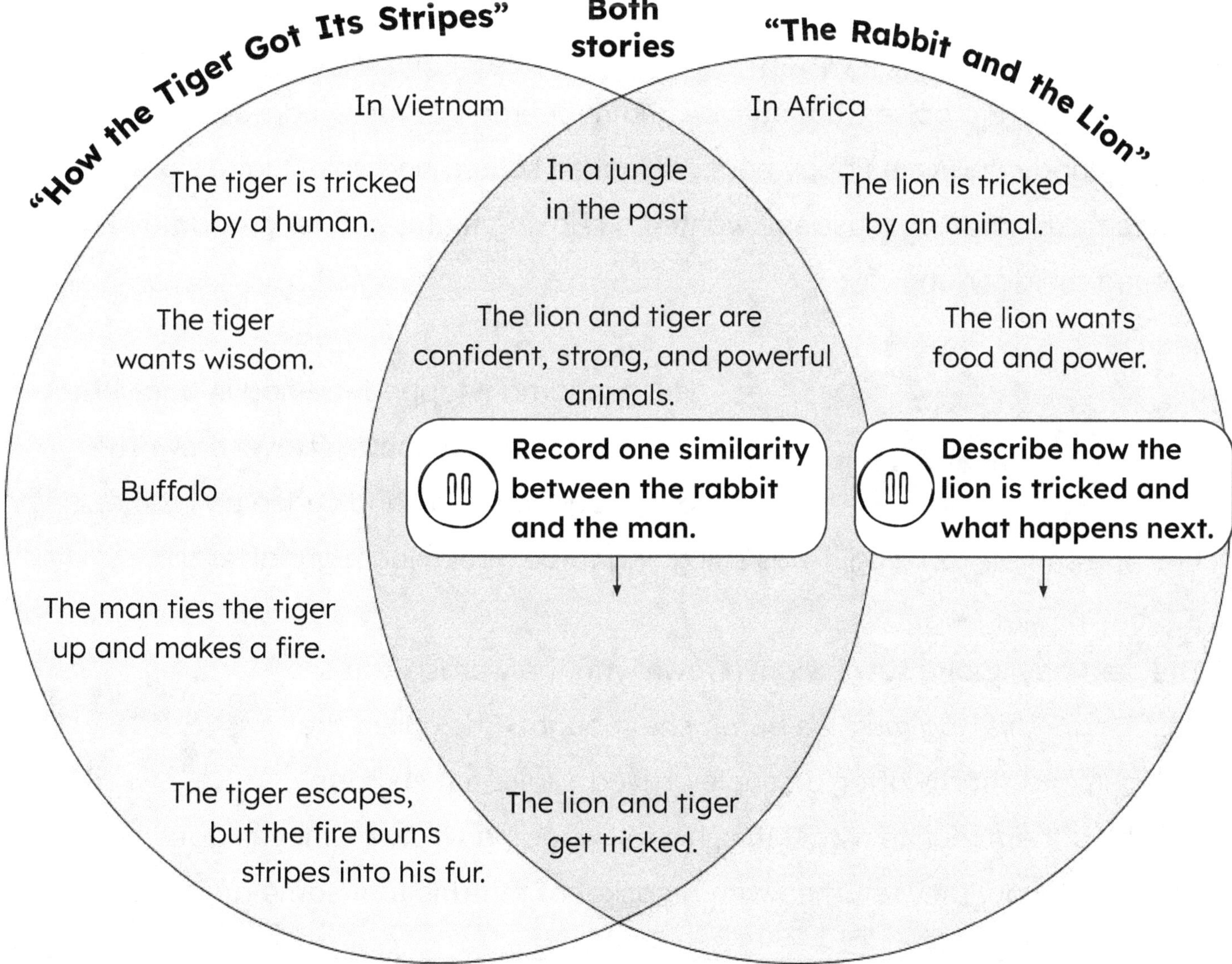

Day 1: Read and Respond

Step 1: Read the story below, or click or scan the QR code to listen. As you read, think about the setting, characters, and plot.

Claire and the Lost Dog

Claire lived in a peaceful mountain village with her grandma, and that's just how she liked it. No loud noises. No surprises. Just calm days outside in nature and quiet nights reading by the fire.

One night, as Claire and her grandma were sitting on the sofa sipping cups of tea, they heard a noise from outside. Claire peered out the window and saw a large, muddy dog with floppy ears. He looked scared and cold. Claire sighed. She felt frustrated because she wanted a relaxing night, but her grandma opened the door anyway.

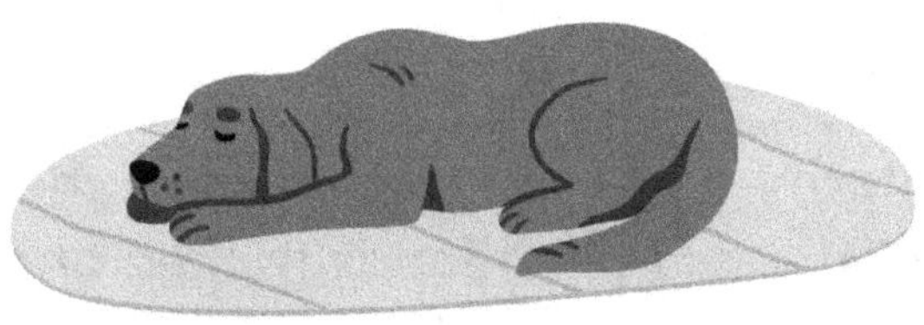

Her grandma wrapped the dog in a towel, and Claire gave it some leftover stew. The dog wagged its tail and curled up by the fire. She smiled, realizing it was still going to be a relaxing night after all.

The next day, Claire saw a sign in town with the words "Rufus: Lost Dog." *This dog must be Rufus!* she thought. She called the number, and shortly after, a couple arrived. Claire felt so happy watching them reunite with Rufus, his tail wagging wildly as they hugged him. As a thank you, they returned with a basket of muffins that same afternoon.

Day 1: Read and Respond

Step 2: Read the story below, or click or scan the QR code to listen. As you read, think about the setting, characters, and plot.

Zara's Visitor From Space

Zara lived on a quiet farm with her dad. She liked the fresh air and open space, but she often felt a little bored. "I wish something exciting would happen around here," she sighed.

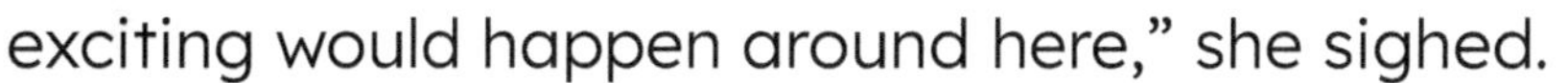

One night, while her family was sleeping, something *did* happen. Zara saw a bright light flash across the sky. BOOM! Something crashed in the field near the barn. She put on her boots and raced outside.

In the tall grass, she found a small, dented spaceship. An alien, no bigger than a cat, peeked out with wide, worried eyes. Zara gasped with excitement. "Wow!" she exclaimed. The alien had crashed his spaceship and was scared of her. Zara smiled softly at it. "Don't worry! I can help," she said.

Zara ran to the shed, grabbed her dad's tools, and rushed back to fix the spaceship. With some twisting and tapping, the spaceship's lights flickered on. The alien made a happy beeping noise and then climbed inside and soared into the stars.

The next morning, Zara told her dad everything, but he just laughed. "A spaceship?" Her dad said, raising his eyebrows. Zara just smiled. She didn't mind that he didn't believe her. She was just happy that, finally, something exciting happened on the farm!

Day 1: Read and Respond

Turn the paper to read the instructions and do the activity!

Step 3: Complete the Venn diagram about the two stories: "Claire and the Lost Dog" and "Zara's Visitor from Space." Record the main similarities and differences about the settings, characters, and plot.

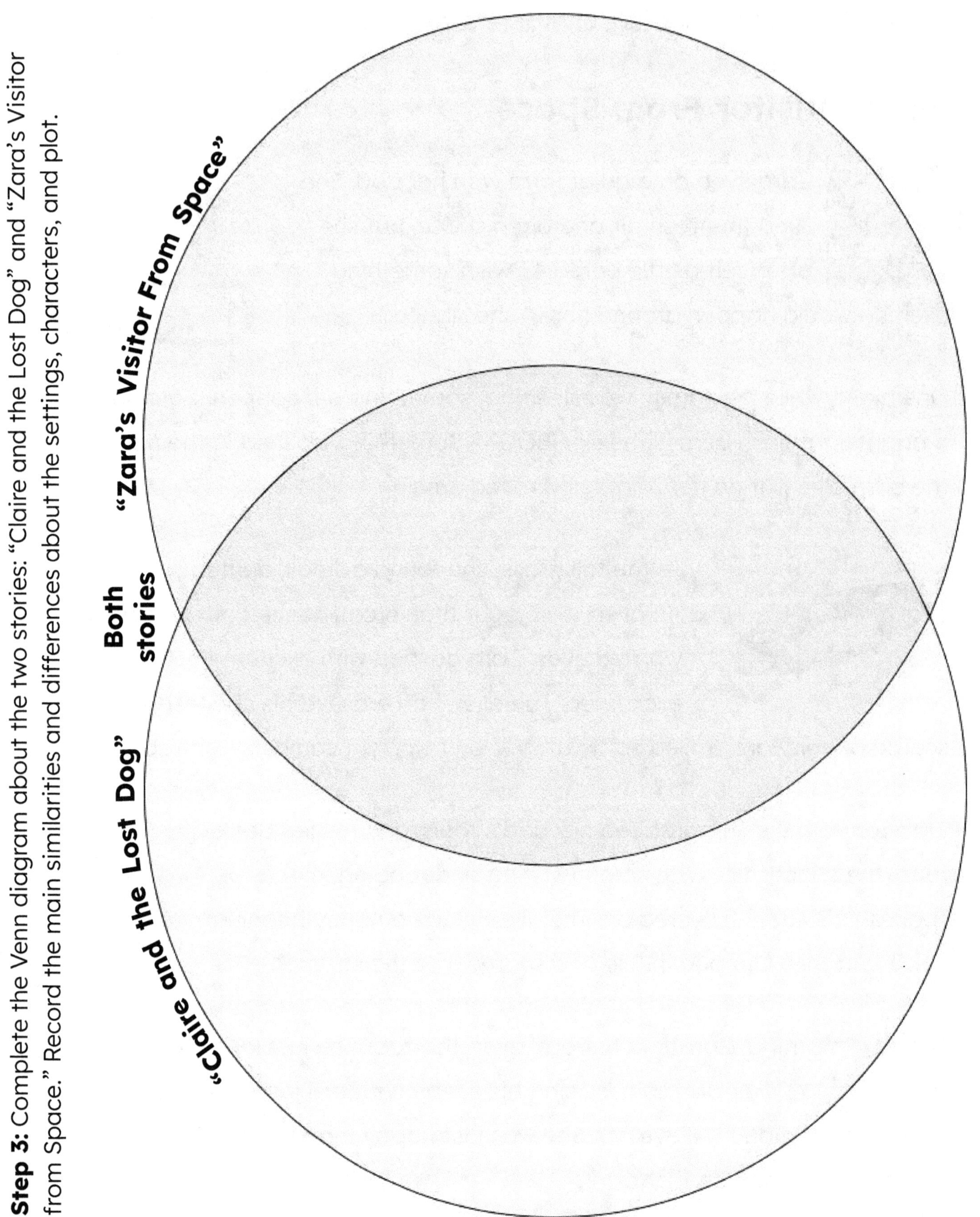

Day 2: Language Lab

Read the mini-lesson. Then, practice the skill in parts 1 to 3.

Homophones are words that sound the same but have different meanings and spellings, such as "flour" and "flower."

Flour is used in baking.
→ *I need flour to bake bread.*

A **flower** is a plant.
→ *That's a beautiful flower.*

Part 1: Match the words that sound the same.

plane	sale
week	which
sail	hole
whole	plain
witch	son
sun	weak

Day 2: Language Lab

Part 2: Complete each sentence with the correct homophone.

Tip: Look at the whole sentence to figure out the correct word. You can also use a thesaurus or dictionary to help you!

one **won**

1. Alice ______________ first place at the dance competition.
2. There's only ______________ cupcake left on the table.

see **sea**

3. When it's hot, I love swimming in the ______________ in summer.
4. Can you ______________ properly without your glasses?

know **no**

5. My little brother doesn't ______________ how to tie his shoes.
6. Casey hesitated then replied, "______________, I don't want to go."

would **wood**

7. The new table and chairs are made of strong ______________.
8. Jack and Hannah ______________ love to go to the park with us.

threw **through**

9. The boy ______________ the ball across the field then ran toward it.
10. On my way home, I walked ______________ the long tunnel.

Day 2: Connect and Reflect

Follow the prompts to deepen your understanding of the lesson.

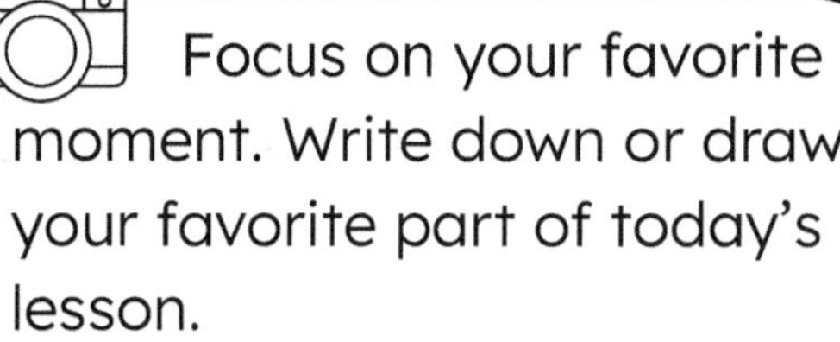

Focus on your favorite moment. Write down or draw your favorite part of today's lesson.

Pack your bags! What's something you learned that you want to take with you and remember later?

Make a real-world connection. Think about a time when you had to choose between two things, like two games, snacks, or movies.

Rate how you feel about this week's "Language Lab" skill:
I can identify and use common homophones.

Rate how you feel about this week's skill:
I can compare and contrast two stories using my knowledge of the setting, characters, and plot.

Day 3: Words To Explore (Unit 3)

Step 1: Review the "Words To Explore" from this unit. Add your own picture to help you remember what the word means.

Word	Definition/Example	Picture
Sprouted	Started to grow or come out, like when a seed grows into a little plant *The plant sprouted out of the soil.*	
Cautiously	To act in a slow and careful way because you want to be safe *The girl walked cautiously, trying not to make a noise.*	
Chuckle	To laugh quietly *The kids always chuckle at Dad's jokes.*	
Pounding	Hitting again and again with force or making a loud, repeated sound *I heard someone pounding on my door.*	
Smirk	Smile in a mean or sneaky way *Anna and Jack smirk, excited about their secret plan.*	
Stunned	Very surprised or shocked *Mom was stunned when she heard the news.*	

Day 3: Words To Explore (Unit 3)

Sequence	The order that things happen in *We put the pictures in the right sequence so that they made sense.*	
Relieved	Feeling happy and calm after being worried *I felt relieved when Harry found the missing key.*	
Dented	Bent or pushed in, usually from being hit or bumped *The side of the car was dented after the accident.*	

Step 2: Circle the correct bold word in each sentence below.

1. Bob was **relieved / stunned** at his surprise party. He wasn't expecting it!
2. The little kids **smirk / relieved** when they're not being very kind.
3. My heart was **pounding / cautiously** so loudly that I couldn't hear a thing.
4. I'm so glad to finally be home! I'm **dented / relieved** that I can relax.
5. Anna tried not to **chuckle / smirk** during the funny part of the movie.
6. New grass **stunned / sprouted** in the yard after the rain.
7. The floor was still wet, so I walked **cautiously/relieved** so I didn't slip.

Optional Support

Dig Deeper

Want more practice with comparing and contrasting stories?

Read the two stories below. Then, compare and contrast them by filling in the blanks in the Venn diagram below. Some have been completed for you!

Jake's Story
Nine-year-old Jake ran through the park, holding the string of his new kite. A strong wind whooshed past, yanking the kite into the sky. Suddenly, the string snapped, and the kite soared away. He chased it past trees and benches until it landed by a pond. "I'm so glad I found it!" Jake said, smiling.

Fred's Story
Fred walked along the sunny beach, wearing a hat that he'd just been given for his ninth birthday. All of a sudden, a gust of wind blew it right off his head and sent it tumbling across the sand. He ran after it, but the wind was so strong that he lost sight of it. He was so upset that he began to cry.

Jake's Story

The setting is ______________.

Jake loses ______________.

Jake **finds** the kite at the end.

Jake feels ______________ at the end.

Both stories

It was a ______________ day.

The main characters are ______________ boys.

They ______________ something in the wind.

They **chase after** the lost objects.

Fred's Story

The setting is **a sunny beach**.

Fred loses ______________.

Fred ______________ his hat at the end.

Fred feels ______________ at the end.

Optional Support

Climb Higher

Ready for a challenge with comparing and contrasting? **Turn the page sideways to get started!**

We can compare and contrast more than stories! Choose one of these pairs to explore what's similar and different: two animals, two characters from different stories, or two of your friends.

Now, add titles to the Venn diagram, then record the similarities and differences between the pair. Think about their personality and appearance, how they behave, where they live, what they like to do or eat, and what makes them special.

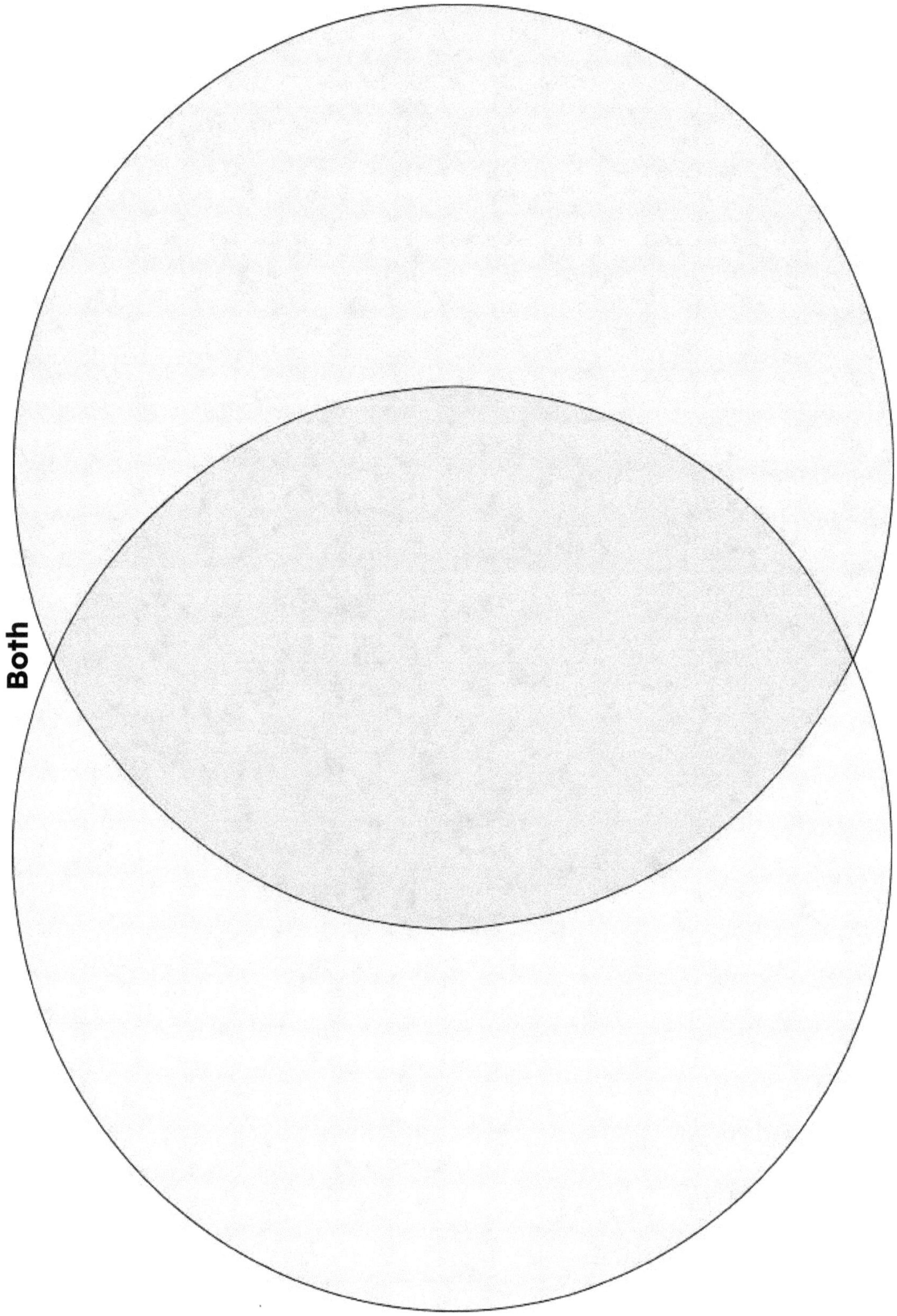

Both

Unit 4: How Authors Write: Text Structures and Features

Day 1

- ❏ Video and Guided Notes
- ❏ Read and Respond
- ❏ Online Practice Levels 1 and 2

Day 2

- ❏ Language Lab
- ❏ Connect and Reflect
- ❏ Online Practice Levels 3 and 4
- ❏ Optional: Dig Deeper or Climb Higher

Lesson Goal: I can identify text features and tell how they help me find and understand important information.

Record your thoughts: What do you do when you want to learn about something new?

Record your thoughts on the right! →

A Word To Explore:

Something or someone that helps you find your way or understand something

Example(s): A map can be a guide to help you find a place. A person can be a guide to show you around a museum.

Day 1: Guided Notes

Follow along with Bea to complete the guided notes below.

Text features

are items in or around a text that ____________ or ____________ important information and help readers ______________ the text.

Costa Rica

Travel Guide

Table of Contents

Title -	**Table of contents -**
the name of a book, article, or other piece of writing that tells what the text is __________	list of chapters or sections in the __________ they will appear in the book, with __________ numbers

Day 1: Guided Notes

Follow along with Bea to complete the guided notes below.

 **Heading -**	**Subheading -**
similar to a __________ but for a specific part of the text	come __________ headings for smaller sections of text

Amazing Animals 

Costa Rica is home to many amazing animals! You can find colorful birds, like toucans and parrots. Monkeys swing through the trees, and sloths move slowly along branches. There are also frogs, butterflies, and big cats, like jaguars.

Sloths

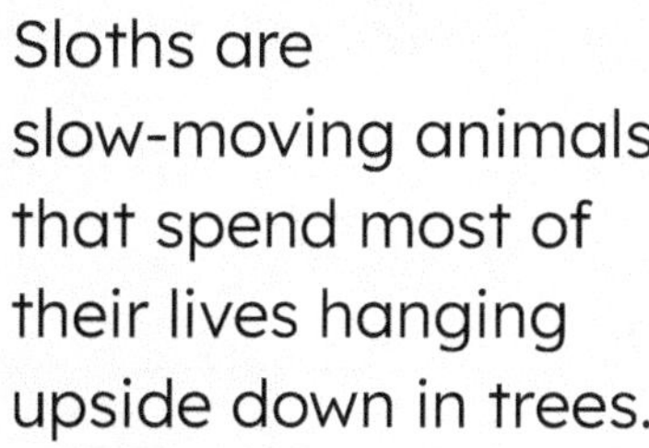

Sloths are slow-moving animals that spend most of their lives hanging upside down in trees.

5

They eat leaves, sleep up to 20 hours a day, and move so slowly that **algae** can grow on their fur!

Toucans

Toucans live in the rainforests of Central and South America. They are easy to spot because of their big, bright beaks, which can be yellow, orange, red, or even green!

A toucan's beak is light but strong — perfect for picking fruit!

6

Illustration - 	**Caption -** 
drawings that help readers __________ what the author is talking about	explains what is shown in a photo or illustration and gives more __________

Day 1: Guided Notes

Follow along with Bea to complete the guided notes below.

Glossary

Algae - tiny green plants that grow in water or on wet surfaces

Amphibian - an animal that lives part of its life in water and part on land, like a frog

Cacao - a plant that grows beans used to make chocolate; grows in Costa Rica's warm climate

Index

Glossaries and **indexes** are written in ________________ order.

Glossaries list important ________ and their ______________.

Indexes list specific topics and their __________ number.

Today we learned...

 Text features help readers find information quickly and understand the text

Text features include...

- Titles
- Table of contents
- Headings/subheadings
- Illustrations/photographs
- Glossaries
- Indexes

Day 1: Read and Respond

Part 1: Read the passage about traveling, or scan or click the QR code below to listen to an audio recording of this passage. Mark the following text features in the passage when you spot them. You can highlight or underline using the different colors shown below, or you can use the suggested symbols. Need help? Look at your guided notes to review what each text feature looks like. On the next page, match each riddle to the correct feature.

Heading	Mark in red or...	Underline with a wavy line
Subheading	Mark in blue or...	Draw a star next to it ☆
Bolded glossary word	Mark in purple or...	Circle it
Illustration	Mark in orange or...	Draw a smiley next to it ☺
Caption	Mark in green or...	Draw a heart next to it ♡

Traveling

Traveling means going to new places. It can be far away or close to home. When we travel, we get to see and try new things.

Where To Travel

You can choose your **destination**! Mountains are great for hiking and seeing nature. Beaches are fun for swimming and building sandcastles. Cities have tall buildings and museums. Forests are quiet and full of trees, birds, and animals.

You need a **passport** to travel to other countries.

How To Travel

There are lots of ways to travel. You can ride in a car, fly in a plane, or take a train or bus. If your trip is close, you might even walk or ride a bike. Each way of traveling can be exciting!

Day 1: Read and Respond

Part 2: Read each riddle below. Draw a line to match it with the correct text feature.

Riddle	Text feature
I come at the beginning of a book. I help you find chapters or sections and their page number. What am I?	Glossary
You can find me under a heading. I break the text into smaller parts and tell what each part is about. What am I?	Subheading
You can find me at the back of the book. I list specific topics and the pages where you can find them. What am I?	Caption
I am a sentence found near an illustration or photograph. I explain what the picture shows or give more information about the text. What am I?	Index
I am found at the back of the book. I explain what bold or new words mean. What am I?	Table of Contents

Day 2: Language Lab

Read the mini-lesson. Then, practice the skill in parts 1 and 2.

Alphabetical order, **or ABC order**, is a way to organize words using the order the letters appear in the alphabet.

Dictionaries, glossaries, and indexes all use alphabetical order so you can find information quickly!

Steps To Alphabetize Words

1 Look at the first letter of each word.

Find which letter comes first in the alphabet. That word goes first. Then, find the next letter in ABC order. Keep going until all the words are in order.

apple banana cheese

2 If two or more words have the same first letter...

Look at the second letter of each word with the same first letter. Find which letter comes first in the alphabet. That word goes first. Then, find the next letter in ABC order. Keep going until all the words are in order.

apple  

Only look at the second letter in the words that have the same FIRST letter.

3 If two or more words have the same second letter...

Move on to the third letter in the word and use this to put the words in ABC order

  doughnuts

Day 2: Language Lab

A B C D E F G H I J K L M N O P Q R S T U V W X Y Z

Use the alphabet to put each set of words in ABC order.

fruit apple orange blueberry	1. ______ 2. ______ 3. ______ 4. ______
pencil picture paint pull	1. ______ 2. ______ 3. ______ 4. ______
watch went sand ball	1. ______ 2. ______ 3. ______ 4. ______
club clip clown book	1. ______ 2. ______ 3. ______ 4. ______

Day 2: Connect and Reflect

Follow the prompts to deepen your understanding of the lesson.

Focus on your favorite moment. Write down or draw your favorite part of today's lesson.

Pack your bags! What's something you learned that you want to take with you and remember later?

Make a real-world connection. Have you ever seen things that look like text features in places other than books? Where?

Rate how you feel about this week's "Language Lab" skill: I can alphabetize to the third letter.

Rate how you feel about this week's skill: I can identify text features and tell how they help me find and understand important information.

Optional Support

Dig Deeper

Want more practice identifying text features and their purpose?

1. Cut out the puzzle pieces and mix them up.
2. Match each picture to the correct text feature.
3. Complete each puzzle piece with the purpose of the feature.

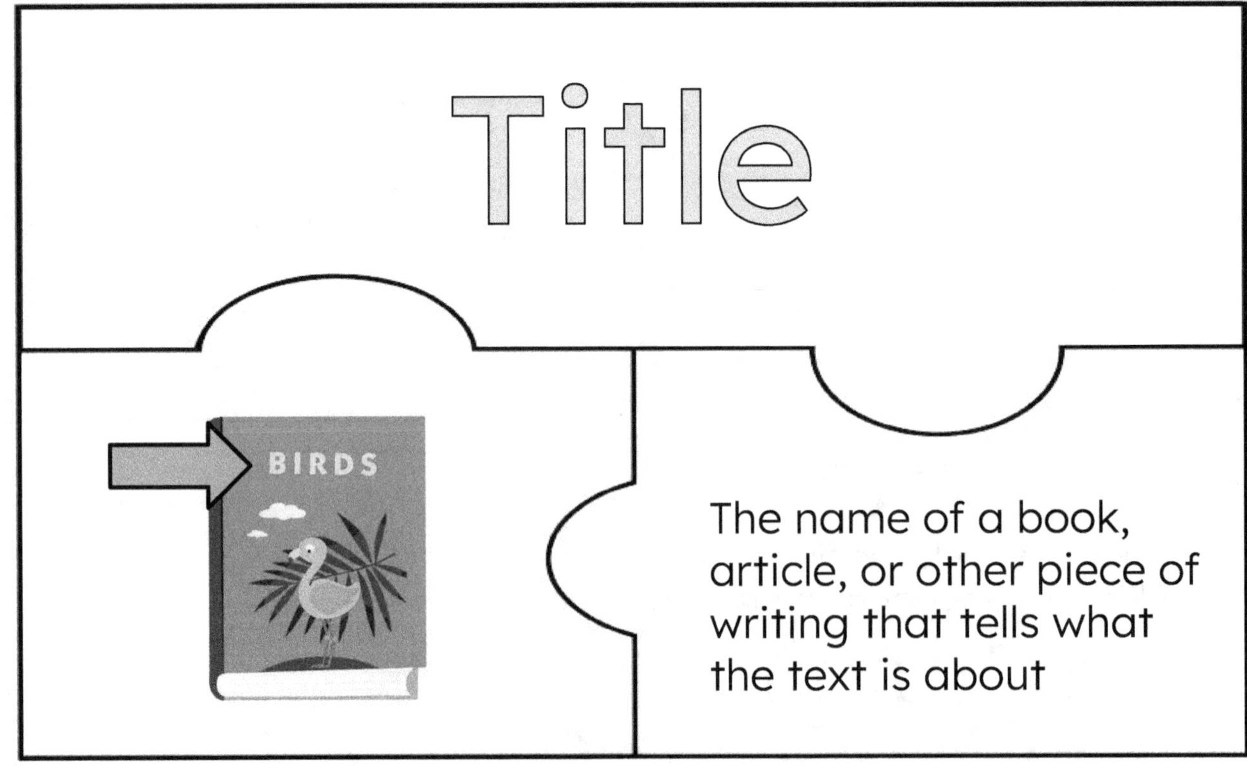

Optional Support

Dig Deeper

Want more practice identifying text features and their purpose?

1. Cut out the puzzle pieces and mix them up.
2. Match each picture to the correct text feature.
3. Complete each puzzle piece with the purpose of the feature.

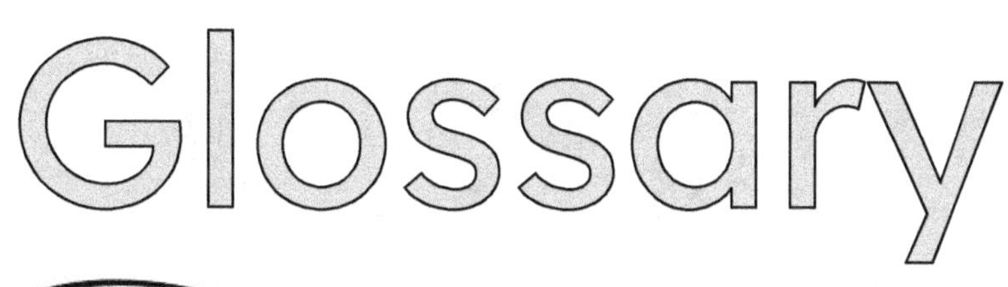

Adaptation - a change in an animal that helps it live in its environment

Amphibian - an animal that lives part of its life in water and part on land

A list of important words and their definitions in ABC order found in the back of a book

Table of contents

Beautiful Butterflies	5
Stage 1: Egg	7
Stage 2: Caterpillar	9
Stage 3: Chrysalis	11
Stage 4: Butterfly	14

A list of sections or chapters in the order they appear with page numbers

Optional Support

Dig Deeper

Want more practice identifying text features and their purpose?

1. Cut out the puzzle pieces and mix them up.
2. Match each picture to the correct text feature.
3. Complete each puzzle piece with the purpose of the feature.

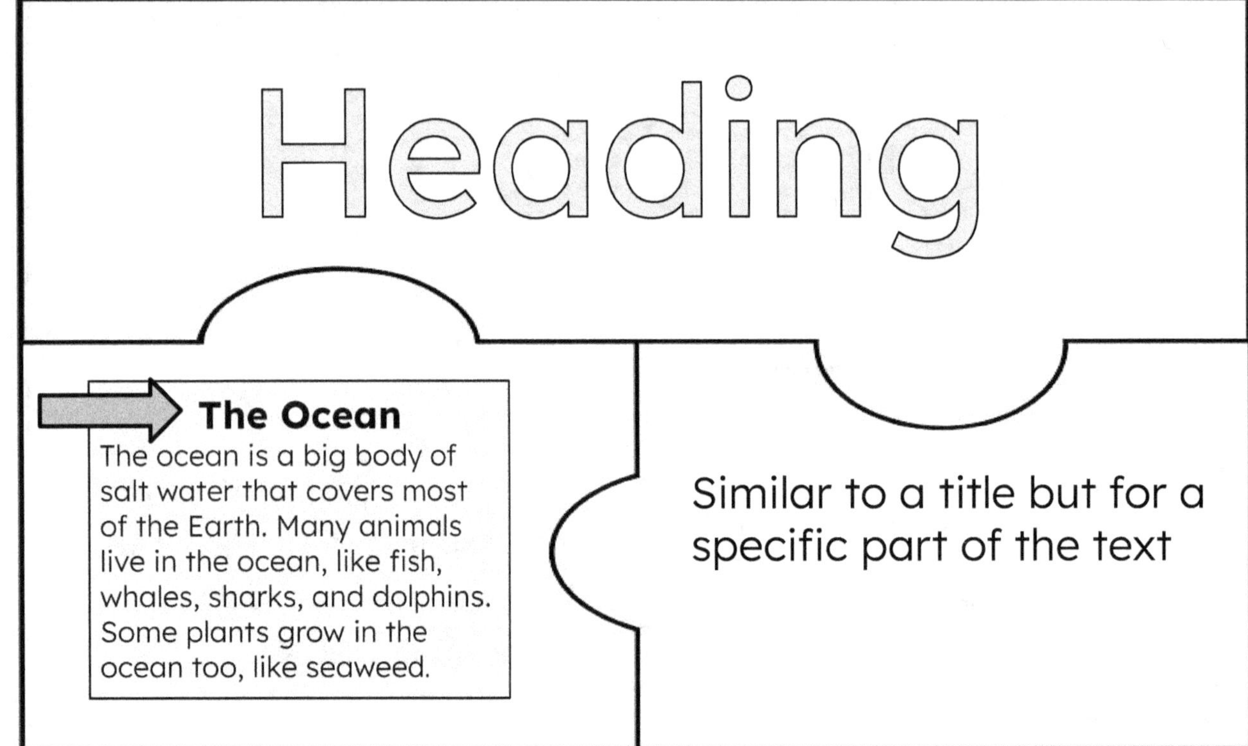

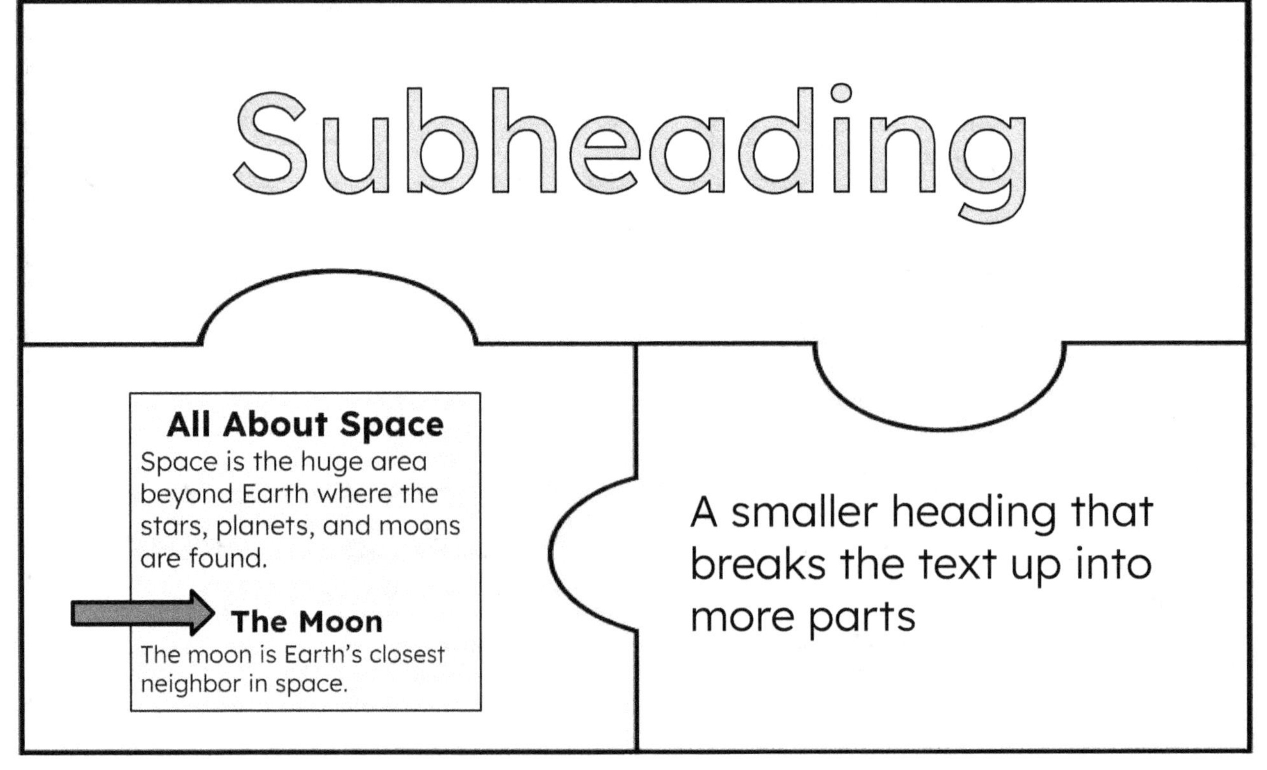

Optional Support

Dig Deeper

Want more practice identifying text features and their purpose?

1. Cut out the puzzle pieces and mix them up.
2. Match each picture to the correct text feature.
3. Complete each puzzle piece with the purpose of the feature.

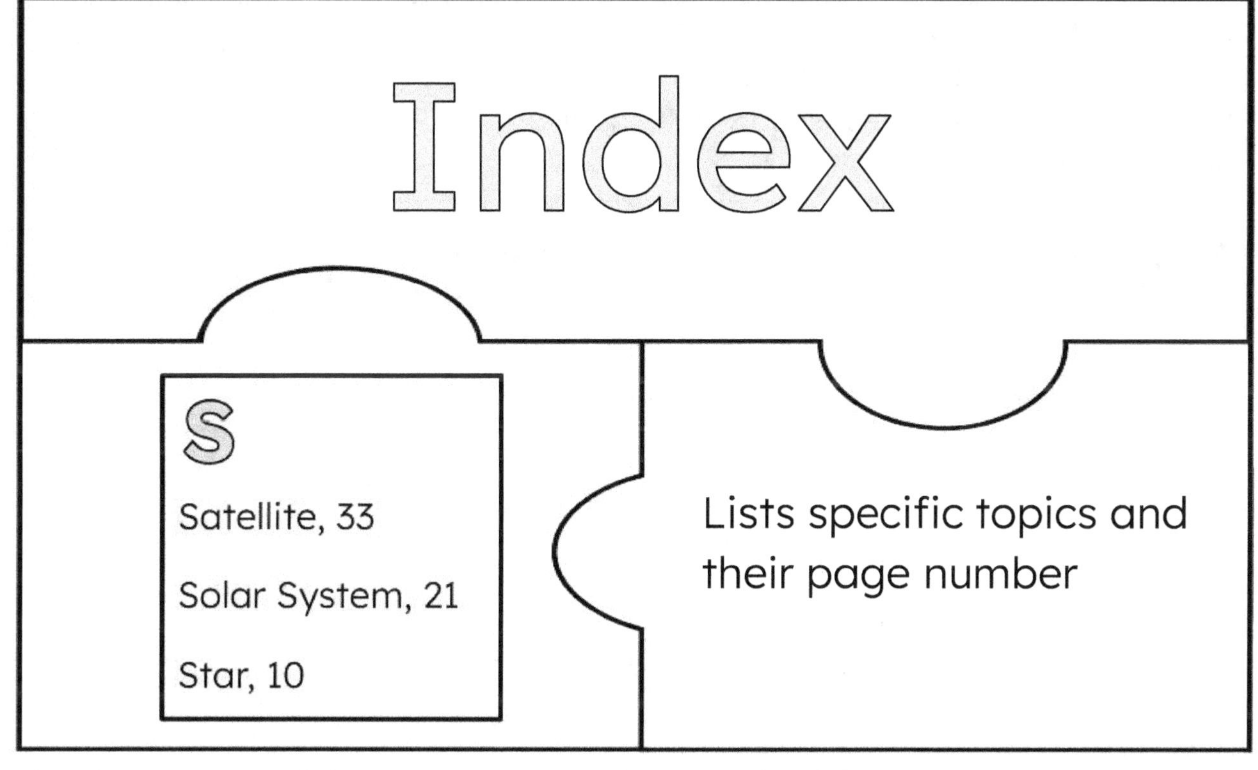

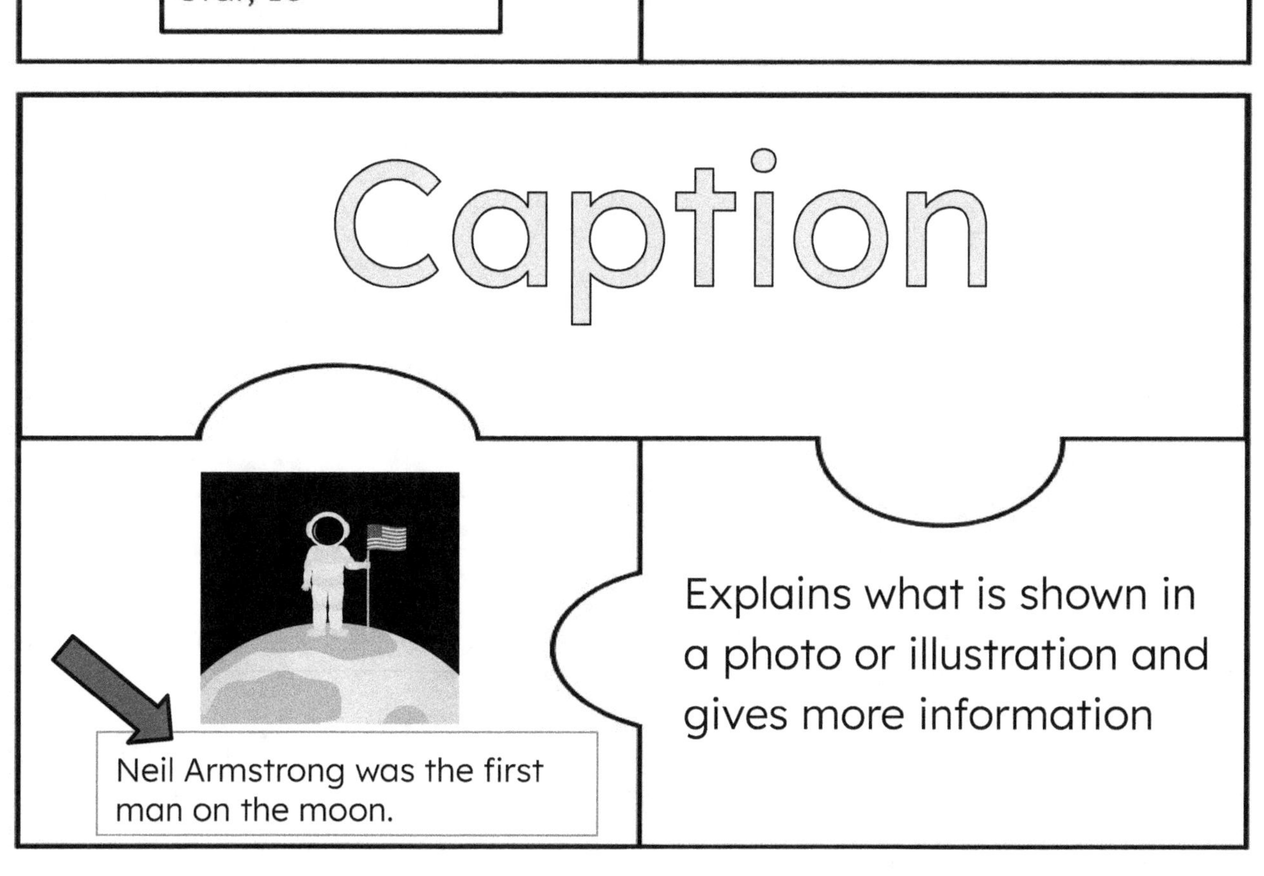

Optional Support

Climb Higher

Ready for a challenge when it comes to text features?

Not every text will have ALL these text features. You can use more than one text — or even create your own text feature for a fun challenge!

Text Feature Hunt

1. Choose a nonfiction book, article, or online passage.
2. Search for text features using the checklist below. Find at least three different text features.
3. Check off each feature as you find it.
4. Explain what the feature helped you learn or understand.

Text Feature	What It Taught Me
❏ Table of Contents	
❏ Illustration	
❏ Caption	
❏ Heading	
❏ Subheading	
❏ Glossary	
❏ Index	

Day 1

- ❑ Video and Guided Notes
- ❑ Read and Respond
- ❑ Online Practice Levels 1 and 2

Day 2

- ❑ Language Lab
- ❑ Connect and Reflect
- ❑ Online Practice Levels 3 and 4

Day 3

- ❑ Extend Your Skills
- ❑ Online Practice Level 5
- ❑ Optional: Dig Deeper/Climb Higher

Lesson Goal: I can use text features to locate information and answer questions in a nonfiction text.

Record your thoughts:
What do you already know about how dictionaries work?

Record your thoughts on the right! →

A Word To Explore:

Diagram

A simple picture that shows what something looks like, how it works, or how parts fit together; usually have labels, arrows, or lines to help explain each part and make the information easier to understand

Day 1: Guided Notes

Follow along with Bea to complete the guided notes below.

Using Text Features

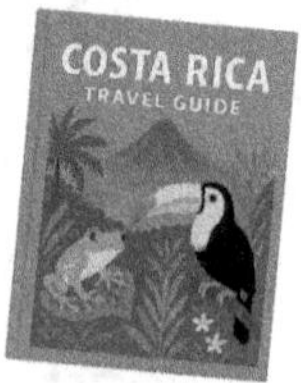

Table of Contents

Section or chapter name

Page number the section starts on

Find and circle the section about **volcanoes** in the table of contents. Drag your finger across to find the page number. Then, record it below.

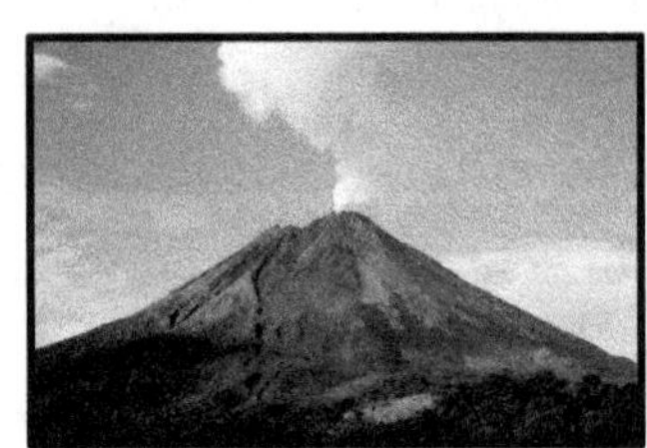

Page Number ___________

Day 1: Guided Notes

Follow along with Bea to complete the guided notes below.

Heading - the heading should match the section or chapter name you selected from the table of contents

Volcano Adventures

What are Volcanos?

Volcanoes are openings in the Earth where melted rock, gas, and ash can come out. Sometimes they erupt with a big blast, and other times they bubble quietly.

Volcanoes can shape the land and even create new mountains!

Volcano Safety

When visiting volcanoes, it's important to stay safe. Always follow warning signs and listen to park guides. Stay on marked paths, and never get too close to the crater or hot steam vents.

Volcanoes Across the Country

Costa Rica is home to over 60 volcanoes! Some are active, which means they still erupt or release steam and heat, while others are **dormant**. These volcanoes are part of what makes Costa Rica special. They create warm hot springs, rich soil for plants to grow, and tall mountains with amazing views. Some volcanoes are even inside national parks.

Subheading - tells what a smaller section of text focuses on

Circle the subheading Bea should focus on to learn more about volcanoes in Costa Rica. Then, record what else you notice in this section below.

____

____

Day 1: Guided Notes

Follow along with Bea to complete the guided notes below.

Remember the glossary is organized in alphabetical, or ABC, order. Start by looking for the letter your word starts with!

Glossary

Algae - tiny green plants that grow in water or on wet surfaces

Amphibian - an animal that lives part of its life in water and part on land, like a frog

Cacao - a plant that grows beans used to make chocolate; grows in Costa Rica's warm climate

Destination - the place someone is going to

Dormant - a volcano that is not active right now but could erupt again in the future

Elevation - how high something is above sea level

Erupt - when a volcano explodes or releases lava, ash, or gases

Find the word **dormant** in the glossary. Then, record its definition below.

____

____

____

Day 1: Guided Notes

Follow along with Bea to complete the guided notes below.

Index

Agouti, 7
Anteater, 8
Arenal Volcano, 12

Bahía Ballena, 19
Black Howler Monkey, 9
Breakfast Foods, 21

Corcovado National Park, 18

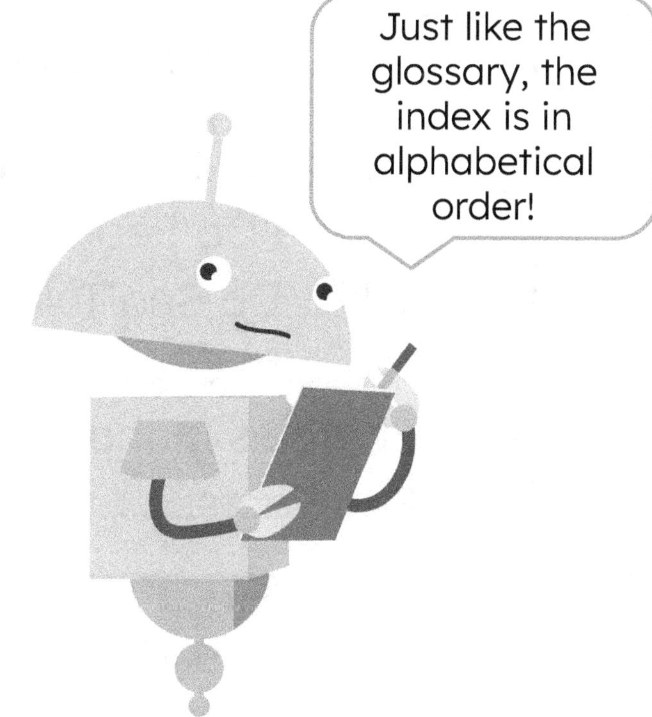

Find the word **Arenal** in the index. Record the page number below.

Page Number __________

Today we learned...

How to use text features to locate information and answer questions in a nonfiction text

Reflection Question: Which text feature did you find the most helpful?

Day 1: Read and Respond

Part 1: Use the table of contents to answer the questions below.

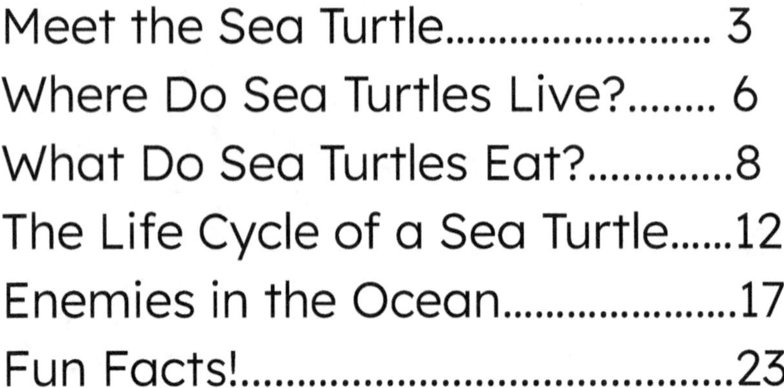

Table of Contents:

Meet the Sea Turtle........................ 3
Where Do Sea Turtles Live?........ 6
What Do Sea Turtles Eat?.............8
The Life Cycle of a Sea Turtle......12
Enemies in the Ocean......................17
Fun Facts!..23

1. On which page would the reader learn about what sea turtles eat?

___

2. What will the reader likely learn about on Page 12?

___

___

___

3. Which section would best help the reader answer the following question: How do sea turtles protect themselves from danger in the ocean?

___

4. On which page can the reader find fun facts about turtles?

___

5. How many chapters or sections are in this book?

___

Day 1: Read and Respond

Part 2: Use the glossary and index to answer the questions below.

Glossary	Index
A	**H**
Algae - a plant that grows in the water	Habitat, 6 Hatchling, 13
C	**K**
Conch - a creature similar to a snail with a spiral shell	Kemp's Ridley Turtle, 4
Current - the flow of water in the ocean that moves in a certain direction	**L**
	Leatherback Turtle, 4 Loggerhead Turtle, 5
E	**N**
Endangered - an animal is called endangered when there are very few left in the world and it might disappear forever if it's not protected	Nesting Beach, 13
	O
	Olive Ridley Turtle, 5

1. What is the definition of **current**?

____

____

____

2. On which page can the reader learn more about loggerhead turtles? _______

3. What does it mean if an animal is **endangered**?

____

____

____

4. On which page can the reader learn more about a turtle's habitat? __________

Day 2: Language Lab

Read the mini-lesson. Then, practice the skill on the next page.

Don't know what a word means? Look it up in a dictionary! A dictionary can be a book or an online tool that tells you what a word means, how to say it, and what kind of word it is — like a noun, verb, or adjective!

Just like a glossary, a dictionary is organized in alphabetical (ABC) order. Most dictionaries will include the following for each word:

- ★ **Pronunciation:** How to say the word; usually found in parenthesis
- ★ **Part of Speech:** Is it a noun, verb, adjective, or adverb?
- ★ **Definition:** The word's meaning
- ★ **Example Sentence:** Some dictionaries will show how to use the word in a sentence; this is often in italics.

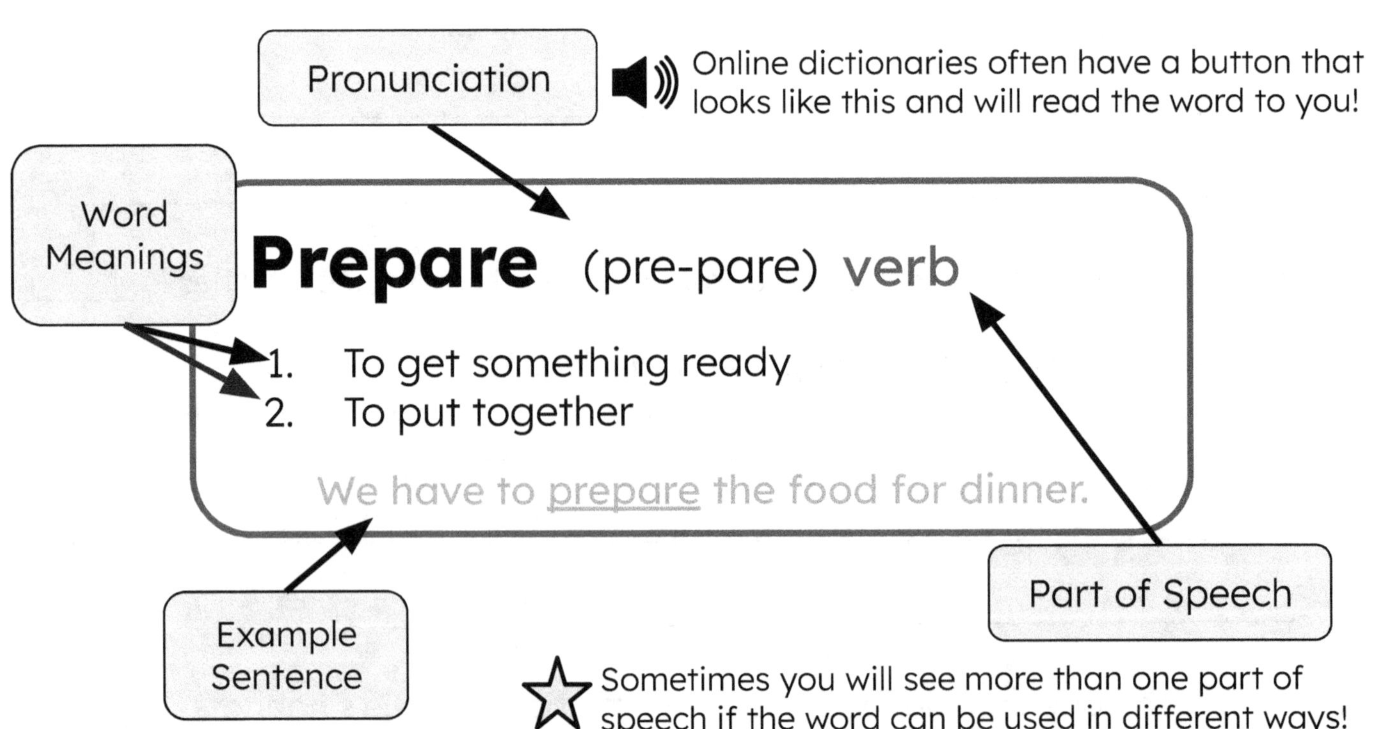

Dictionary Detective

With the help of a grown-up, find a dictionary (book or online) and use it to find a definition and part of speech for each word.

Word	Part of Speech	Definition
Flutter		
Bold		
Imitate		
Coast		

Choose one word from above and use its definition to write it in a sentence.

___

___

___

Day 2: Connect and Reflect

Follow the prompts to deepen your understanding of the lesson.

Focus on your favorite moment. Write down or draw your favorite part of today's lesson.

Pack your bags! What's something you learned that you want to take with you and remember later?

Make a real-world connection. What text features have you used to help you learn more about a topic?

Rate how you feel about this week's "Language Lab" skill: I can use print or digital dictionaries to determine or clarify the meaning of a key word.

Rate how you feel about this week's skill: I can use text features to locate information and answer questions in a nonfiction text.

Day 3: Extend Your Skills

Digital Text Features

Text features aren't just found in books; you can find them online too! Digital text features help you find information, answer questions, and learn about nonfiction topics. Some are just like the ones you see in books, and some are brand new!

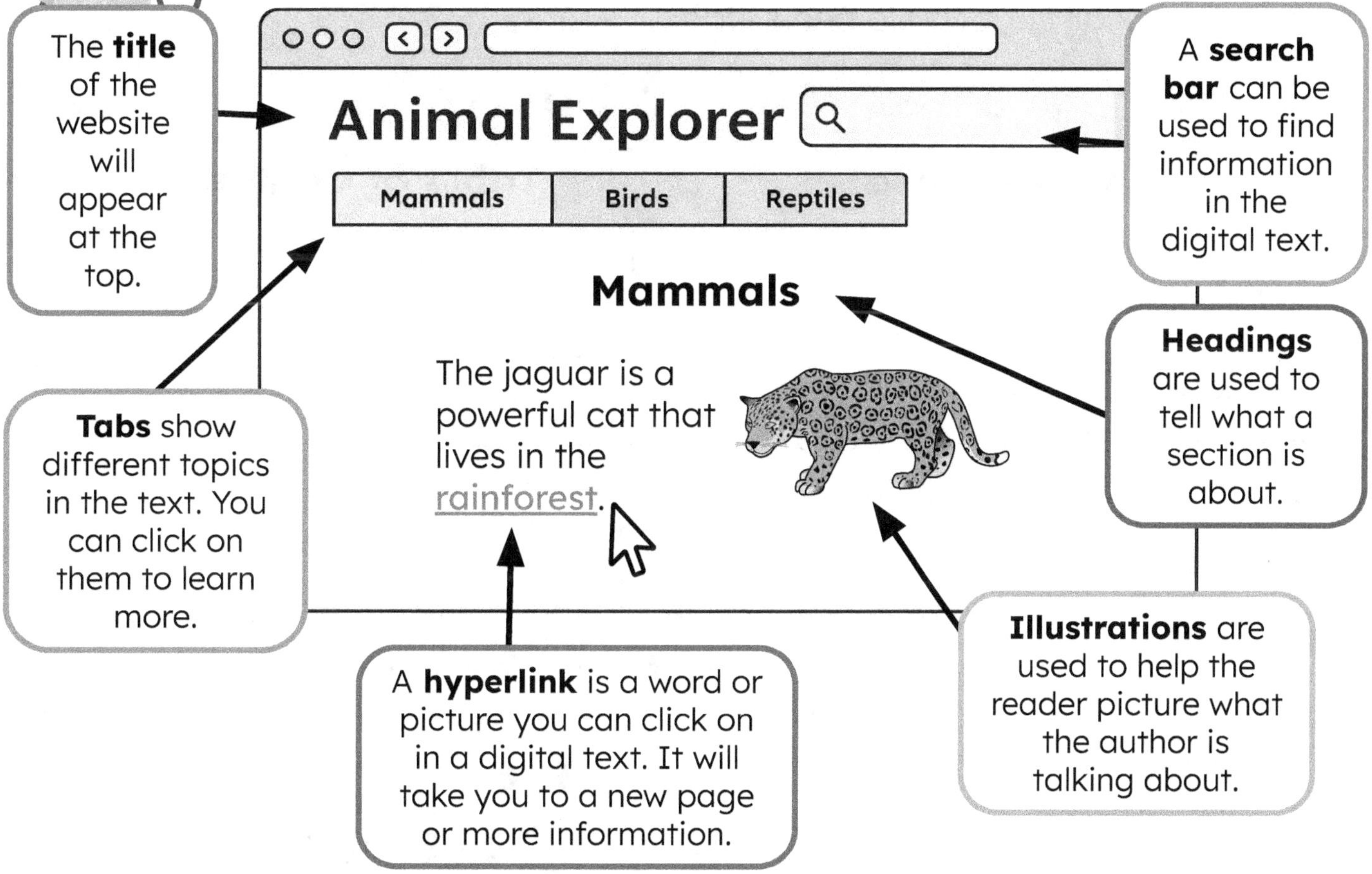

Animal Explorer

Mammals | Birds | Reptiles

Mammals

The jaguar is a powerful cat that lives in the rainforest.

The **title** of the website will appear at the top.

A **search bar** can be used to find information in the digital text.

Headings are used to tell what a section is about.

Tabs show different topics in the text. You can click on them to learn more.

A **hyperlink** is a word or picture you can click on in a digital text. It will take you to a new page or more information.

Illustrations are used to help the reader picture what the author is talking about.

Explore a website of your choice with a trusted adult. See if you can find each digital text feature shown above. Record a digital text feature you found and what it helped you find or learn.

Optional Support

Dig Deeper

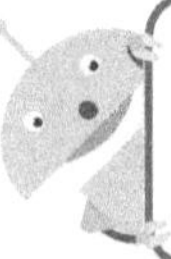

Want more practice with text features?

Directions: This game can be played with a single player or up to eight players. Cut apart the cards. Shuffle and deal all the cards out completely among the players. The player with the first card reads their "I have..." statement aloud and then asks "Who has..." for the next feature. The game continues until all cards have been read.

I have...

The first card

Who has...

The feature that gives readers an overview of book chapters and sections with their page number

I have...

Table of Contents

Fabulous Frogs	5
Stage 1: Egg	7
Stage 2: Tadpole	9
Stage 3: Froglet	11
Stage 4: Adult Frog	13

Who has...

The feature that tells what a large section of text is about

I have...

Heading

Fabulous Frogs

Frogs are amazing animals that live on land and in fresh water. They have strong legs for jumping, long tongues for catching bugs, and big eyes to help them see!

Who has...

The feature that tells what a smaller section of text is about

I have...

Subheading

Fabulous Frogs

Frogs are amazing animals that live on land and in fresh water. They have strong legs for jumping, long tongues for catching bugs, and big eyes to help them see!

What Do Frogs Eat?

Frogs love to eat bugs! They use their long, sticky tongues to catch flies, mosquitoes, and other insects.

Who has...

The feature that can help you define a bolded word in the text

Optional Support

Dig Deeper

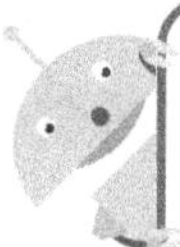

Want more practice with text features?

Directions: This game can be played with a single player or up to eight players. Cut apart the cards. Shuffle and deal all the cards out completely among the players. The player with the first card reads their "I have..." statement aloud and then asks "Who has..." for the next feature. The game continues until all cards have been read.

I have...

Glossary

Tadpole - a baby frog that hatches from an egg and lives in water

Toad - a kind of frog with dry, bumpy skin and short legs

Who has...

The feature in the back of a text that gives you page numbers for specific topics

I have...

Index

Habitat, 6

Hibernation, 14

Who has...

The feature that tells you more about an illustration or photograph and adds information to the text

I have...

Caption

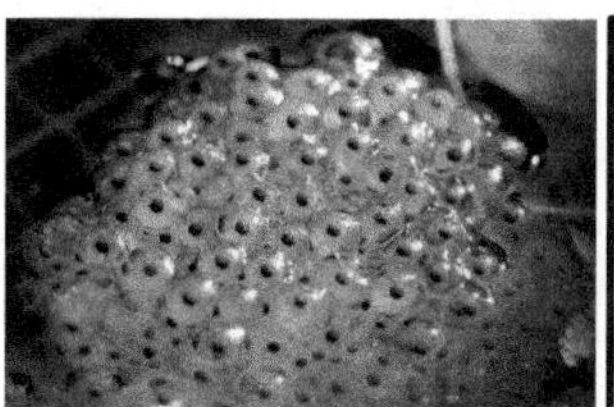

These are frog eggs. Tiny baby frogs will hatch from them soon!

Who has...

The feature that is a drawing that helps the reader picture what the author is talking about

I have...

Illustration

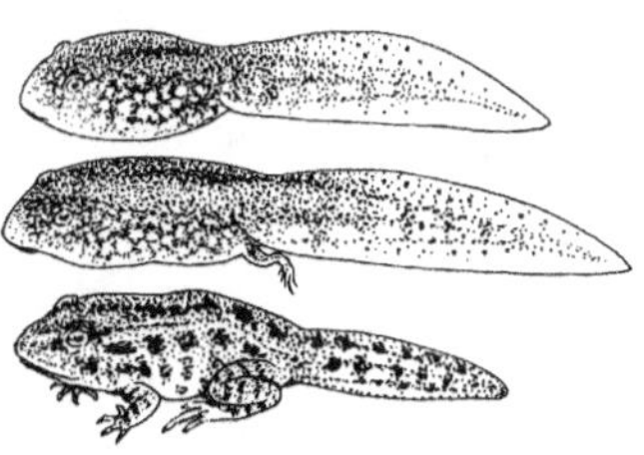

This is the last card!

Optional Support

Climb Higher

Ready for a challenge when it comes to alphabetizing and using a dictionary?

Create a Mini-Glossary

1. Choose a nonfiction topic you are interested in.
2. Come up with five words related to the topic.
3. Put the words in ABC order below.
4. Use a dictionary to write a definition for each word.

My Glossary

Day 1

- ❏ Video and Guided Notes
- ❏ Read and Respond
- ❏ Online Practice Levels 1 and 2

Day 2

- ❏ Language Lab
- ❏ Connect and Reflect
- ❏ Online Practice Levels 3 and 4
- ❏ Optional: Dig Deeper or Climb Higher

Lesson Goal: I can identify visual text features, including maps, diagrams, and timelines, and explain how they help readers.

Record your thoughts: What would a timeline of your morning look like?

Record your thoughts on the right! →

A Word To Explore:

Visual

Something you can see

Day 1: Guided Notes

Follow along with Bea to complete the guided notes below.

Visual Text Features

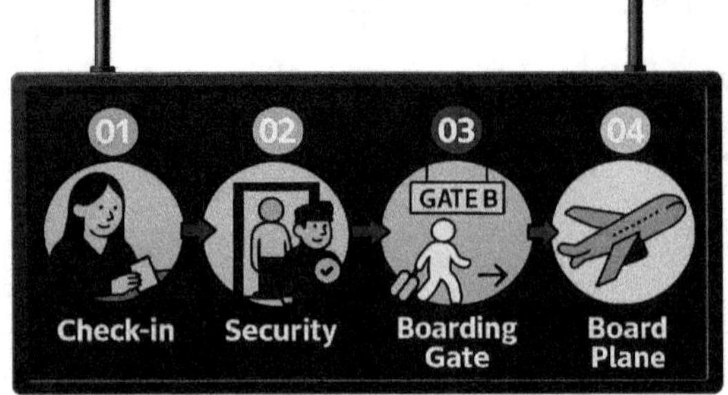

Diagrams are usually paired with text labels so each part is easy to spot and understand. You'll also often see arrows, lines, or numbers guiding you through the information.

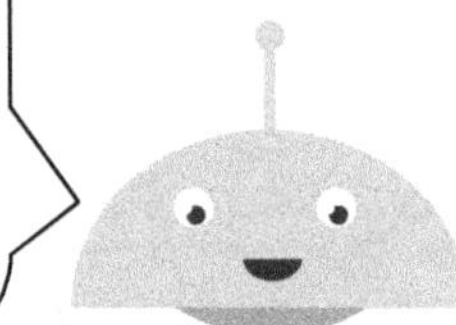

Diagram - a simple ____________ that shows what something looks like, how it works, or how parts fit together

Take a look at the diagram. What do you notice? What does it teach you?

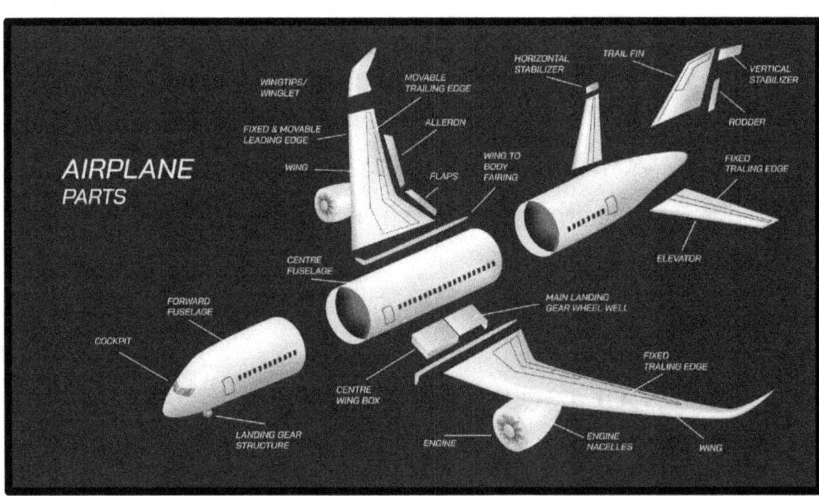

____

____

____

Day 1: Guided Notes

Follow along with Bea to complete the guided notes below.

This is a world map. Maps can also show you the way around smaller places, like cities, schools, malls, parks, or the airport!

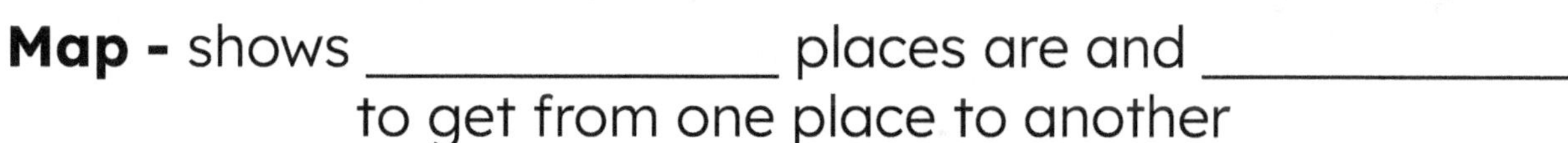

Map - shows ______________ places are and ______________ to get from one place to another

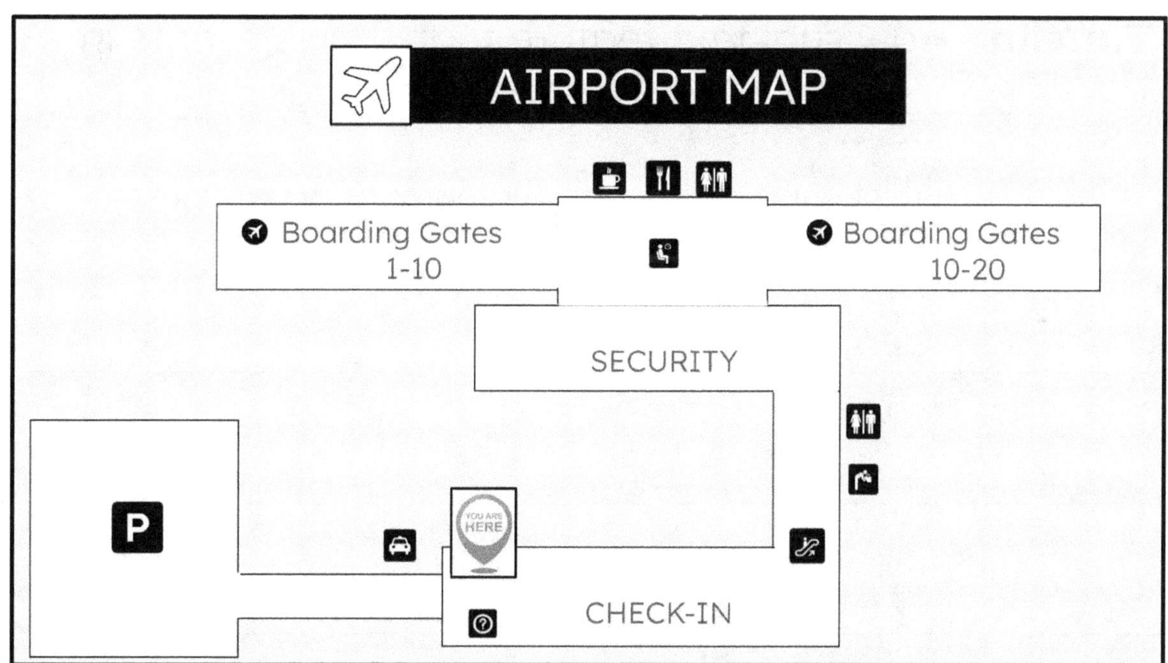

Take a look at this airport map. What do you notice? How is it similar to or different from the world map or another map you've used before? Record your thoughts.

____

____

Day 1: Guided Notes

Follow along with Bea to complete the guided notes below.

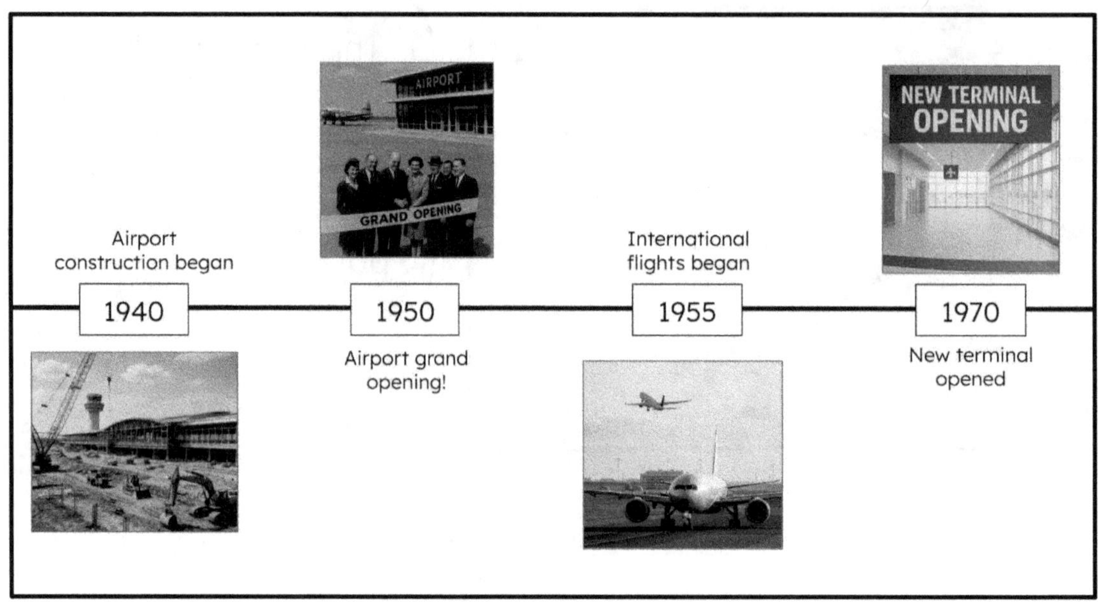

Timeline - a visual text feature that shows events in ________________ from past to present

Why do you think this timeline has photographs and not just text? Pause the video and record your thoughts.

____

____

____

Today we learned...

We use visual features, like diagrams, maps, timelines, and photographs every day to help us understand the world around us. When combined with text, they add information and help us better understand people, places, ideas, and information, answering questions like what, where, when, why, and how.

Day 1: Read and Respond

Each box below includes a section of text and a related text feature. Read the passages, or click or scan the QR codes, and explore how the text features help you understand the information. Then, answer the questions that follow.

All About Honeybees!

Honeybees are small but very important insects. They help plants grow by moving pollen from one flower to another. This is called pollination. Bees also make something we all love: honey!

1. Which text feature is shown above? ________________
2. How does this feature help the reader?

____

____

The Body of a Honeybee

A honeybee's body has three parts: the head, thorax, and abdomen. The head has eyes, antennae, and a jaw called a mandible that helps with chewing. The thorax is the middle part where the wings and six legs are attached. The abdomen is in the back and helps with digestion and stinging.

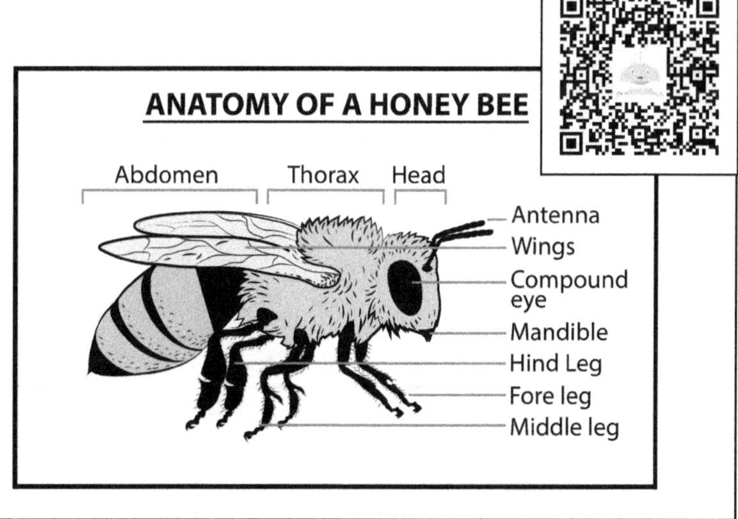

1. Which text feature is shown above? ________________
2. Which helps you understand the parts of a honeybee better: the paragraph or the diagram? Why?

____

____

____

Day 1: Read and Respond

Where Does Honey Come From?

The top five honey-producing countries are China, Turkey, Argentina, Ukraine, and Russia. Honey comes in many colors, like light yellow, amber, and even dark brown. Some honey is very light and sweet, while darker honey can taste stronger.

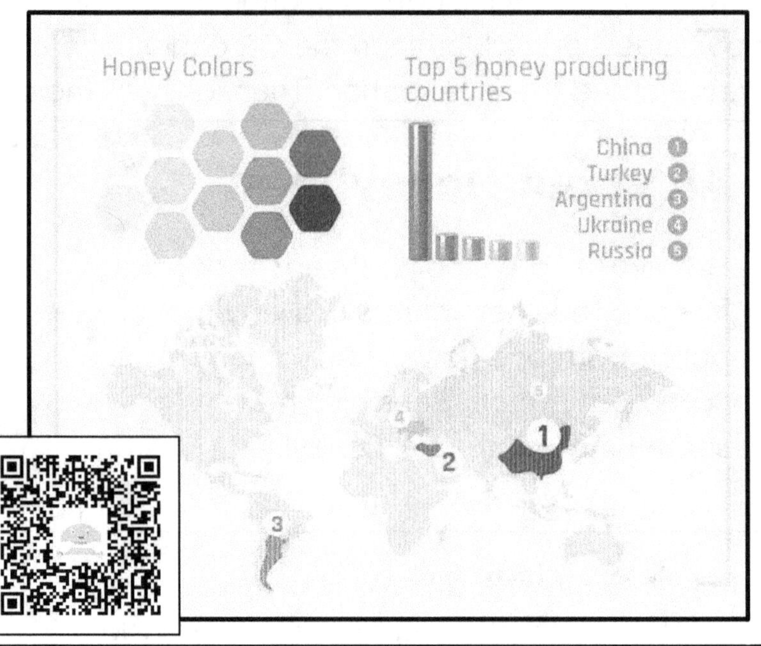

1. Which text feature is shown above? ________________
2. How does the text feature make the information easier to understand or find?

____

____

____

---

1. Which text feature did you find the most helpful? Why?

____

____

____

____

Day 2: Language Lab

Read the mini-lesson. Then, practice the skill in parts 1 and 2.

Homophones

Words that **sound the same** but are spelled differently and have different meanings

write	right
pair	pear
hear	here

Part 1: Which words sound the same? Read the words below and draw lines to connect the pairs of homophones.

mail •	• tail
tale •	• male
flour •	• board
bored •	• flower

Day 2: Language Lab

Part 2: Complete each sentence with the correct homophone. If you need help, use a dictionary to help you find the different meanings.

Words	Sentences
bee be	We are going to __________ late. I saw a __________ on the flower.
blue blew	She painted the walls __________. She made a wish and __________ out the candles.
aloud allowed	I am not ______________ to walk alone at night. The teacher read the book ______________ to the students.
eight ate	I _____________ a snack. I am _____________ years old.
bear bare	We walked on the beach with _________ feet. We saw a _________ in the woods.

Day 2: Connect and Reflect

Follow the prompts to deepen your understanding of the lesson.

Focus on your favorite moment. Write down or draw your favorite part of today's lesson.

Pack your bags! What's something you learned that you want to take with you and remember later?

Make a real-world connection. Where have you seen visual text features like maps, charts, or labels outside of books or school? How did they help you find information or understand something more easily?

Rate how you feel about this week's "Language Lab" skill: I can identify homophones and use them correctly in a sentence.

Rate how you feel about this week's skill: I can identify visual text features and explain how they help organize information, locate key details, and answer questions.

Optional Support

Dig Deeper 

Want more practice with visual text features and homophones?

Visual Feature Scavenger Hunt

Go on a scavenger hunt through a nonfiction book, article, or magazine. As you read, look for different visual text features, such as diagrams, maps, and timelines. Each time you find one, record what the feature is and what it helped you learn or understand. For example, a map might help you see where something happened, or a diagram might show how something works.

Homophone Matching/Memory Game

Write homophones, like "hair/hare," "heal/heel," and "mousse/moose," on slips of paper or index cards. Then, write simple definitions or draw small pictures that match each word on separate slips of paper. Mix them up and match each word to its correct meaning or picture. You may also choose to turn it into a memory-style game by laying all the cards face down and taking turns flipping over two at a time to find a matching pair.

Climb Higher 

Ready for a challenge when it comes to visual text features and homophones?

Create Your Own Visual Text Feature

After reading a nonfiction text, create your own diagram, map, or timeline to show the information in a visual way. Explain how your visual text feature adds to the text and helps others understand the topic better.

As an alternative, you may choose to create a diagram, map, or timeline about something from your own life, such as a map of your home, a timeline of your day, or a diagram showing the parts of your favorite toy.

Use Homophone Pairs

Choose a homophone pair and write a sentence that uses both words correctly. Draw pictures to go with each sentence.

Example(s):

- I can see the sea from my window.
- While baking, I got flour all over my flower shirt.

Day 1

- ❏ Video and Guided Notes
- ❏ Read and Respond
- ❏ Online Practice Levels 1 and 2

Day 2

- ❏ Language Lab
- ❏ Connect and Reflect
- ❏ Online Practice Levels 3 and 4

Day 3

- ❏ Extend Your Skills
- ❏ Online Assessment
- ❏ Optional: Dig Deeper or Climb Higher

Lesson Goal: I can use information gained from text and visual features to answer questions in nonfiction texts.

Record your thoughts: What would a map of your home or neighborhood include?

Record your thoughts on the right! →

A Word To Explore:

Recognize

To recognize something means to know it because you've seen it or experienced it before

Day 1: Guided Notes

Follow along with Bea to complete the guided notes below.

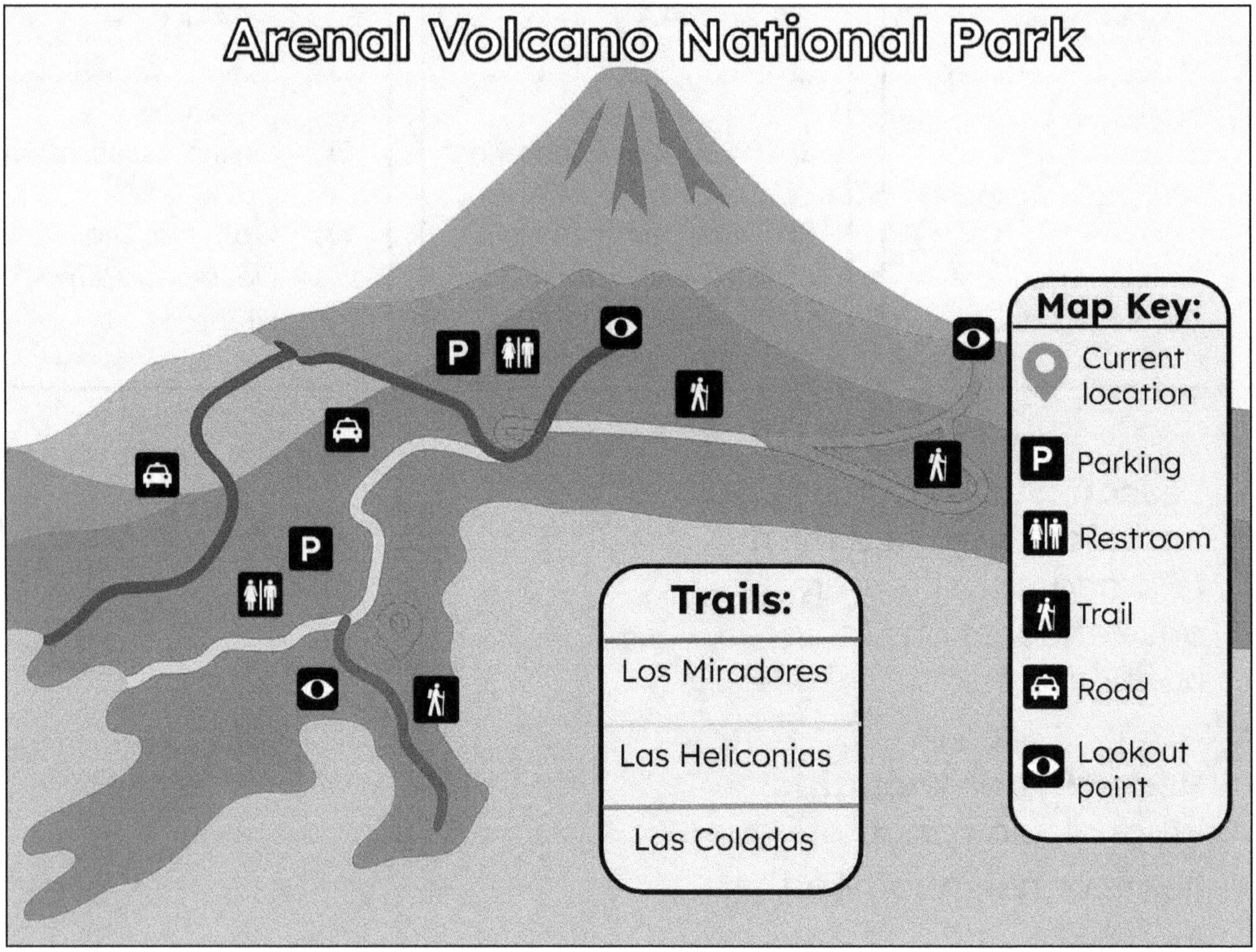

Arenal Volcano National Park

Map Key:
- Current location
- P Parking
- Restroom
- Trail
- Road
- Lookout point

Trails:
- Los Miradores
- Las Heliconias
- Las Coladas

Take a look at the map. What does it teach you? What information is missing, or what are you left wondering?

____

____

____

____

Day 1: Guided Notes

Follow along with Bea to complete the guided notes below.

Parts of a Toucan
Toucans are colorful birds that live in the rainforests of Central and South America.

Beak
A toucan's beak may look large and heavy, but it's actually very light! The beak helps the toucan reach fruit on branches that are too small to sit on. It also helps the toucan grab insects or small lizards.

Claws
Claws help the toucan grip onto branches so it doesn't fall. They're important for climbing and staying safe in the trees.

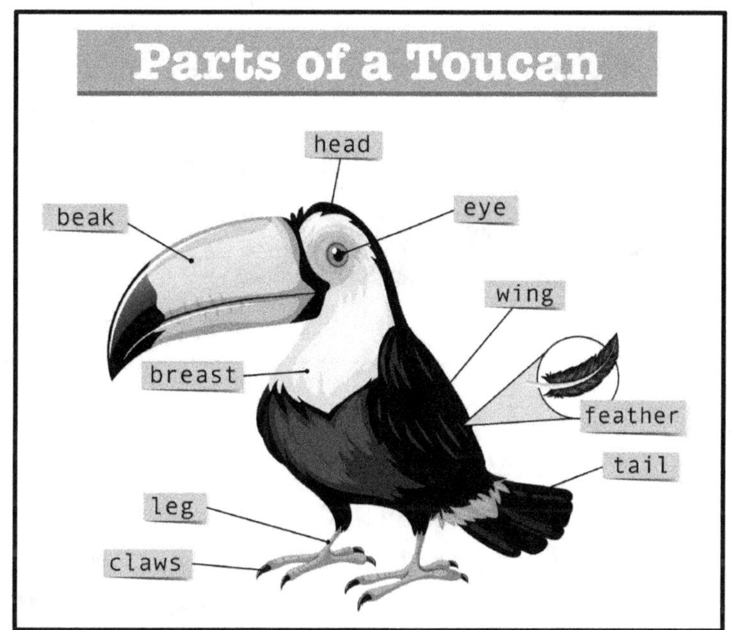

Wings
Toucans have strong wings that help them fly from tree to tree. Even though they are not long-distance fliers, their wings are great for quick, short flights.

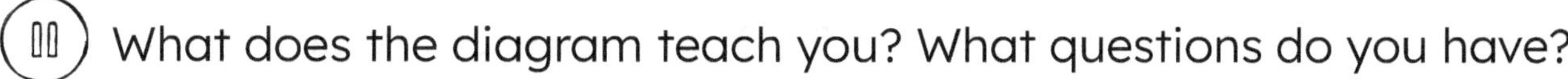

What does the diagram teach you? What questions do you have?

____

____

____

Text and visual features work together! Always read the surrounding text to find the answers to your questions. Remember headings/subheadings can help you easily find the topics you are looking for!

Day 1: Guided Notes

Follow along with Bea to complete the guided notes below.

From 1968 to 2010, the volcano stayed very active. It had many eruptions during that time. Some were small, and a few were much bigger, but none compared to the one in 1968. In this time frame, scientists counted over 100 lava flows! After a final eruption in 2010, Arenal became quiet again, and it hasn't erupted since.

Bea's Questions:
What happened between 1968 and 2010?
How many more eruptions were there?

Use the text to find the answers to Bea's questions.

____

____

____

Day 1: Read and Respond

Part 1: Read the passage below, or click or scan the QR code to listen to it. Then, use information from the text and the map to answer the questions below.

Tropical Rainforests

Tropical rainforests grow near the middle of the Earth. They are hot, rainy, and full of trees, animals, and plants. The largest is the Amazon rainforest in South America. Others are in Africa, Asia, Central America, and near Australia.

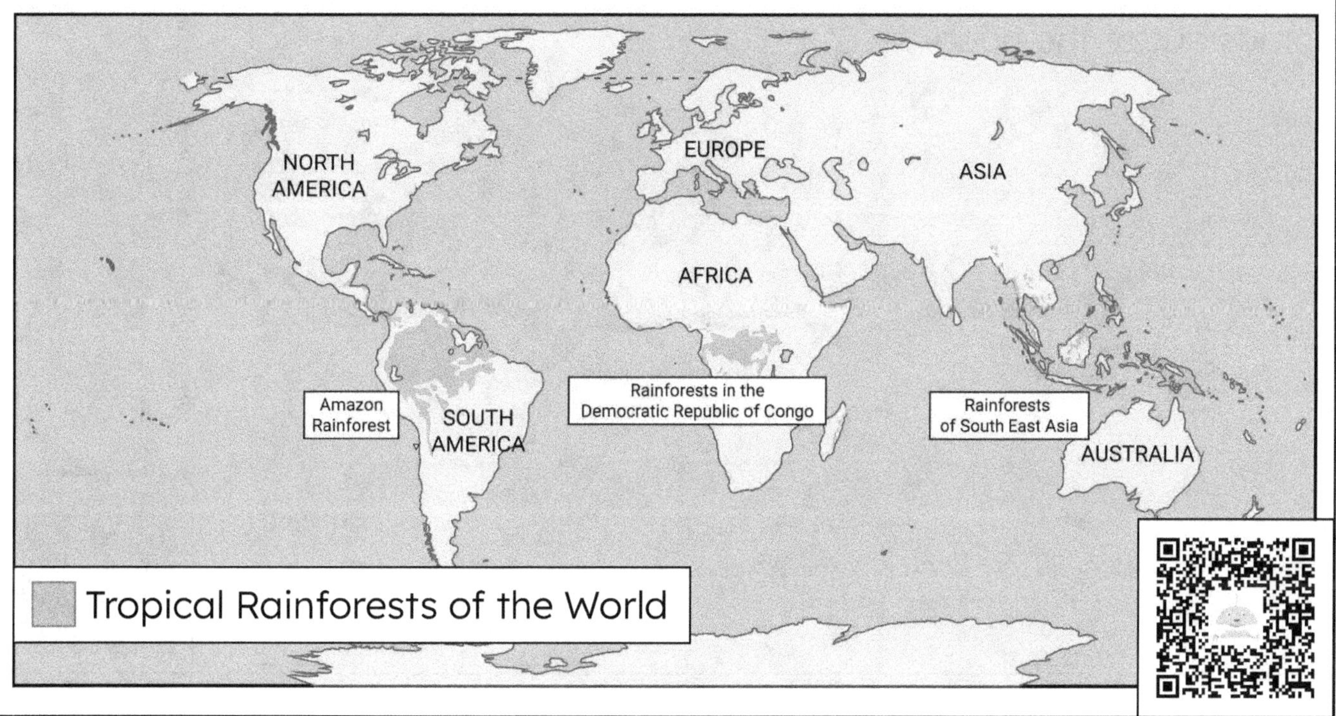

1. What color shows rainforests on the map?

____

2. Which rainforest is the largest?

____

3. Where is the largest rainforest?

____

Part 2: Read the passage below, or click or scan the QR code to listen to it. Then, use information from the text and the diagram to answer the questions.

Butterfly Life Cycle

Butterflies go through four stages in their life. First, the butterfly lays eggs on a leaf. Then, the egg hatches into a caterpillar. The caterpillar eats a lot and grows bigger. Next, the caterpillar forms a pupa, also called a chrysalis. Inside, it changes into a butterfly. Last, a beautiful butterfly comes out of the pupa.

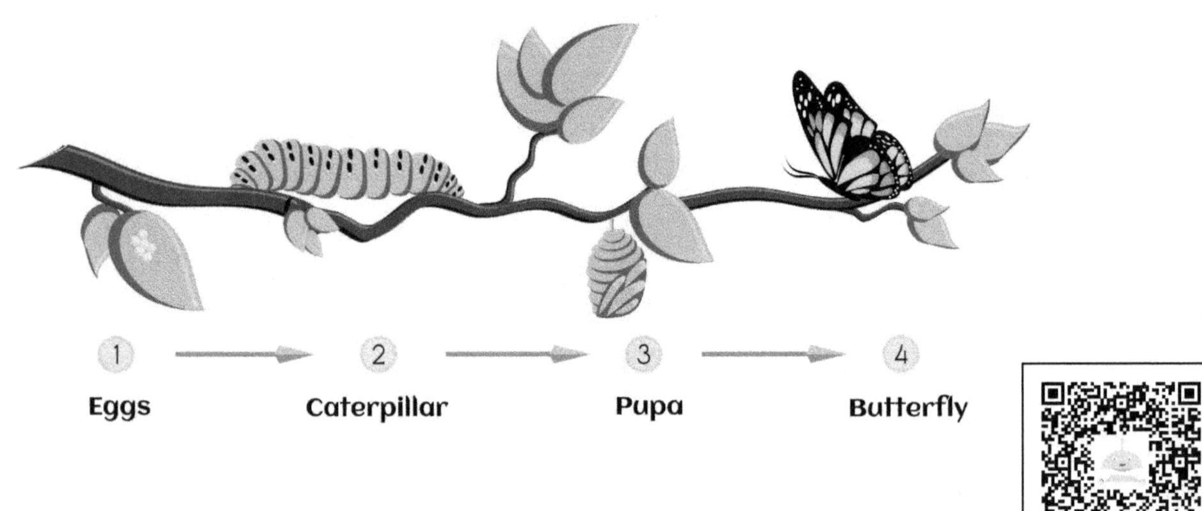

1. Where does a butterfly lay its eggs?

____

2. What are two different names for the third stage of a butterfly's life cycle?

____

3. What is the second stage of a butterfly's life cycle?

____

Day 2: Language Lab

Read the mini-lesson. Then, practice the skill in parts 1 and 2.

Some words can have **multiple meanings**. One word can mean different things depending on how it's used in a sentence. These are called homographs. Read the examples of homographs below.

Homographs

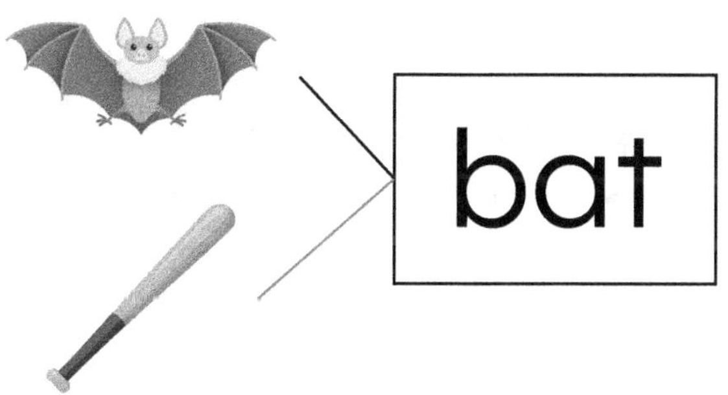

bat

The **bat** flew out of the cave and into the night sky.

She hit the baseball with her **bat** and ran to first base.

park

We had a picnic at the **park** and played on the swings.

We had to **park** the car across the street from our house.

Sometimes, even though homographs are spelled the same, they are pronounced differently, like the word "dove."

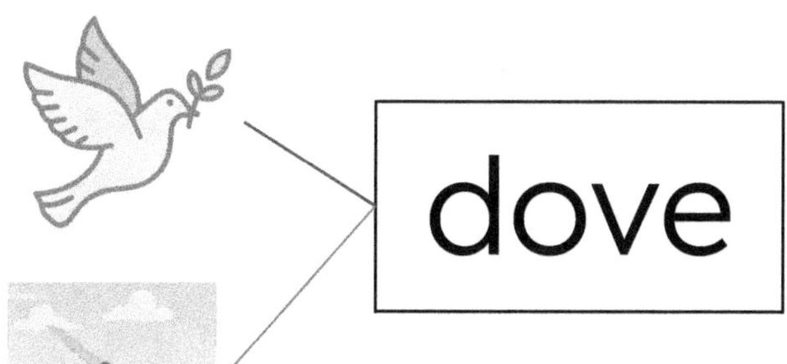

dove

A **dove** flew by my window.

He **dove** into the pool.

Day 2: Language Lab

Part 1: Draw a simple picture to match each meaning of the word.

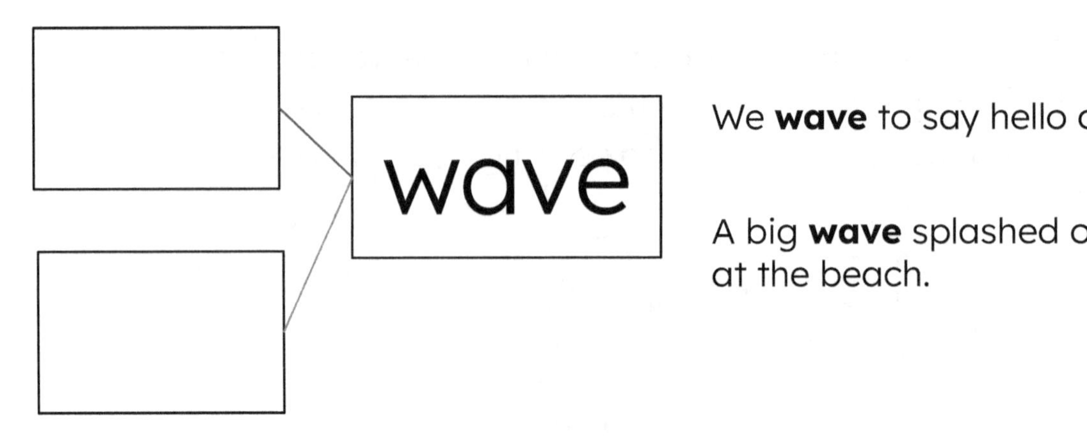

We **wave** to say hello or goodbye.

A big **wave** splashed onto the sand at the beach.

Part 2: Read each sentence and select the correct definition for the word. Circle the homophone that can be pronounced in different ways. As a challenge, write a sentence with the other meaning of each word.

1. We had to **duck** under the rope to get through.
   a. A type of animal
   b. To bend down

2. The rock will **sink** if you drop it in the pond.
   a. A bowl used to wash hands
   b. To fall below the water

3. He stayed home from school because he had a **cold**.
   a. A sickness; runny nose and cough
   b. Low temperature; Opposite of warm

4. I sent him a **letter** wishing him a happy birthday.
   a. A character or symbol in the alphabet
   b. A written message sent to someone

5. She had to **bow** before the queen.
   a. To bend forward
   b. A ribbon

6. He **left** his phone in the car.
   a. Opposite of right; a direction or side of the body
   b. To leave or go away from

Day 2: Connect and Reflect

Follow the prompts to deepen your understanding of the lesson.

Focus on your favorite moment. Write down or draw your favorite part of today's lesson.

Pack your bags! What's something you learned that you want to take with you and remember later?

Make a real-world connection. Can you think of a time when you had to read something that included both words and visuals to figure something out or make a decision?

Rate how you feel about this week's "Language Lab" skill: I can identify homographs and determine their meaning within a sentence.

Rate how you feel about this week's skill: I can use information gained from text and visual features to answer questions in nonfiction texts.

Day 3: Extend Your Skills

Read the passage about ladybugs below, or listen to it by clicking or scanning the QR code. Then, use what you learned to complete the diagram. Add a number in each circle and a text label in each rectangle to show the stages explained in the text. Explain to someone at home how the two features work together.

The Life Cycle of a Ladybug

Ladybugs go through four stages in their life cycle. First, the ladybug lays tiny yellow eggs on the bottom of a leaf. These eggs are usually laid in clusters. Next, the eggs hatch into larvae. The larvae look like tiny alligators with black and orange bodies. They crawl around and eat lots of aphids. After a few weeks, the larvae attach to a leaf and become a pupa. Inside the pupa, the ladybug changes shape. Finally, a grown ladybug comes out of the pupa. It has a hard red shell with black spots. The adult ladybug is now ready to fly and lay eggs of its own!

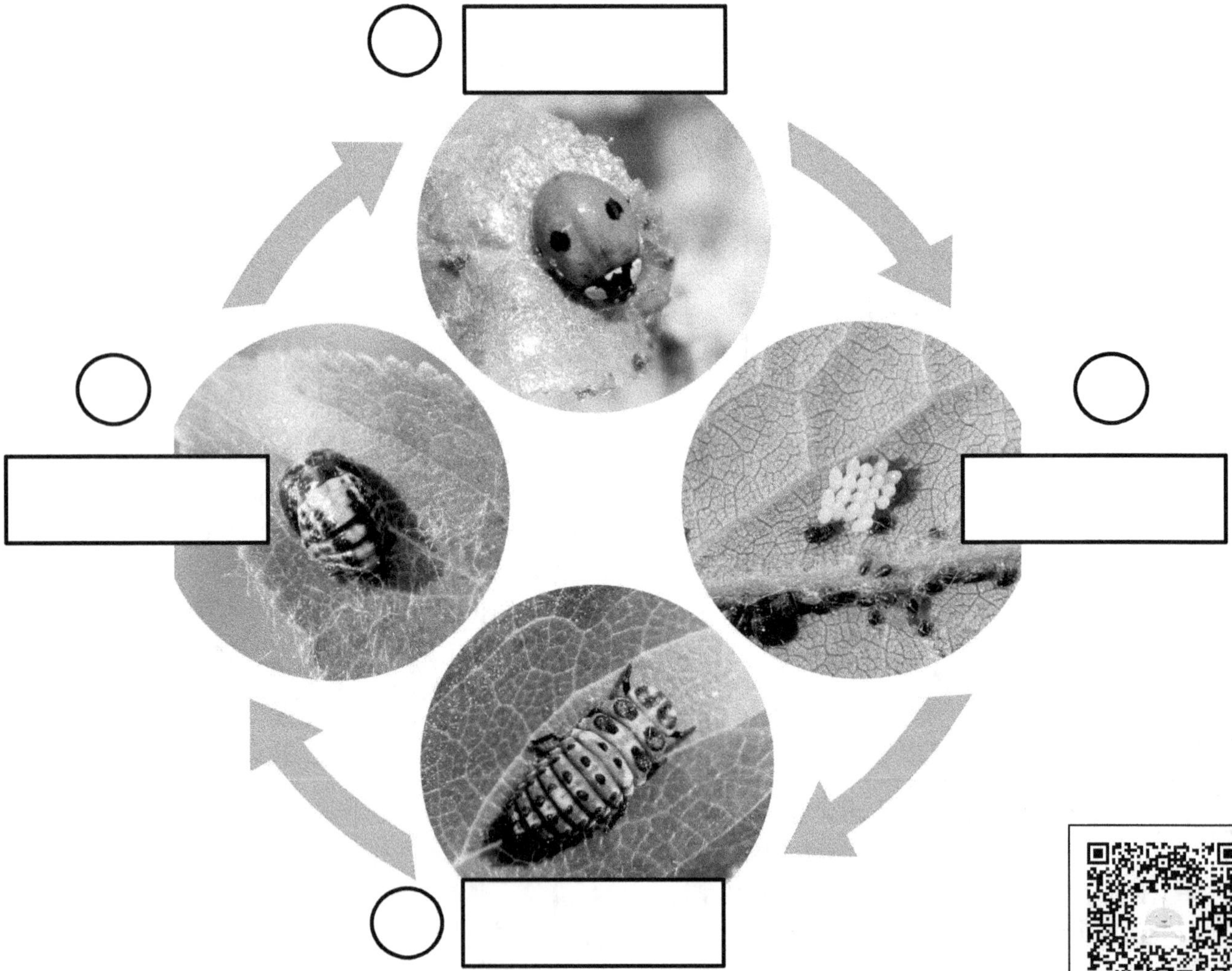

Optional Support

Dig Deeper

Want more practice with how text and visual features work together?

Read each text. Then, draw a line to the visual feature that supports it.

We wash our hands to stay healthy. We scrub our palms, fingers, nails, and thumbs to remove germs. Each step helps keep our hands clean.

There are seven continents in the world. They are North America, South America, Europe, Asia, Africa, Australia, and Antarctica. Each continent is a big piece of land with different people, animals, and places.

A click beetle's life cycle has four steps. It starts as an egg, hatches into a wireworm, becomes a pupa, and then grows into an adult beetle.

We use our five senses to learn about the world. We see with our eyes, hear with our ears, smell with our noses, taste with our tongues, and touch with our skin.

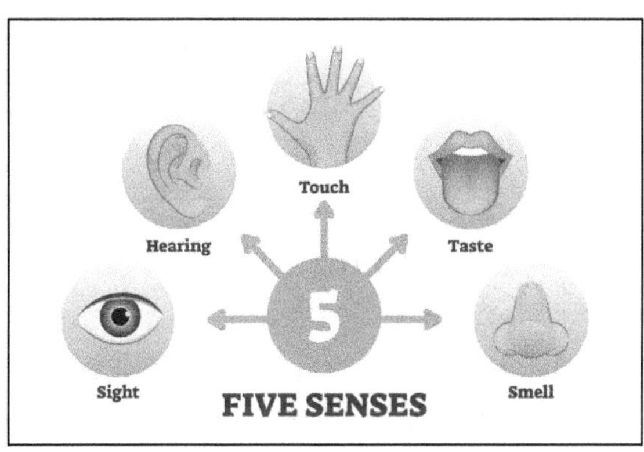

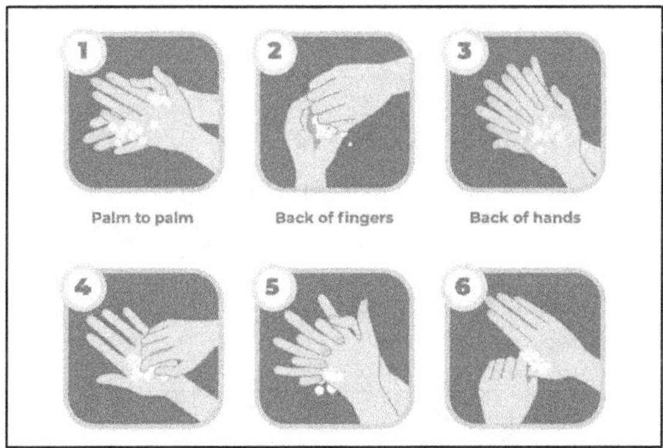

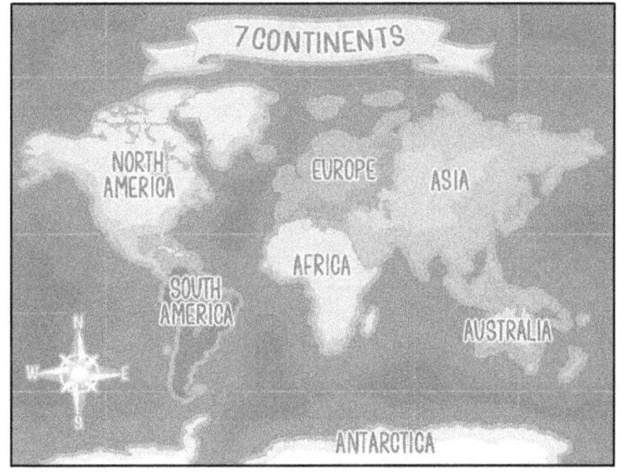

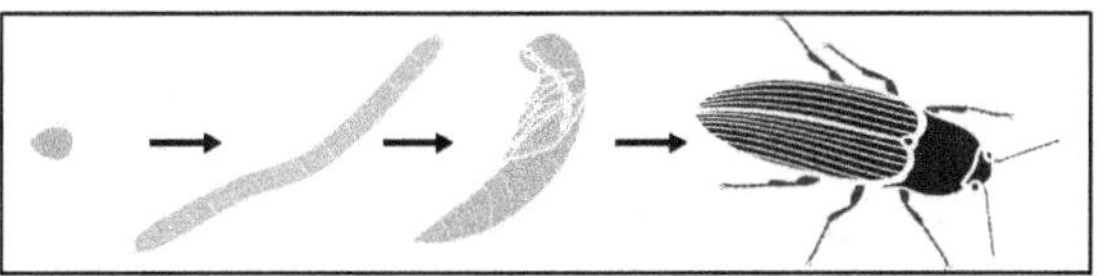

Optional Support

Climb Higher

Ready for a challenge when it comes to using visual features alongside text?

Get ready to become a nonfiction expert and take the spotlight as the host of your very own **Text Feature Talk Show**! In this activity, you'll explore a topic you love, use visual features like maps and diagrams, and teach your audience like a pro.

1. **Pick a Topic:** Choose a nonfiction topic you love (volcanoes, sharks, or space). Then, give your talk show a fun name! You can use your own name or be creative just like Bea did with her channel, "Read and Roam."
2. **Find Visual Features:** Look in books or online for maps, diagrams, timelines, or photographs. Select at least two visual features.
3. **Study & Prepare:** For each feature, ask yourself: What does this show me? What question does it help me answer? How does it help me better understand the topic?
4. **Host the Show:** Ask a parent, family member, or friend to interview you. Show each visual feature and explain it like an expert!
5. (Optional): Record your show and/or write a short summary of what you shared below.

Talk Show Name: ____________________

Topic: ____________________

Summary:

____

____

____

____

Day 1

- ❑ Video and Guided Notes
- ❑ Read and Respond
- ❑ Online Practice Levels 1 and 2

Day 2

- ❑ Language Lab
- ❑ Connect and Reflect
- ❑ Online Practice Levels 3 and 4
- ❑ Optional: Dig Deeper or Climb Higher

Lesson Goal: I can identify common text structures, such as description, sequence, and problem/solution, and explain how each one organizes information and helps readers understand how ideas are connected in a nonfiction text.

Record your thoughts: Why does sequence matter when you're building, cooking, or fixing something?

Record your thoughts on the right! →

A Word To Explore:

Structure

How something is built or organized

Day 1: Guided Notes

Follow along with Bea to complete the guided notes below.

Text structure

is the way that authors ______________ information.

Description Text Structure

Tells about a person, place, or thing using ___________ about how it looks, feels, smells, or sounds, and sometimes gives examples too. When authors use description, their goal is to help readers visualize a topic.

Sequence Text Structure

Tells the ______________ of events or the ______________ in a process and helps the reader understand a process clearly, one part at a time.

Problem/Solution Text Structure

Describes a ______________, something that isn't working or needs to change and then explains how it was or could be______________. This structure of writing helps readers see how people solve real-life challenges.

Day 1: Guided Notes

Follow along with Bea to complete the guided notes below.

Name That Text Feature

1	To plant a sunflower, first dig a small hole in the soil. Then, drop the seed into the hole and cover it with dirt. Next, water the seed gently. After a few days, you'll see a sprout start to grow.

Record which kind of text structure this has. Is it a description of something, a sequence of events in order, or a problem/solution?

____

2	Polar bears live in the cold Arctic. They have thick white fur to keep them warm and help them blend into the snow. Their large paws help them walk on ice and swim in icy water. They have small dark eyes, a long neck, and a black nose that stands out against their thick white fur.

Record which text structure the author used.

____

3	Many people enjoy putting up bird feeders to watch colorful birds eat seeds. But there's one big problem: squirrels that climb up and eat the birdseed! To fix this, some people use bird feeders that close when a squirrel lands or add a slippery cone to keep them from climbing.

Record the structure. Explain how you know.

____

____

____

Day 1: Read and Respond

Read the passages, or listen to them by clicking or scanning the QR codes. Identify which text structure was used. Then, explain why the author chose this structure and how it helps the reader.

The rainforest is a warm, wet place filled with tall green trees and colorful plants. The air is humid, and sunlight shines through the thick leaves above. Birds sing from the treetops, and monkeys swing from vines. The ground is soft with fallen leaves and buzzing with insects. Everywhere you look, the rainforest is full of life and color.

Which text structure did the author use? ____________________

Why did the author use this structure? How does it help the reader?

____

____

____

In the town of Maple Creek, many people were having trouble crossing the busy street near the grocery store. There was no crosswalk, and cars drove by too fast. This made it unsafe for kids and older adults. To solve the problem, the town built a crosswalk with flashing lights and had a crossing guard during busy hours.

Which text structure did the author use? ____________________

Why did the author use this structure? How does it help the reader?

____

____

____

Day 1: Read and Respond

Read the passages, or listen to them by clicking or scanning the QR codes. Identify which text structure was used. Then, explain why the author chose this structure and how it helps the reader.

To build a paper airplane, follow these steps. First, take a piece of paper and fold it in half. Next, open it and fold the top corners down to the middle. Then, fold the sides down to make the wings. Finally, hold the bottom and throw it gently.

Which text structure did the author use? ____________________

Why did the author use this structure? How does it help the reader?

____

____

____

The river near town was filled with trash, like plastic bags and bottles. It made the water look dirty, and fish started to disappear. To solve the problem, the community held a river clean-up day. People wore gloves and picked up trash together. They also added signs to remind everyone not to litter.

Which text structure did the author use? ____________________

Why did the author use this structure? How does it help the reader?

____

____

____

Day 2: Language Lab

Read the mini-lesson. Then, practice the skill in parts 1 through 3.

Synonyms are words with the same or similar meanings.

For example, "**angry**" and "**mad**" are synonyms because they both describe someone who is upset or not happy.

To find a synonym, you can ask yourself: What's another word I could use the same way as this word?

Tip: Try replacing a word in a sentence with a synonym. Does the sentence have the same meaning? If yes, you've found a good synonym!

Part 1: Color each pair of synonyms in a matching color. Each pair should be a different color. One pair has been colored for you as an example.

hard	yell	rest	difficult
ill	relax	shout	sick
scared	fast	afraid	quick

Day 2: Language Lab

Part 2: Read each sentence. Find a synonym for each underlined word in the box and write it next to the sentence.

below	smell	road	grin	pretty
leaped	enjoyed	stone	loud	fix

1. I threw a rock in the lake. ______________
2. The frog jumped from one lily pad to another. ______________
3. I ran down the street to catch the bus. ______________
4. The school halls were noisy. ______________
5. The builder had to repair the roof after the big storm. ______________
6. The dog stopped to sniff the flowers in the garden. ______________
7. He had a big smile on his face. ______________
8. The flowers are beautiful. ______________
9. I really liked the movie. ______________
10. The cat curled up under the table. ______________

Part 3: Read each sentence. Come up with your own synonym for the underlined word. Record it on the line next to the sentence.

1. Will you close the window? ______________
2. She gave me a gift for my birthday. ______________
3. I am so glad to see you! ______________
4. I got the answer correct. ______________
5. She was very nice. ______________

Day 2: Connect and Reflect

Follow the prompts to deepen your understanding of the lesson.

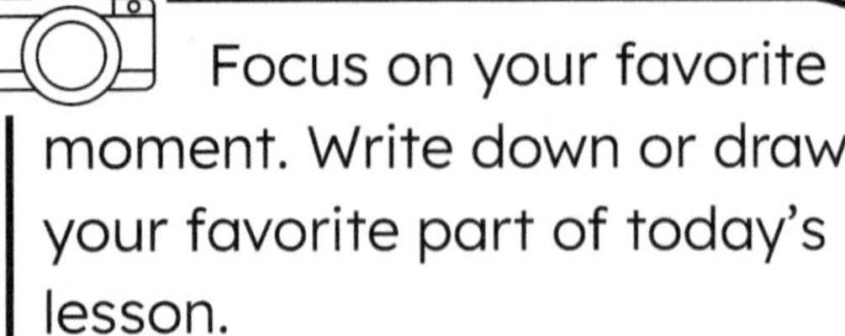

Focus on your favorite moment. Write down or draw your favorite part of today's lesson.

Pack your bags! What's something you learned that you want to take with you and remember later?

Make a real-world connection. Where have you seen a sequence text structure?

Rate how you feel about this week's "Language Lab" skill: I can identify and use synonyms.

Rate how you feel about this week's skill: I can identify and explain common text features.

Optional Support

Dig Deeper 

Want more practice with text structures?

Structure Scavenger Hunt
Go on a scavenger hunt through texts of your choice (nonfiction books, cookbooks, how-to guides, magazines, or even articles online). Try to find at least one example of each common text structure: description, sequence, and problem/solution. Explain how each structure helps you understand the information better as a reader.

Extension: Structure Scavenger Hunt Drawing Activity
Try drawing a picture to match each text structure you find. For a sequence text, you might draw a series of steps. For description, create a detailed illustration or a labeled diagram that shows what the text is describing. If the text uses a problem/solution structure, draw two pictures: one that shows the problem and another that shows how it was solved.

Climb Higher 

Ready for a challenge when it comes to text structures?

Description Writing
Take a nature walk or choose an interesting object at home. Look closely at an object of your choice and describe it using sensory details. What does it look like? How does it feel and/or smell? Does it make a sound? Write a paragraph that paints a clear picture in your reader's mind. For a fun challenge, read your paragraph aloud to someone at home and ask them to draw what they hear. If they're missing details, add more to make your writing even clearer!

Sequence Writing
Think about your daily routine. What do you do first when you wake up? What happens next, and what do you do after that? Keep going until you get to the last part of your day. Now, write a sequence paragraph that tells your day step by step. Use words like first, next, then, and finally to help your reader follow along in the right order.

Problem/Solution Writing
Think of a problem you or someone you know has had recently. It could be something simple, like losing a library book or dealing with a rainy day when you wanted to play outside. Talk to a friend or family member about how the problem was solved or what could be done to fix it. Then, write a paragraph that explains the problem clearly and describes one or more solutions.

Day 1

- ❑ Video and Guided Notes
- ❑ Read and Respond
- ❑ Online Practice Levels 1 and 2

Day 2

- ❑ Language Lab
- ❑ Connect and Reflect
- ❑ Online Practice Levels 3 and 4

Day 3

- ❑ Extend Your Skills
- ❑ Online Practice Level 5
- ❑ Optional: Dig Deeper or Climb Higher

Lesson Goal: I can identify and explain cause-and-effect relationships within fiction and nonfiction texts.

Record your thoughts: Can you think of a time when something you did caused something else to happen?

Record your thoughts on the right! →

A Word To Explore:

An effect is what happens because of something else; the result or outcome of an action or event

Day 1: Guided Notes

Follow along with Bea to complete the guided notes below.

Cause and Effect

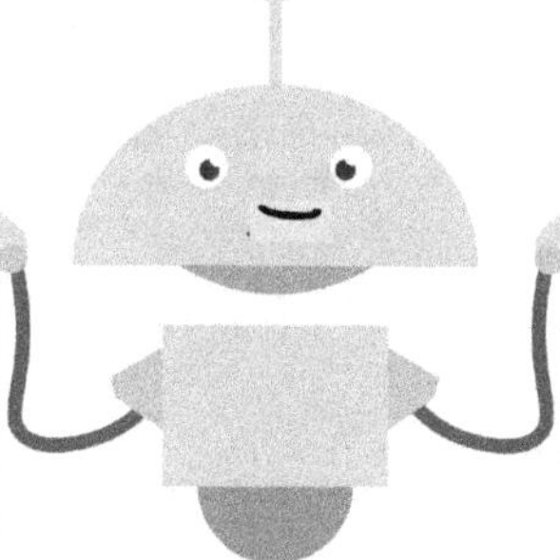

Why?
Helps us understand ________ something happened

What?
Tells us ________ happened after as a result

Show us how one thing ____________ to another

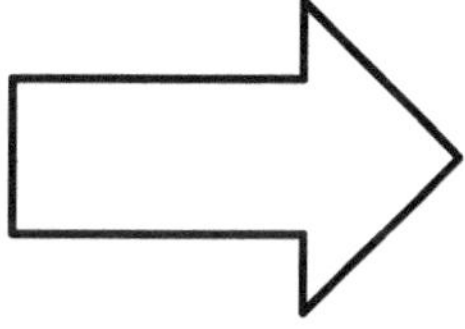

Cause: Stayed up late reading

Effect: Tired the next day

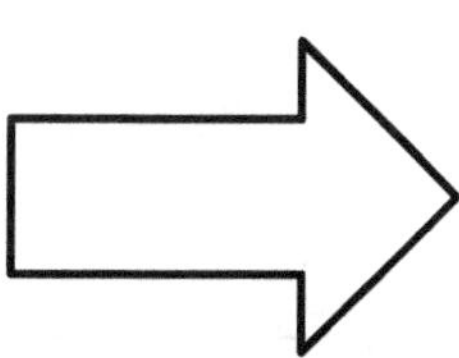

Cause: Sun and rain

Effect: Rainbow

Day 1: Guided Notes

Follow along with Bea to complete the guided notes below.

In the fall, when the days get shorter and there is less sunlight, trees stop making as much food. As a result, the green color in the leaves begins to fade, and we start to see bright reds, oranges, and yellows.

Circle the cause, and **underline** the effect. Then, explain the connection between the cause and effect.

____

____

____

The leaves were torn, and several ripe tomatoes had been eaten. Amina ran outside when she heard her brother shout, "The goats are in the garden!" "Uh-oh," Amina thought. She had forgotten to close the gate to her family's goat pen that morning.

Circle the cause, and **underline** the effect. Then, explain the connection between the cause and effect.

____

____

____

Today we learned...

Authors use cause and effect to show us how one thing leads to another. This helps us understand **WHY** something happened, which is the **cause**, and **WHAT** happened as a result, which is the **effect**. This structure can be found in fiction and nonfiction.

Day 1: Read and Respond

Read the passages below, or click or scan the QR codes to listen. Identify which part is the cause and which part is the effect.

In the winter, food becomes harder to find. As a result, some animals go into hibernation to save energy. During hibernation, animals like bears, bats, and groundhogs sleep for a long time. Their bodies slow down, so they don't need to eat as much. This helps them survive until spring, when food is easier to find again.

1. Is the text underlined in purple a cause or effect? ________________
2. Is the text circled in blue a cause or effect? ________________

Lila's socks were soaked, and her shoes made a squishing sound as she walked. She had accidentally walked into a deep puddle. "I should have worn my rain boots!" she said.

1. Is the text underlined in orange a cause or effect? ________________
2. Is the text circled in red a cause or effect? ________________

Sometimes, after it rains, the sun comes out. When sunlight shines through raindrops, a rainbow appears in the sky. We see colors like red, orange, yellow, and blue.

1. Is the text underlined in green a cause or effect? ________________
2. Is the text circled in pink a cause or effect? ________________

Remember, even though the cause always happens first in real life, it isn't always written in that order in the text!

Day 1: Read and Respond

Read or listen to the passages below. Then, follow the steps below.

1. Circle the cause.
2. Underline the effect.
3. On the lines below the passage, explain the connection between the cause and effect.

The doctor explained that I had a sunburn. This happened because I didn't wear strong enough sunscreen. He told me that sunscreen has an SPF number. The higher the number, the more it protects your skin.

Jamal forgot to set his alarm last night, so he missed the bus. "Oh, no!" he shouted. "I overslept!" He quickly got ready and ran out the door.

Day 2: Language Lab

Read the mini-lesson. Then, practice the skill in parts 1 through 3. .

Antonyms are words with **opposite** meanings.

For example, "hot" and "cold" are antonyms because they describe opposite temperatures.

I love the cold winter weather.

No way! I can't wait for a nice hot summer day.

Part 1: Color each pair of antonyms in a matching color. Each pair should be a different color. One pair has been colored for you as an example.

loud	above	old	quiet
empty	young	below	full
last	dry	first	wet

Day 2: Language Lab

Part 2: Read each sentence. Find an antonym (or opposite) for each underlined word in the box and write it next to the sentence.

late	sour	night	up	happy
small	sharp	sold	light	short

1. The tree was tall and sturdy. ______________
2. The apple was sweet and juicy. ______________
3. The bear was big and furry. ______________
4. The day was cold and dark. ______________
5. I took the dull pencil from my pencil box. ______________
6. Allison bought a car this weekend. ______________
7. He was feeling very sad today. ______________
8. I arrived at the party early. ______________
9. I looked down the stairs. ______________
10. My bag was very heavy to carry. ______________

Part 3: Read each sentence. Write an antonym for the underlined word.

1. Will you close the door? ______________
2. She lost the race. ______________
3. Ashton's room was messy. ______________
4. I got the answer right. ______________
5. She was very nice to her sister. ______________

Day 2: Connect and Reflect

Follow the prompts to deepen your understanding of the lesson.

Focus on your favorite moment. Write down or draw your favorite part of today's lesson.

Pack your bags! What's something you learned that you want to take with you and remember later?

Make a real-world connection. Think about your day so far. Can you come up with a cause-and-effect scenario from something that happened?

Rate how you feel about this week's "Language Lab" skill: I can identify and use antonyms.

Rate how you feel about this week's skill: I can identify cause-and-effect relationships and explain how they connect ideas.

Day 3: Extend Your Skills

Read the story. Then, cut and paste to complete the cause-and-effect chart.

The Great Puppy Escape

One sunny morning, Max was rushing to get to school. While feeding Scout in the backyard, he forgot to close the gate. Scout slipped out without Max noticing.

Excited to explore, Scout wandered through the neighborhood. When he saw a butterfly, he chased it through a muddy yard. Soon, he was covered in mud from his paws to his nose!

That afternoon, Max saw muddy paw prints on the porch. He followed the footprints and found Scout hiding under the deck, wagging his muddy tail. Max smiled. "Next time, I'll remember to close the gate!"

Cause →	Effect

Max forgot to close the gate.	He was covered in mud from his paws to his nose.
Max followed the muddy footprints.	Scout got out.
Scout chased a butterfly through a muddy yard.	He found Scout under the deck.

Optional Support

Dig Deeper

Want more practice with cause-and-effect relationships?

Read each cause and effect below. Draw a line to match each cause with an effect on the right.

Cause		Effect
It snowed six inches!	• •	She had to wear a cast on her leg.
Nana planted seeds in the garden.	• •	We grabbed our umbrellas.
Sarah broke her leg playing soccer.	• •	We had to shovel the driveway and sidewalk.
It was raining outside.	• •	He stayed home to rest.
Tommy didn't feel well this morning.	• •	Vegetables began to grow.

Optional Support

Climb Higher

Ready for a challenge
when it comes to cause-and-effect structures?

Sometimes, one cause can lead to more than one effect. Read the passage below, then identify the cause and list three effects in the graphic organizer.

Nibbles, our class pet, escaped from his cage in Mrs. Lee's classroom! He knocked over a stack of books, left tiny paw prints on the windowsill, and startled a group of students who had just come back from lunch. Be on the lookout. Nibbles is small, sneaky, and surprisingly fast!

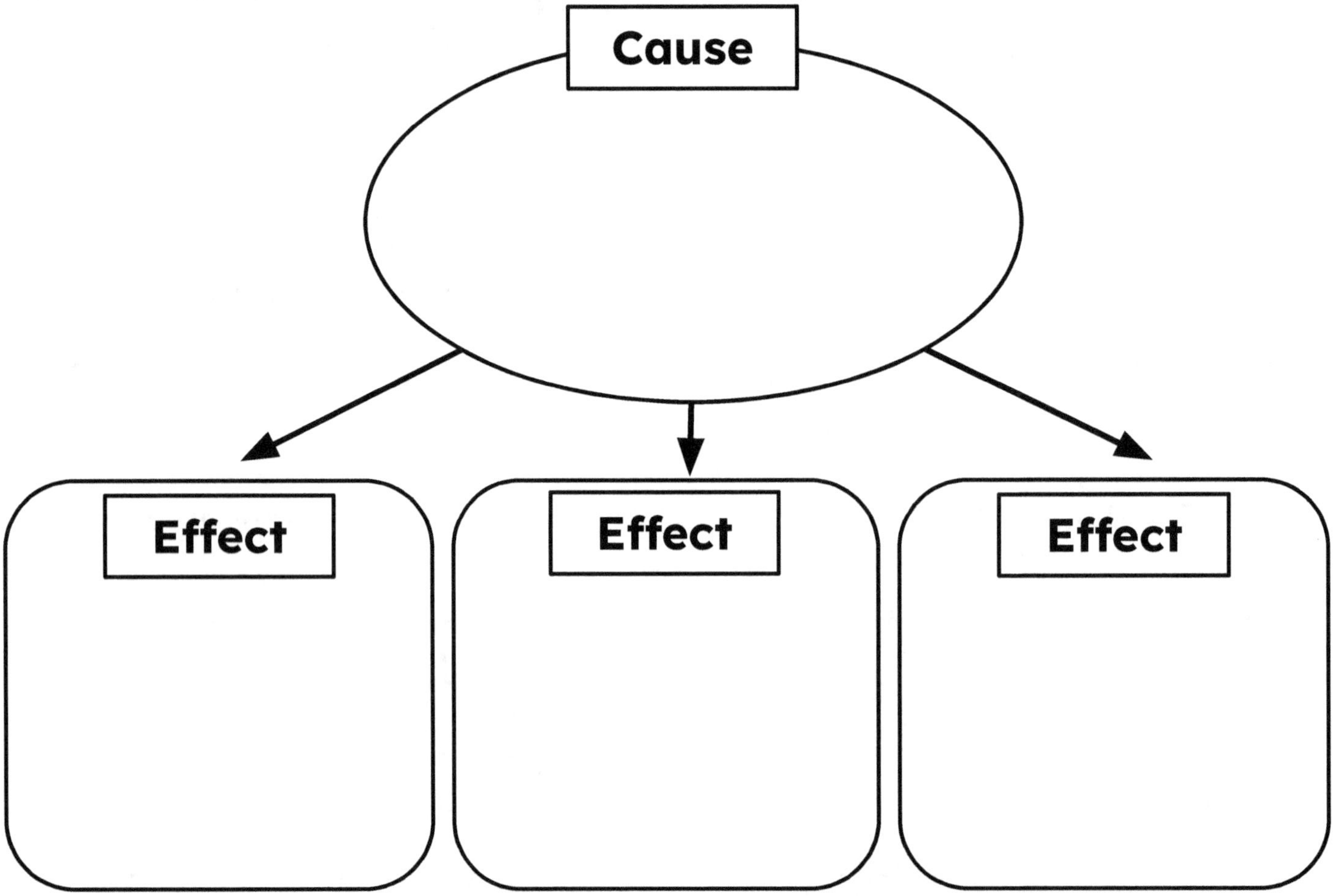

Cause

Effect | **Effect** | **Effect**

Day 1

- ❏ Video and Guided Notes
- ❏ Read and Respond
- ❏ Online Practice Levels 1 and 2

Day 2

- ❏ Language Lab
- ❏ Connect and Reflect
- ❏ Online Practice Levels 3 and 4
- ❏ Optional: Dig Deeper or Climb Higher

Lesson Goal: I can find compare-and-contrast text structures in nonfiction and use a Venn diagram to show what's the same and what's different.

Record your thoughts: How are reading and writing the same? How are they different?

Record your thoughts on the right! →

A Word To Explore:

Similar

When two or more things are almost the same

Day 1: Guided Notes

Follow along with Bea to complete the guided notes below.

Compare and Contrast

A nonfiction **text structure** that helps the reader understand how two or more things are ____________ and ____________.

Clue Words

Comparing Words:

Both
Similar
Alike

Contrasting Words:

But
However
While

Venn Diagram

Used to compare two topics

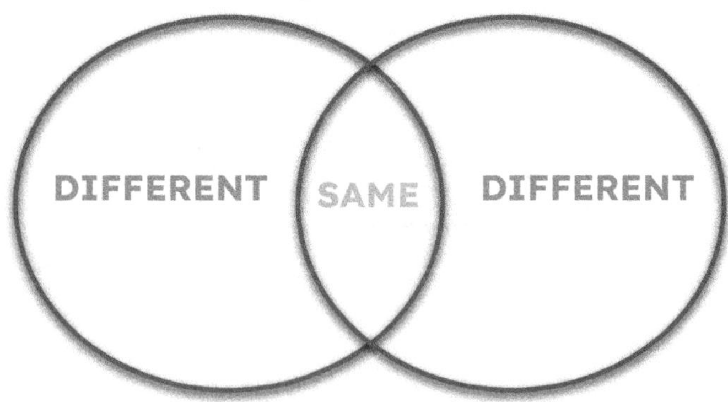

Day 1: Guided Notes

Use the article below to fill in the Venn diagram.

Books or Movies

Books and movies both tell stories. They can have exciting characters and surprising endings. However, books use words to describe the story, while movies show the story with pictures and sound. Books are meant to be read, while movies are meant to be watched.

Find the ways the author compares and contrasts book and movies. Record the similarities in the middle of your Venn diagram and the differences on the outside.

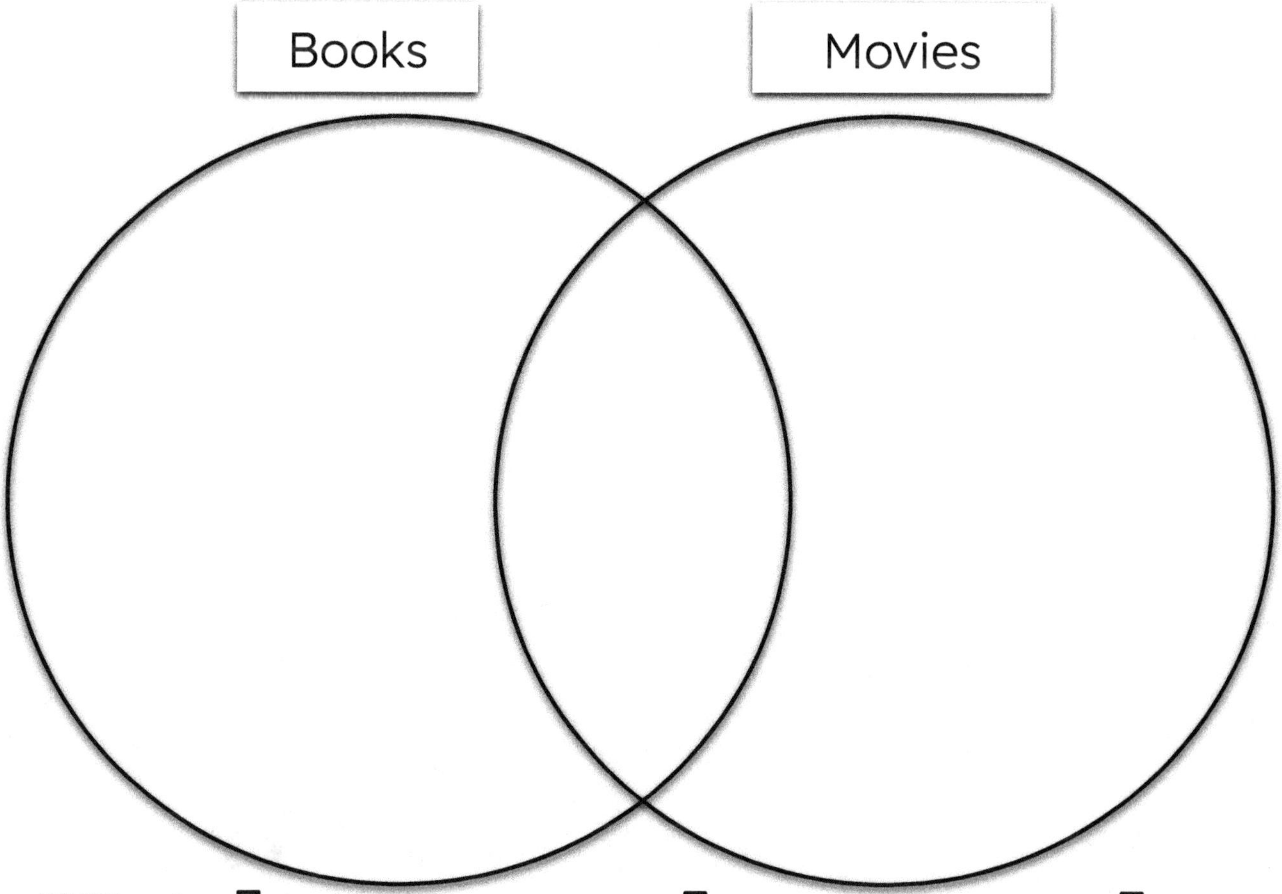

Books

Movies

Today we learned...

Compare-and-contrast text structure helps us see that two topics can be connected in ways we might not think about. When we look at similarities AND differences, we can see that ideas and topics have more in common than if we had just learned about them separately.

Day 1: Read and Respond

Read the passage below, or listen to it by clicking or scanning the QR code. Then, list the similarities and differences in the Venn diagram on the next page.

Bicycles and Scooters

Bicycles and scooters are both fun ways to travel short distances. They are similar because they both have wheels and handlebars. However, a bicycle usually has two big wheels, while a scooter has two small wheels. You sit on a bicycle, but you stand on a scooter. Bikes also have pedals that you push with your feet, but scooters are pushed by using one foot on the ground.

Day 1: Read and Respond

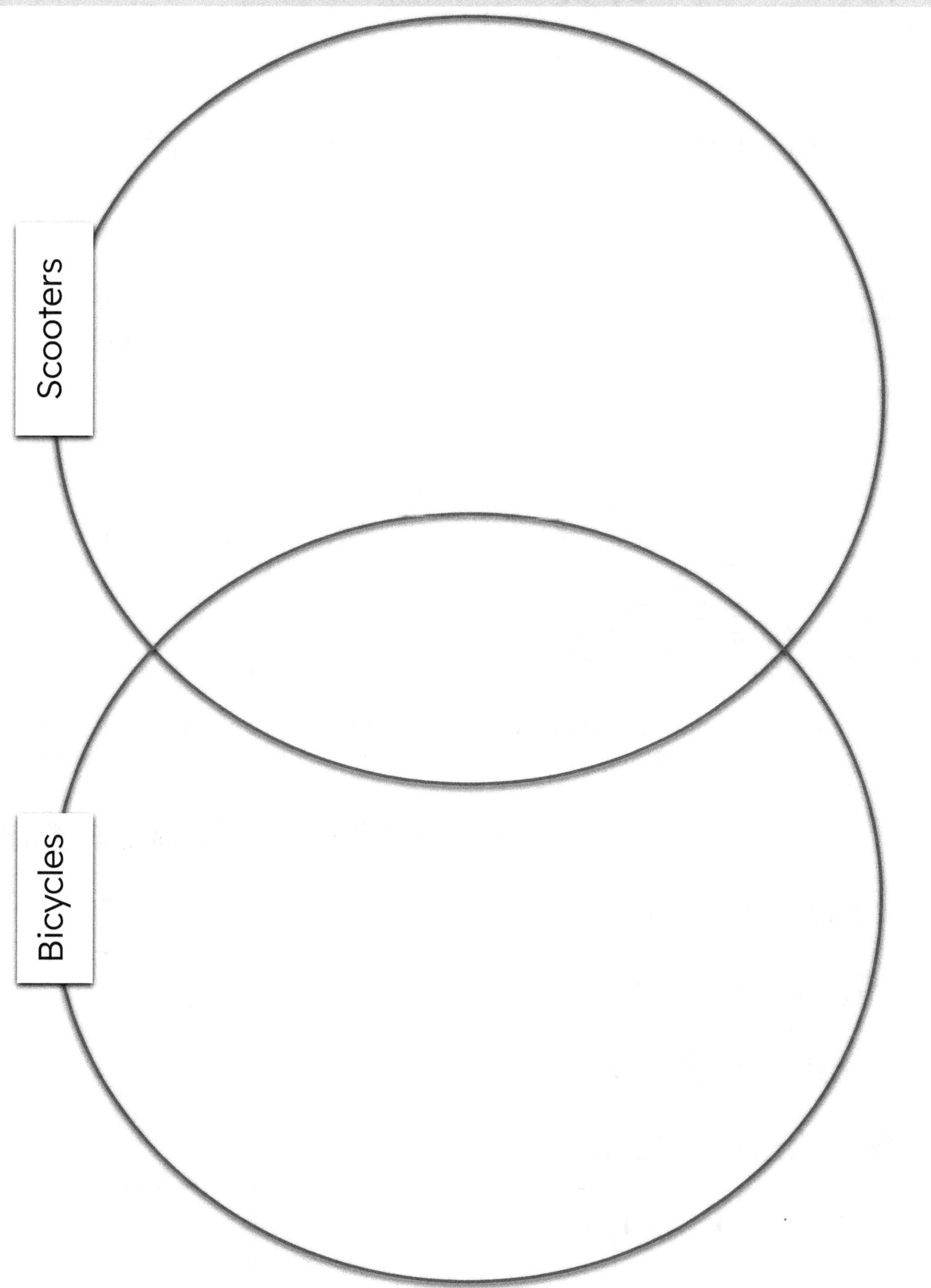

Day 2: Language Lab

Read the mini-lesson. Then, practice the skill in parts 1 and 2.

Synonyms

are words with the **same** or similar meanings.

What's another word for **fast**?

Speedy or **quick**!

Antonyms

are words with **opposite** meanings.

Whew! I'm getting **old**!

Not me! I'm still **young**.

Part 1: Read each pair of words below. Decide if the words are synonyms (the same) or antonyms (the opposite). Put a check mark in the correct box. The first one has been done for you.

	Synonyms	Antonyms
fast and **slow**		✓
clean and **dirty**		
yell and **shout**		
bright and **dark**		
sad and **unhappy**		

Day 2: Language Lab

Part 2: Write a synonym and antonym for each word. Use the words from the box below.

correct	afraid	awake	ill	easy
difficult	frown	happy	brave	huge
wrong	hot	chilly	mean	sleepy
small	healthy	grin	angry	friendly

	Synonym	Antonym
1. Sick	____________	____________
2. Hard	____________	____________
3. Smile	____________	____________
4. Tired	____________	____________
5. Mad	____________	____________
6. Kind	____________	____________
7. Scared	____________	____________
8. Big	____________	____________
9. Cold	____________	____________
10. Right	____________	____________

Day 2: Connect and Reflect

Follow the prompts to deepen your understanding of the lesson.

Focus on your favorite moment. Write down or draw your favorite part of today's lesson.

Pack your bags! What's something you learned that you want to take with you and remember later?

Make a real-world connection. Have you ever explained to someone why you like one thing better than another? What did you say that showed how they were alike or different?

Rate how you feel about this week's "Language Lab" skill: I can identify synonyms and antonyms.

Rate how you feel about this week's skill: I can identify compare-and-contrast structure, explain how it helps readers, and use a Venn diagram to organize similarities and differences.

Optional Support

Dig Deeper 

Want more practice with compare-and-contrast text structures?

Structure Scavenger Hunt

Go on a scavenger hunt in nonfiction texts of your choice.

1. Find at least two examples of compare-and-contrast text structure.
2. Draw a diagram to help you organize the similarities and differences.

Think about the following questions:

- Why might the author have used compare and contrast instead of another structure? (Other structures include description, sequence, problem/solution, and cause and effect.)
- What does it help you understand better?

Climb Higher 

Ready for a challenge when it comes to compare-and-contrast text structures?

Write Your Own Compare/Contrast Paragraph

1. Choose two topics you know well.
    - Ex. two holidays, two sports, two animals, etc.
2. Write one paragraph with...
    - At least two similarities
    - At least two differences
    - At least two clue words from your guided notes.
3. Challenge — Answer the following questions:
    - Why is compare and contrast the best structure for your topic?
    - How would your writing be different if you used description, sequence, problem/solution, or cause and effect instead?

Day 1

- ❑ Video and Guided Notes
- ❑ Read and Respond
- ❑ Online Practice Levels 1 and 2

Day 2

- ❑ Language Lab
- ❑ Connect and Reflect
- ❑ Online Practice Levels 3 and 4

Day 3

- ❑ Writing With Mia
- ❑ Online Practice Level 5
- ❑ Optional: Dig Deeper or Climb Higher

Lesson Goal:
Use context clues to determine the meanings of new words

Record your thoughts:
What do you do if you come across a word you don't know while reading?

Record your thoughts on the right! →

A Word To Explore:

A journey or search for something, usually long and difficult

Day 1: Guided Notes

Follow along with Bea to complete the guided notes below.

Context clues

are ____________ that readers use to find the

_______________ of unknown words.

Since local farmers provide our ingredients, our dishes feature **seasonal** produce, such as strawberries in spring, pumpkins in fall, and citrus fruits in the winter!

Based on the examples, the word "seasonal" might mean

____.

As Jack **hoisted** the bucket out of the well, he struggled to keep pulling it up since his arms were so tired.

Underline the context clue that helps you understand the meaning of the word "hoisted."

Think: Why might the author have included the word "struggle" in this context clue.

____

____

Day 1: Guided Notes

Follow along with Bea to complete the guided notes below.

As the knight prepared for her quest, she stuffed her bag with **provisions**: sandwiches wrapped in cloth, a canteen of water, a small sack of apples, and climbing gear. She was ready for the challenge ahead.

Underline the examples that can help you understand the meaning of the word "provisions."

Based on the examples, the word provisions probably means

____.

Today we learned...

Context clues are hints that readers use to find the meaning of unknown words

To find clues, we...

Think of what is already known about the word

Check the surrounding text

Look for clues like **definitions** and **examples**

Day 1: Read and Respond

Step 1: The following text has some words that the author has included context clues for. As you read or listen along by clicking or scanning the QR code, **underline** the context clues that help you understand the meaning of the highlighted words.

How Coffee Is Made

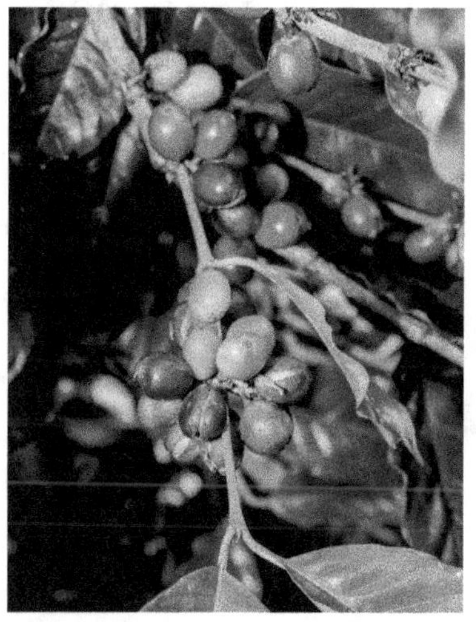

Did you know that every cup of coffee starts out as a tiny seed? There are many steps in the coffee-making process, and each one is important in creating the drink that is loved by people all over the world.

Coffee starts as a seed that grows on a plant called a coffee shrub. These seeds, known as coffee beans, are found inside a bright red fruit called a coffee cherry. Farmers **harvest** the cherries from the shrub when they are ripe. Once the cherries have been removed, the coffee beans are taken out of the cherries in a process called "pulping."

Once the beans have been removed from the cherries, they are **roasted**. This means the beans are heated slowly until they turn brown and develop a stronger flavor. As the beans roast, they also release an **aroma**, like the smell of chocolate or nuts. After being roasted, the beans are broken down by machines into tiny pieces called **grounds**.

To make coffee that's ready to drink, the coffee grounds are first placed in a filter. Hot water is poured over the grounds, and the heat helps **brew** the coffee, bringing out the flavor and mixing it into the water. This liquid coffee drips through the filter, leaving the grounds behind.

Coffee grounds can be used for more than just making coffee. While most people throw them away, grounds can be **repurposed** as fertilizer for plants, added to compost piles, or even spread in gardens to keep insects away. Finding new uses for coffee grounds helps reduce waste and protect the environment.

From seed to cup to garden, every step in making coffee plays a part in making the drink people enjoy every day.

Day 1: Read and Respond

Step 2: Based on the context clues you found, put a check mark next to the word that best matches the definition.

1. __________ - heated slowly over time, usually to bring out more flavor

☐ Grounds ☐ Roasted ☐ Aroma

2. __________ - a noticeable smell

☐ Grounds ☐ Roasted ☐ Aroma

3. __________ - small, broken up pieces of something

☐ Grounds ☐ Roasted ☐ Aroma

Step 3: Create a written or drawn definition of each word based on what you know from the context clues.

Harvest	
Brew	
Repurpose	

Day 1: Read and Respond

 **Step 4:** Answer the following spiral review questions about the passage.

1. Write a summary of the passage. Remember to think about the main idea and supporting details you find while reading.

____

____

____

____

____

____

____

2. What type of text features does the passage include?

____

3. How do these text features help you understand more about the topic?

____

____

____

____

____

Day 2: Language Lab

Read the mini-lesson. Then, practice the skill in parts 1 through 3.

Prefixes are groups of letters that are added to the beginning of a base word that change the word's meaning. Recognizing and learning prefixes can help you understand new words when you find them.

Base words are words that can stand alone and still have meaning and can be combined with other words or groups of letters to form new words. There are many prefixes we can use to modify base words! Practice with some three common prefixes below.

- ★ The prefix **un-** means "not" or "the opposite of."
  - Example: **un**<u>happy</u> = not happy
- ★ The prefix **re-** means "again."
  - Example: **re**<u>make</u> = make again
- ★ The prefix **mis-** means "wrongly."
  - Example: **mis**<u>treat</u> = treat wrongly

Part 1: Identifying Word Parts

For each word, circle the prefix and <u>underline</u> the base word.

unlucky reread misuse refill misplace unzip

Part 2: Creating Words

Write the word that matches the definition on the left by combining a prefix with the base word. The first one has been completed for you.

do again =	redo
not well =	
behave wrongly =	
view again =	

Part 3: Complete the Sentence

The bolded word in each sentence is missing a prefix. Add the prefix un-, re-, or mis- to create a word that makes sense in the sentence, and rewrite the sentence with the new word.

1. I need to **fill** my cup since I drank all my water.

____

____

2. I **heard** the instructions and didn't know what to do.

____

____

3. I had to **tie** my shoes to take them off.

____

____

4. When I **counted** in my math homework I had to redo it.

____

____

Day 2: Connect and Reflect

Follow the prompts to deepen your understanding of the lesson.

Focus on your favorite moment. Write down or draw your favorite part of today's lesson.

Pack your bags! What's something you learned that you want to take with you and remember later?

Make a real-world connection. How might context clues help you in everyday life?

Rate how you feel about this week's "Language Lab" skill. I can use prefixes to identify the meanings of words.

Rate how you feel about this week's skill. I can use context clues to find the meanings of new words.

Day 3: Writing With Mia

For this activity, you'll be creating your own context clues within creative writing. Follow the steps below to build your knowledge and start writing!

Step 1: Explore the new vocabulary words below by reading their definitions and examples.

Terrain - the surface features of an area of land
- Examples: mountains, rivers, desert, forest, rocky ground

Beacon - a light or signal that helps guide travelers
- Examples: lighthouse, flare, lantern, fire

Artifact - an object from the past that is important or interesting
- Examples: pottery, ancient coins, tools, jewelry

Landmark - a noticeable or interesting object that is easy to see or find
- Examples: tall tree, water tower, mountain peak, rock formation, colorful house

Step 2: Study some popular guide words and phrases that can be used to signal the different types of context clues.

Definition Signals	Example Signals
• is, are, means, refers to Sentence example: The missing artifacts **are** important objects from the past.	• like, for example, such as, including, for instance Sentence example: The museum was full of artifacts, **like** old pottery, ancient coins, and famous statues.

Step 3: Write your own adventure! On the next page, write a paragraph or short story about an adventure. You must write at least one context clue using one of the vocabulary words above. Your context clue can be a definition, example, or both! Feel free to get creative and write about any kind of adventure you'd like! For a challenge, include as many of the new vocabulary words as you can!

Day 3: Writing With Mia

Optional Support

Dig Deeper

Want more practice with context clues?

Step 1: Read the passage below, or listen along by clicking or scanning the QR code. **Highlight** the word that you think each of the underlined context clues is describing.

The Science of Shadows

Have you ever noticed your shadow on a sunny day? A shadow <u>is a dark shape that forms when something blocks light</u>. For example, when you stand in the sun, your body blocks the sunlight, and a shadow appears on the ground behind you.

Shadows change depending on the position of the light source, <u>like the sun or a lamp</u>. When the sun is low in the sky during the morning or evening, shadows are long and stretch out across the ground. But when the sun is high in the sky at noon, shadows become much shorter.

Some materials can block light completely, while others let light pass through. <u>Materials that block all the light are called</u> opaque, like wood, metal, or stone. For example, a tree is opaque because it blocks the sunlight, creating a shadow underneath its branches.

Other materials <u>let some light through but not all</u>, which causes the light to scatter. They are called translucent materials. Things like frosted glass, wax paper, or thin fabric fit into this group.

Transparent materials, <u>like clear glass or plastic</u>, don't create shadows at all because the light goes straight through them.

Optional Support

Dig Deeper Continued

Step 2: Circle whether each context clue from the text gives a definition or example.

1. ...is a dark shape that forms when something blocks light

   Definition OR Example

2. like the sun or a lamp

   Definition OR Example

3. Materials that block all the light are called...

   Definition OR Example

4. ...let some light through but not all...

   Definition OR Example

5. ...like clear glass or plastic...

   Definition OR Example

Step 3: Reread the passage. There are three other context clues that describe words you've already found. Underline each new context clue you find.

Optional Support

Climb Higher

Ready for a challenge
when it comes to using context clues?

Context Clue Scavenger Hunt: Grab a book or have a friend or family member find a new text for you to read! Use the chart below to record new words you come across and the context clues you find!

New Word	Context Clue

Day 1

- ❑ Video and Guided Notes
- ❑ Read and Respond
- ❑ Online Practice Levels 1-3

Day 2

- ❑ Language Lab
- ❑ Connect and Reflect
- ❑ Online Assessment
- ❑ Optional: Dig Deeper or Climb Higher

Lesson Goal: I can explain how a nonfiction text is organized and choose text features that help readers understand the topic better.

Record your thoughts: If you could interview the author of the nonfiction book or article you read today, what would you ask them?

Record your thoughts on the right! →

A Word To Explore:

To make something clearer or easier to understand

Day 1: Guided Notes

Follow along with Bea to complete the guided notes below.

Text Features and Structures

Text Features

- Table of contents
- Heading
- Subheading
- Caption
- Photograph
- Illustration
- Map
- Timeline
- Index
- Glossary

Text Structures

- Description
- Sequence
- Problem/solution
- Cause and effect
- Compare and contrast

Leila's Writing

Why Are Bees Disappearing?

Bees are disappearing in many parts of the world. One cause is pesticides, which make it hard for them to survive. Another is habitat loss because flowers and fields are replaced by buildings.

Which text structure did Leila use? ______________________________

Which text feature should she add? Why?

____

____

Day 1: Guided Notes

Follow along with Bea to complete the guided notes below.

Ezra's Writing

In 2014, Flint, Michigan, had a big problem. The water was unsafe to drink, and many people were getting sick! People spoke up to get help to fix the problem. In 2016, the government gave Flint money and provided families with clean bottled water. Starting in 2017, old pipes were replaced, and scientists tested the water to make sure it was getting better. By 2021, most homes had clean water again.

Which text structure did Ezra use? ______________________________

Which text feature should he add? Why?

____

____

Jeremiah's Writing

The sun and moon are both in the sky, but only the sun is a star. It gives us light and heat, while the moon shines at night by reflecting sunlight. The sun is much larger than Earth, while the moon is much smaller.

Which text structure did Jeremiah use? ______________________________

Which text feature should he add to his writing to make the differences clear? Why?

____

____

Day 1: Read and Respond

Review the text structures we've learned in this unit using the chart below. Use the questions to help you figure out the structure of different nonfiction texts as you read!

Text Structure	Definition/Purpose	Ask Yourself...
Description	This tells about a person, place, or thing using details about how it looks, feels, smells, or sounds, and sometimes gives examples too. When authors use description, their goal is to help readers visualize a topic.	Is this **describing** something?
Sequence	This tells the order of events or the steps in a process and helps the reader understand a process clearly, one part at a time.	Is this teaching me **steps** to complete something or telling me the **order** of events?
Problem/Solution	This describes a problem, something that isn't working or needs to change, and then explains how it was or could be solved. This structure of writing helps readers see how people solve real-life challenges.	Is this telling me a **problem** and how it was **solved**?
Cause and Effect	This helps the reader understand what happened and why. It shows how one thing leads to another.	Is this explaining **why** something happened?
Compare and Contrast	This helps the reader understand how two or more topics are connected, but not exactly the same, by showing similarities and differences.	Is this telling me how two or more things are **alike** or **different**?

Day 1: Read and Respond

Review the text features below! Use this as a guide as you pick the best feature for different nonfiction pieces.

Example	Feature	Example	Feature
Egg......................5 Caterpillar........8 Chrysalis...........10 Butterfly...........12	**Table of contents -** a list of sections or chapters in the order they appear with page numbers	**Butterfly Life Cycle** A butterfly goes through four stages in its life cycle: egg, caterpillar, chrysalis, and adult.	**Heading -** similar to a title but for a specific part of the text
Butterfly Life Cycle A butterfly goes through four stages in its life cycle: egg, caterpillar, chrysalis, and adult. **Egg** The butterfly life cycle begins when the butterfly lays tiny eggs on a leaf.	**Subheading -** a smaller heading that breaks the text up into more parts	 	**Illustration -** drawing **Photograph -** real image taken with a camera *Both help the reader picture the topic.
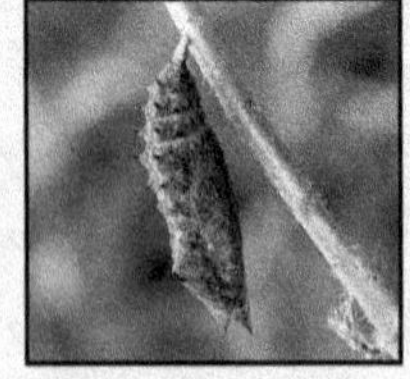 This is a chrysalis, where the caterpillar changes into a butterfly.	**Caption -** explains what is shown in a photo or illustration and gives more information		**Map -** shows where places are and how to get from one place to another
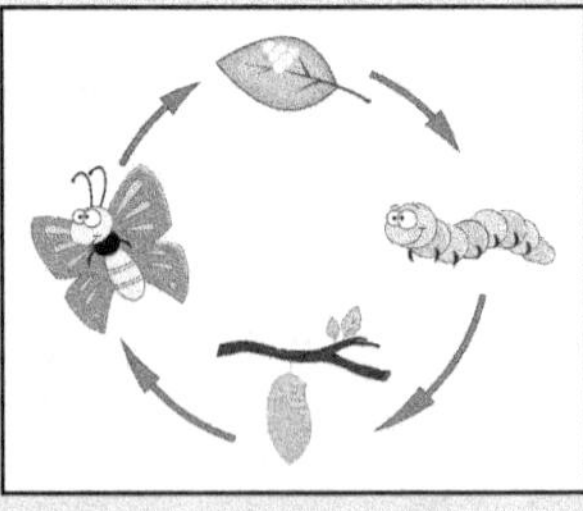	**Diagram -** a simple illustration that shows what something looks like, how it works, or how parts fit together	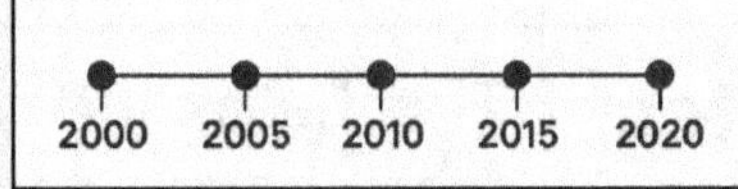 	**Timeline -** shows events in order from past to present
 **Compound eyes -** special eyes on a butterfly that help it see in many directions at once **Camouflage -** colors or patterns that help a butterfly blend in with its surroundings to stay safe from predators	**Glossary -** a list of important words and their definitions in ABC order found in the back of a book	 Metamorphosis, 8 Monarch Butterfly, 12	**Index -** lists specific topics and their page number

Day 1: Read and Respond

Read the passages, or listen by scanning the QR codes. Then, answer the questions. Use the charts on the two previous pages to help you.

All About Sea Turtles

What Do Sea Turtles Look Like?

Sea turtles have large, round shells and strong flippers that help them glide through the water. Their shells can be green, brown, or yellow and often have beautiful patterns. They have big, dark eyes and a small head that sticks out when they come up for air. Their bodies are built for swimming, not walking, and they look graceful as they move through the sea.

Where Do Sea Turtles Live?

Sea turtles live in warm oceans all around the world. They swim slowly and gently, almost like they are flying underwater. You can sometimes find them resting near coral reefs or floating close to the surface. When it's time to lay eggs, sea turtles crawl onto sandy beaches, where they dig holes to bury their eggs safely.

Which text structure did the author use? ____________________

Which text feature(s) would help the reader better understand the topic? Why?

____

____

____

____

Day 1: Read and Respond

Black Bears and Grizzly Bears

Two types of bears that live in North America are the black bear and the grizzly bear. Both of these bears are **omnivores**, which means they eat plants and animals. They also like to live alone, spending most of their time by themselves.

Even though they share some traits, there are many differences between them. Grizzly bears are usually bigger. They can grow up to 8 feet tall and weigh about 800 pounds. Black bears are smaller, growing to about 5 to 6 feet tall and weighing between 200 and 600 pounds.

In the winter, both grizzly bears and black bears **hibernate**. They go into a deep sleep where their heart rate slows down, they don't eat or drink, and they stay in dens for months. However, black bears sometimes hibernate for a shorter time than grizzlies.

Which text structure did the author use? ____________________

Which text feature(s) would help the reader better understand the topic? Why?

____

____

____

____

Day 2: Language Lab

Read the mini-lesson. Then, practice the skill in parts 1 through 3.

Suffixes are groups of letters that are added to the **end** of a word to change the meaning.

Just like **prefixes** are added to the **beginning** of a base word, **suffixes** are added to the **end**.

Prefix	+	Base word	=	New Word
Base word	+	**Suffix**	=	New Word

Remember: Base words are words that can stand alone or be combined with other words or groups of letters to form new words. Practice with some common suffixes below.

★ The suffix **-ful** means "full of."
- ○ Example: color**ful** = full of color

★ The suffix **-able** means "can be" or "able to be."
- ○ Example: break**able** = can be broken

★ The suffix **-less** means "without."
- ○ Example: fear**less** = without fear; not afraid

★ The suffix **-est** means "most."
- ○ Example: fast**est** = the most fast

Part 1: Identifying Word Parts

For each word, circle the suffix and underline the base word.

thankful	readable	careless	longest
tallest	hopeless	moveable	playful

Day 2: Language Lab

Part 2: Creating Words

Write the word that matches the definition on the left by combining a suffix with the underlined base word. The first one has been completed for you.

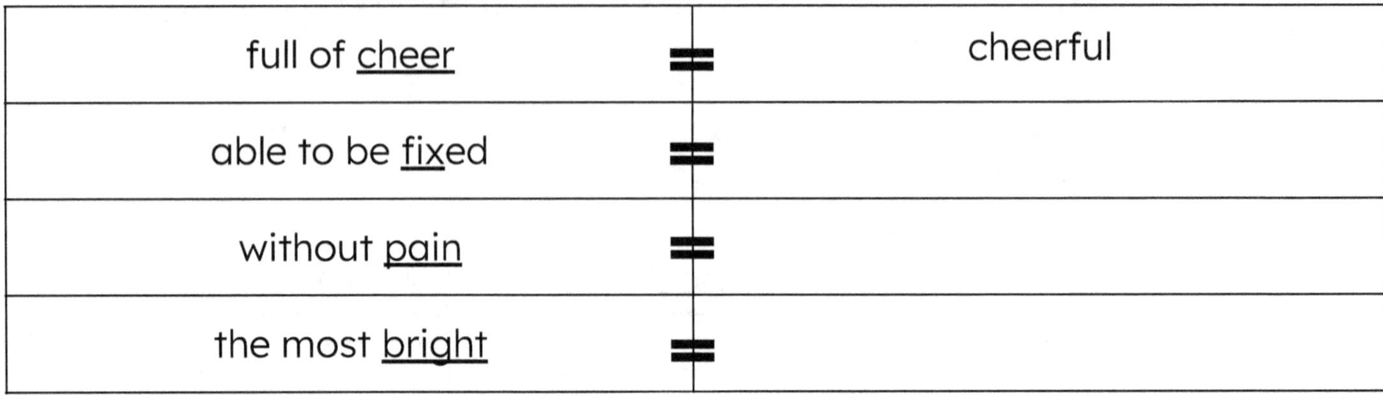

full of cheer	=	cheerful
able to be fixed	=	
without pain	=	
the most bright	=	

Part 3: Completing the Sentence

The bolded word in each sentence is missing a suffix. Add the suffix -ful, -able, -less, or -est to create a word that makes sense in the sentence. Then, rewrite the sentence with the new word. Each suffix will be used once.

1. It was freezing! Definitely the **cold** day of the year so far!

____

2. My shirt is **wash**, so it's easy to clean.

____

3. The desert was completely **water**. Not a drop could be found.

____

4. Please be **care** when you carry the glass of water.

____

Day 2: Connect and Reflect

Follow the prompts to deepen your understanding of the lesson.

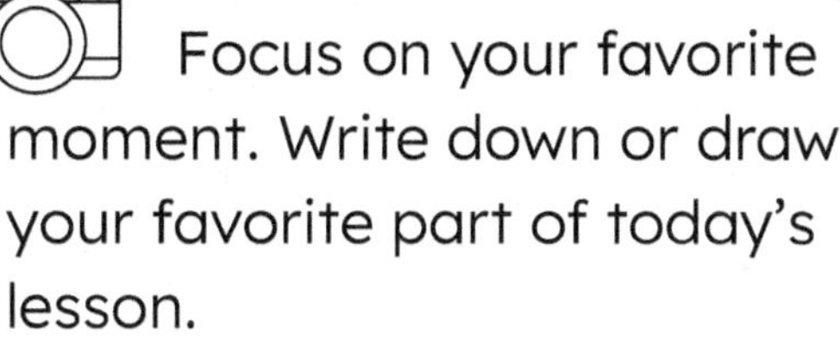

Focus on your favorite moment. Write down or draw your favorite part of today's lesson.

Pack your bags! What's something you learned that you want to take with you and remember later?

Make a real-world connection. Find your favorite nonfiction book. What structure does it use? Are there any text features?

Rate how you feel about this week's "Language Lab" skill: I can identify and use suffixes.

Rate how you feel about this week's skill: I can explain how a nonfiction text is organized and choose text features that help readers understand the topic better.

Optional Support

Dig Deeper

Want more practice with text features and structures?

This game can be played with a single player or up to 12 players. Cut apart the cards. Shuffle and deal all the cards out completely among the players. The player with the first card reads their "I have..." statement aloud and then asks "Who has..." for the next feature or structure. The game continues until all cards have been read.

I have...

The first card

Who has...

A text structure that describes a person, place, or thing using details about how it looks, feels, smells, or sounds?

I have...

Description Text Structure

Who has...

A text feature that helps readers picture what a topic looks like in real life?

I have...

Photograph — which is a real image taken with a camera!

Who has...

A text structure that tells a problem and gives a way to fix it?

I have...

Problem/Solution Text Structure

Who has...

A text feature that shows where things are or how to get from one place to another?

Optional Support

Dig Deeper

Want more practice with text features and structures?

This game can be played with a single player or up to 12 players. Cut apart the cards. Shuffle and deal all the cards out completely among the players. The player with the first card reads their "I have..." statement aloud and then asks "Who has..." for the next feature or structure. The game continues until all cards have been read.

I have...

Map

Who has...

A text structure that tells steps to do something or the order of events?

I have...

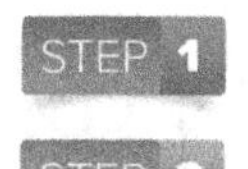

Sequence Structure

Who has...

A text structure that compares two or more things with similarities and differences?

I have...

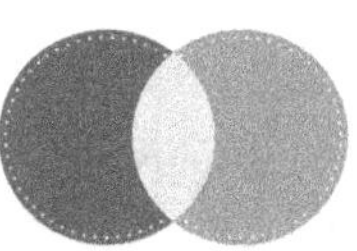

Compare-and-Contrast Structure

Who has...

A text structure that explains what happened and why?

I have...

Cause-and-Effect Structure

Who has...

A text feature that shows what something looks like, how it works, or how parts fit together?

Optional Support

Dig Deeper

Want more practice with text features and structures?

This game can be played with a single player or up to 12 players. Cut apart the cards. Shuffle and deal all the cards out completely among the players. The player with the first card reads their "I have..." statement aloud and then asks "Who has..." for the next feature or structure. The game continues until all cards have been read.

I have...

Parts of a plant
Flower
Leaf
Shoot System
Fruit
Stem
Root System
Root

Diagram

Who has...

A text feature that pairs well with a sequence structure because it shows the order of events from past to present?

I have...

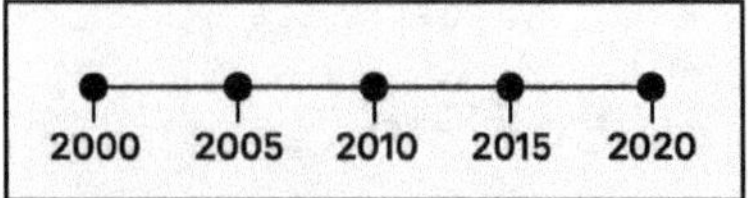

Timeline

Who has...

A text feature that you can find in the back of a book that defines words from the text?

I have...

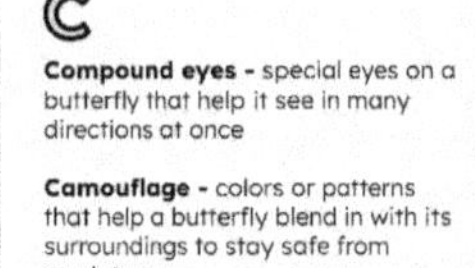
C

Compound eyes - special eyes on a butterfly that help it see in many directions at once

Camouflage - colors or patterns that help a butterfly blend in with its surroundings to stay safe from predators

Glossary

Who has...

A text feature that lists specific topics and their page number?

I have...

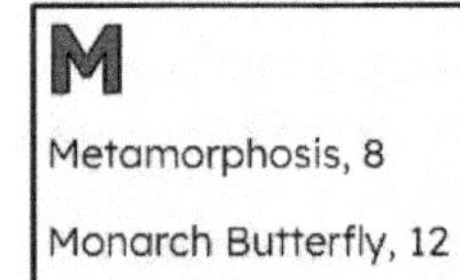
M

Metamorphosis, 8

Monarch Butterfly, 12

Index

This is the last card.

Optional Support

Climb Higher

Ready for a challenge when it comes to pairing text structures with text features?

The passage below is missing important text features! Transform the text by adding a heading, subheading, and an illustration or diagram to help readers understand the topic!

____

Sunflowers are bright, beautiful plants that stand tall in gardens and fields. Sunflowers are easy to spot because of their bright yellow petals and round brown centers. The petals open wide, like rays of the sun. This is how the sunflower got its name! The center of the sunflower is made of tiny flowers called florets. These florets hold seeds that can grow into new plants.

Sunflowers can grow taller than most kids. Some even grow taller than adults! Their long, green stems help hold them up straight. When they are young, sunflowers follow the sun across the sky during the day. This is called heliotropism.

____

Every part of a sunflower has an important job. The roots grow deep in the ground and soak up water and nutrients from the soil. The stem holds the plant up and carries water and food between the roots and the leaves. The leaves are large and green. They use sunlight to make food for the plant in a process called photosynthesis. The center of the flower, or the disc, contains seeds.

www.ingramcontent.com/pod-product-compliance
Lightning Source LLC
LaVergne TN
LVHW060324170826
845315LV00028B/55
2370023849268